P9-DBN-575

Swimmer

Swimmer

By RICHARD MULLINS

FUNK & WAGNALLS COMPANY, INC., NEW YORK

Swimmer

Library of Congress Catalog Card Number 57-10580
Printed in the United States of America

For Michael Mullins,
the Littlest Swimmer of them all

Swimmer

1

As HE MADE the next-to-last turn to start the final two laps of the race, Harry Williams lifted his head out of the water long enough to see that he had a lead of half the length of the pool on Travers of Tech. He took a deep gasping breath, hearing the growing roar of the crowd in the grandstands on both sides of the pool; then he plunged ahead, arms pumping, legs kicking. Only fifty yards to go on the four-forty, and without pressure from behind, he still felt relatively fresh and strong. There would be no record this time—he had known he would not be pushed hard enough by Tech. You have to be pushed into a record.

The water, whitish-green and strong with chlorine, frothed and boiled as he slid through it. Distantly he could hear the spectators yelling his name. "That'sa boy, Harry." "Go it, Harry!" There was not much urgency in the voices, however, for everybody knew the race was won and that the time was slow.

Kicking off on the last turn for the final twenty-five yards, Harry saw he had gained even more on Travers, who was tiring badly. Harry eased up. No need to humiliate Travers too much. He was a nice kid and his parents were probably watching in the stands. Why not give him a break and make him look good?

He plowed ahead, certain he would win, not caring about the clock. He had known that this would not be an exciting race, but he had hoped a little anyhow. He could hear Travers puffing behind him; but there was no more time for generosity, for suddenly the end of the pool was in front of Harry Williams' eyes and he slapped at it with the palm of his hand.

Now that it was over, he felt let down and disappointed. He hung on to the run-off rim, looking at the water, breathing hard, trying to look more tired than he actually was. From the stands he could hear the shouts and yells; just above him were the voices of the rest of the team congratulating him. A few seconds later Travers finished, his breath coming in sobbing gasps.

Harry smiled at the boy across the blue lane marker. "Nice race, Travers. You had me worried there for a while." He had said those very words, or something like them, a hundred times before. Now they were without real meaning.

Travers nodded without speaking. He was close to exhaustion. Better than anyone else, he knew that it had been an effort for Harry to keep the race so close and he was embarrassed by it until Harry came very close to him.

"Travers," he said in a voice no one else could hear, "mind if I give you a clue?"

"About what?" the other asked.

"About your style. It'll probably take ten seconds off your time."

"Are you kidding?"

"No. Listen. Try kicking with your knees stiff; kick from the hips with your legs straight all the way. It'll make a terrific difference."

Travers' breath was almost normal now. His hair was plastered down over his forehead. "I don't think our coach will go for it," he said. "He's pretty strict."

"So is ours," Harry grinned. "But *I* swim stiff-legged. Try it." He started to haul himself onto the apron of the pool. Travers' hand held him back.

"Say, how come you're telling me this?"

"Because I like to see anybody improve his swimming. Makes no difference if you're with Tech or Notre Dame. Besides," Harry added with a smile, "somebody had to tell me once, didn't they?"

Travers had time only to grunt in appreciation and then Bud Hill was helping Harry out of the water. "Nice going, kid," Bud said, slapping his bare back.

As they walked together toward the dressing room, the loudspeaker system was blaring the results: "Order of finish in the Four-Forty: Williams, State, four minutes, fifty-one seconds, the winner; Travers, Tech, five minutes flat, second . . ."

It was no record. In fact, it was exceedingly slow time.

Ahead of him, through the milling crowd of swimmers, officials, divers, and handlers, he could see the frowning face of Coach Barnes. Barnes was waiting at the entrance to the locker rooms. Harry halted and looked up into the stands. A flash of color caught his eye, and he waved instinctively. Dorothy Bryson blew him a kiss from her pretty mouth. She was sitting next to her father, Professor Bryson, who made a modified salute with his right hand. Harry grinned at them and then walked toward Coach Barnes. Bud Hill, spotting the coach, quickly draped a towel around Harry's shoulders and returned to the bench.

"How you feeling, Williams?" Barnes asked lightly. He was a powerfully built man with a red face and short-cropped gray hair. Now he spoke softly, but it did not become him—usually he was bellowing. "Tired?" Barnes asked.

"I'm feeling all right," Harry answered and started to move past the coach to the showers.

"Where you going?"

"I'm going to change."

"Who says?"

Harry looked at him. "I say."

"Nothing doing. Back to the bench with the rest of the squad. You've still got the relay to do."

"Not today. I can't do it."

Barnes folded his massive arms across his chest and squinted his eyes as if he couldn't believe what he was hearing. "Williams. Let's get this straight right now: who is the coach here, me or you?"

"I know what's best for me, Mr. Barnes. The relay is out for me."

"That's for me to decide." Barnes came very close to him and poked a finger into Harry's ribs. "Williams, you loafed in the four-forty. It was fifteen seconds over your best time. Now don't play the martyr with me. We've got a meet to win today and we're not going to win it with you in street clothes."

"Tech is a soft touch," Harry observed. "They offer no competition. I can't swim well against them. Let Holland or someone else do the relay—others need the experience. I don't."

"Lazy?" Coach Barnes sneered. He was making an effort to control his temper.

"No," Harry said mildly. "Are you sore because I didn't set a new record?"

"Could be. You've got it in you, Williams. I'd like to see it come out someday."

"You will, coach. But not against Tech. Not against a Travers."

"Not good enough for the prima donna?" Barnes asked sarcastically.

Harry started to answer and then bit his tongue. That was a term one of the sports writers had used in describing him. *Prima donna.* Just because he knew what he wanted and was willing to sacrifice anything to get it.

"Harry," Barnes said casually, "let's not haggle right here. Okay? Suppose you go back to the bench with the rest of the guys. Maybe I won't tap for the relay—and maybe I will."

"I don't care."

"Well, I do!" Barnes snapped. "It will depend on the score. Remember—I run the team, not you!"

For an instant Harry debated whether or not he should have a showdown with Barnes on the spot. But it wouldn't prove anything, and it wasn't important enough to quarrel over. Not today. He spun on his heel and walked over the wet apron of the pool, ducking under the diving board structure, and sat down on the end of the bench, the place usually reserved for him by the rest of the team. Bud Hill sat next to him, looking straight ahead. Harry did not look up into the grandstand, although he sensed Dotty's eyes on him.

"The Old Man work you over?" Bud asked out of the side of his mouth.

Bud was a cheerful soul, with brick-red hair cut short and a million freckles splattered over his face. Harry had roomed with him for two semesters now and he was about as close a friend as he had on campus. What he liked about Bud was that the redhead was always the same—optimistic and buoyant—and you could depend on him to steady you when the going got rough. There was never any real rivalry over swimming between them—Harry was too good for Bud—and besides, Bud enjoyed life too much to be bothered by any one aspect of it, like swimming. Sure, he liked swimming and did fairly well at it, but he could like golf or tennis or ping-pong just as well. For Harry there was only swimming.

Bud repeated his question.

"Not so much. Why?"

"He's been jumpy all day. There are supposed to be some university trustees in the audience *and* some Olympic scouts. Barney wants to look good."

"He wants *us* to look good," Harry corrected.

"Same thing," Bud said.

Harry glanced at his friend. Trustees. Scouts. So that explained the sudden pressure. Until today he, Harry Williams, had always decided which races he would or would not swim in—and Barnes had always gone along. Both had agreed at the beginning of the season that only Williams could know his mood, shape, and capacities on a given day. For example, on a good day he might swim—and win—the 100-yard free-style, the 440-yard free-style and the 1500-meter. Or he might swim in only one of them. The system had worked well, and although State did not win every meet, he, Harry Williams, had won every race he swam, equaling two national records in the process.

And now, today, Coach Barnes was putting on a show for the folks, as if to say, "This is Harry Williams—*my* creation. Look at him go, folks. The best swimmer this university ever had. Doesn't that prove I deserve another five-year contract? Doesn't that prove I should be one of the Olympic coaches?"

Only Harry Williams was *not* Coach Barnes' creation. In fact, very few of the swimmers owed their talent to Barnes. He was more of a guide than a coach and frequently he had asked Harry for advice about certain of the team members.

Harry studied the boys on the bench. Most of them were lean, hard-muscled youths, with legs and arms as firm as tree trunks. A magnificent collection of physical specimens. Each and every one had trained and sweated and strained for as long as ten years for the honor of sitting on this bench now. And few would ever get more out of it than a few cheers from the crowd or a pat on the rump from Barnes and a "Good race, son," by way of a compliment. The point was, of course, that they *were* here; ready to do their bit for one or two or ten minutes, for the sake of the team and the university. A grueling sport with small rewards—and Harry admired each one of them for having selected swimming.

Bud Hill was speaking again. "The scouts aren't here to see Barney only. You aren't exactly a wallflower, Mr. Williams."

Harry knew that was true. Undoubtedly, the Olympic scouts were on hand to catch him in action, to see if the reports they'd heard about this "human fish" were true. Yet, he simply could not get excited about racing today. It did not matter how many scouts or trustees were in the stands. This was not his day to attack records and he could not pretend or force himself. It was his one weakness—the need for a competitor as good, or nearly as good, as himself, just as greyhounds need mechanical rabbits to make them run. So far this season he had not been pushed to his best time.

The meet proceeded rapidly, with State piling up an insurmountable lead. State's drivers blanketed Tech's; Dixon and Hill were one-two in the backstroke, and Holland was barely nosed out by a Tech man in the fifty-yard sprint. Harry sat and watched, feeling no desire at all to swim again today. Coach Barnes studiously ignored him, although from time to time Harry could see him talking with a group of dignified-looking gentlemen in the special seats. From the way the men glanced over at him, Harry knew he was the subject of their conversation.

At last it was time for the medley relay. With the meet already won, the result of the relay would have no bearing on the outcome. Harry knew that Dixon would do the first hundred yards as the back-stroker, Shaw the second hundred with the butterfly breast-stroke, and then Reynolds or Hill in the orthodox breast-stroke. Anchor man with the hundred-yard free-style would be either himself or Holland.

The crowd quieted down as Coach Barnes stepped to the microphone, consulted his chart, and read off the names.

"Dixon. Shaw. Hill. . . ." He paused and scanned the bench quickly. Harry's heart skipped a beat. He did not look at the coach. He wondered if this would be the moment for the showdown. His hands were slippery with nervous sweat.

"Originally," Barnes said gruffly, "Williams was scheduled to do the anchor; however, he has informed me that he got a charley-horse in the four-forty and will be unable to swim in the relay. Therefore, Holland will swim the final leg."

The audience let out a collective "Oooooh," of disappointment.

Harry felt relief flood over him. So Barnes had backed down, trustees or no trustees. He would not risk a display of insubordination in public for the sake of a race that did not mean much.

Before he got up, Bud Hill turned to Harry. "What's up, kid? Your leg looks okay to me. Barnes being funny?"

Harry did not answer, so Bud shrugged and walked over to the end of the pool, jerking his arms to loosen the muscles. Harry heard whispering ripple through the audience. They were trying to figure out what was the matter. After all, most of them had come to the State-Tech meet mainly in the hope of seeing Williams break a record or two. Now they were to be denied seeing him swim at all.

The relay was fairly close until Holland knifed the water and left the Tech anchor man in his churning wake. He won by fifteen yards, and that was the meet. The crowd tried to work up some enthusiasm, but it didn't work. They felt cheated, and they filed out quietly. A lump of guilt settled in Harry's throat as he joined the rest of the team in the locker room.

Perhaps he should have swum just for the sake of appearances. Nobody believed the coach's line about the charley-horse. For that matter, the way Barnes had said it, no one could believe it. People would think he had been afraid. Nevertheless, in his heart he knew he had done the right thing—for himself. His finely attuned body would have rebelled at swimming a race against a poor team and making that team look even worse than it was.

Bud Hill, still puffing, fell into step with him. "Don't let it get you, Harry. I'm with you all the way."

"Thanks, Bud," Harry said sincerely. Bud understood.

The dressing room was fairly subdued without Coach

Barnes, who was still at the pool talking with the officials. Harry figured he was probably telling them that he was saving Williams for bigger things, that he did not like to risk his star, that other kids needed the experience. Coach Barnes was a pretty good talker.

Harry dressed quickly and went outside. Dotty and her father were waiting on the sidewalk in front of the Fieldhouse. She looked very fresh and clean, her auburn-colored hair wild with curls spun closely above her ears. Next to her he felt even taller than his six feet, and she was so tiny that his hundred and seventy pounds seemed gross and awkward.

"Hello, Harry," she murmured prettily and slipped her hand neatly into the crook of his elbow.

"Hi, Dotty," he said. "Hello, Professor Bryson."

It was the custom after every home meet for him to dine with the Brysons. As usual they would drive home together in the Bryson car, so the three of them headed for the parking lot on the far side of the building.

Professor Paul Edward Bryson, A.B., M.A., Ph.D., Phi Beta Kappa, walked on his daughter's right side. He was probably the most renowned faculty member at a university famous for renowned faculty members. His specialty was English Literature, with emphasis on Shakespeare. Professor Bryson was as tall as Harry, but bigger, much bigger, with a vast barrel of a chest and a clifflike chin and a face that creased into many ridges whenever he frowned or scowled or laughed. At times he resembled the west wall of the Grand Canyon. He had been a swimmer himself in his undergraduate days—a good one—and

Harry always felt a certain degree of camaraderie when they were together.

"Rough in the four-forty?" the professor asked, looking at him over the springy curls on Dotty's head.

"So-so," Harry said. He did not want to discuss it now.

"I noticed Barnes passed you up in the relay. I would have raised the roof. 'This was the most unkindest cut of all.' " He spoke gently, smoothly, his voice rich with culture and a trace of teasing.

"I passed myself up," Harry told him, speaking over Dotty's head. "I told him I didn't want to race in the relay."

Professor Bryson pursed his lips thoughtfully. "Hmmm. That's interesting. Then you did have a charley-horse?"

"No," Harry said evenly. "I just didn't want to swim it."

Both the professor and Dotty looked at him. "Come now," the professor said jocularly. "After all, this was a league meet. Surely you would not jeopardize the team's reputation? That's not like you."

Harry felt a swelling flash of anger, as he had when he had talked with Barnes earlier. "I was thinking about myself, Professor Bryson. Today wasn't my day. I was out of balance. Well, you know how it is, sir. You had off days, too, didn't you?"

There was something wrong about this. It was pleading. He didn't want to have to plead to be understood. It shouldn't be necessary. Professor Bryson should *know*.

"Of course I had off days," Professor Bryson said with

a tight smile. "But nevertheless I always put out for the team."

"Why, Professor?" Harry heard himself asking.

The question brought them all to a halt. Dotty stared up at him, eyes wide. "Harry—what a thing to say." She turned to her parent. "Dad—Harry was just kidding. He always gets a little giddy after swimming. Don't you, Harry?"

The professor's broad forehead was furrowed in consternation. "Forget it, I—"

"But I'm not kidding, Professor Bryson," Harry said, pulling away from Dotty's restraining grip. "*Why* did you always put out for the team? Don't you think it's possible for someone to think of himself first and the team second?" His teeth clamped together. "Isn't it possible for a person to know more about himself than a coach knows? Winning isn't everything, is it?"

Dotty's face had gone pale. She gnawed at her lower lip, uncertain how to cope with this rebellion against the austere authority of her father.

The professor glanced about nervously, for they were still within earshot of other homeward-bound spectators. "That will do, Harry. I don't mind a joke about some things, but team spirit is no joke with me. A man either plays by the rules—plays the game—*plays for the team,* or he might as well turn in his suit." He snapped the brim of his fedora. "I must say, you do an injustice to the name of Henry the Fifth, whose name you carry. *There* was a man who knew the value of working and fighting together."

They had reached the car now, but no one made a move to enter.

"I don't agree with you, sir," Harry said softly, feeling his heart pound again. "I think that it is wrong for anyone to be forced to run or swim or throw if he doesn't feel like it." He turned to Dorothy. "*You* understand, Dotty. You've seen me in all sorts of moods after a meet. If I felt I did not do a good job, no matter how the team did, I would feel bad. My mental attitude is important too."

"Harry—"

Professor Bryson interrupted with, "It's your attitude that I'm worried about, Harry. It's not healthy. Don't ever forget that the university gave you a scholarship based on your ability to swim. You owe it to your fellow students—to us—to do your best *always*."

"Dad," Dotty said miserably, torn between the two men at her side.

Professor Bryson climbed into the car. He was large and imposing, looking straight ahead, his fleshy face unsmiling. "Dorothy," he said sternly.

His daughter hesitated, her small hand on Harry's arm. Harry felt his face redden. He had let his tongue run away with him. He should not have allowed the Professor to rile him so. Dotty's face was taut with concern.

"Dorothy—are you coming?"

So that's the way it was. Just like that the dinner date was canceled. Dotty's eyes begged him to apologize, to be nice to her father.

Harry swallowed thickly. "Dotty, I—"

Biting her lip, Dotty spun away and got into the car

without waiting to hear what he had to say. Her eyes glinted with tears. And that was all he saw, for the Professor stomped on the gas pedal and the big new car hummed and was on its way through the thinning crowd. Harry stared after it.

For a long time he did not move; finally, he walked his solitary way back to the room he shared with Bud Hill.

2

FOR DINNER THAT NIGHT Harry Williams went to Al's, a small but busy restaurant frequented by students who did not eat in fraternity houses or in the university dining halls. He chose a back booth in order to avoid meeting anyone he knew. He still did not want to talk about the Tech meet and he certainly did not want to have to defend himself to anyone who knew nothing about the situation. So he ate broiled lamb chops with baked potatoes and topped them off with a piece of apple pie. Then he paid Al, who greeted him by name, and left.

When he got back to Mrs. Gray's house, where he and Bud rented one of the upstairs rooms set aside for men students, he found a note from Bud saying that he had gone to a movie and would see him later. Harry was just as glad. Tonight he wanted to be alone to think out his problem. For it was a problem, and after the encounter with Professor Bryson, he was beginning to wonder who was right.

It was a nice room, with two huge windows that looked out over a quiet street lined with thick-branched elms. There were twin beds, twin desks, twin dressers, and a couple of odd leather chairs that were ideal for reading or just relaxing. Fortunately, Mrs. Gray was thoughtful enough to tidy up after they left every morning, otherwise the room would simply be a shambles to live in. Mrs. Gray was the widow of Dr. Gray, who had headed the university's zoology department years ago, and she was now looked on as a second mother by the students who stayed in her rooms. She was kind enough to overlook it if they happened to fall behind in their rent, and more than once she had delved into her own savings to help out a needy boy.

Harry was tempted to go straight to Mrs. Gray tonight and ask her for advice, but he knew he couldn't do that—this was his baby to figure out on his own. . . .

He looked at himself in the mirror over the dresser. The image he saw was not altogether an unpleasant one. Tall and lean, he had broad, hard shoulders and a flat, wide chest that tapered to a taut waist and narrow hips. His sand-colored hair was cut short so as to keep it out of his eyes when he swam. The eyes that looked back at him were dark blue and intense, under a smooth brow. His nose was straight and thin.

All in all, not the worst-looking man on campus, but a long way from the handsomest. Outwardly, he knew he gave the appearance of being an average student with little on his mind except passing next week's exams before spring vacation.

This was deceptive. There was a lot on his mind—and most of it had to do with swimming. But, really, it was more than that.

"Harry, boy," Doc Howell had once told him, "a man's got to be true to what he believes is right—he's got to stick to his principles, no matter what. And that goes for all walks of life, whether it's sports or working or loving. . . ."

Doc's words rang in his memory now. Good old Doc. It had been a long time since they had seen one another. A couple of years anyhow, but unless things had changed drastically, Doc would still be in charge of Camp Skylark in the Adirondacks.

Harry Williams picked up his American history book and ensconced himself in his leather chair, preparatory to studying the Civil War again. But the book was heavy and he could not focus his attention on its pages. He let his mind doze and drift back into time, remembering his early years and his still-warm relationship with Doc Howell.

After his parents had died in an airplane crash when he was nine, Harry had gone to live with an uncle, a bachelor. But his uncle did not have much time to devote to Harry and was only too happy to send him off to summer camp. It was a lucky decision, for the camp was Doc Howell's Camp Skylark.

It was there that Harry learned to swim, in the cold, blue waters of the mountain lake that gave its name to the camp. Under the tutelage of Doc Howell, Harry took to the water like a duckling. And like a duckling, his first attempts were laughable.

"Don't worry, Harry boy," Doc would tell him when the older boys chortled at his splashings. "Someday you'll be better than all of them put together."

Although he was not a great swimmer himself, Doc knew how to teach swimming. The trick was that he really made the boys teach themselves, allowing them to develop their own styles, to "find their own depths."

From the start he told Harry that he was a natural and that any formal kind of instruction would hurt rather than help him. Then he would tell him stories of how the great Hawaiian, Duke Kahanamoku, had learned to swim by himself in the surf at Waikiki Beach, maybe diving for coins thrown by tourists from the luxury liners as they steamed into the harbor. In time The Duke became one of the world's greatest swimmers, and then he had turned to helping other young Hawaiians and to encouraging them to break records all over the world. The Duke was a case of the self-made swimmer, Doc said, and he had successfully resisted any changes suggested by coaches who did not know as much as he did.

Harry would listen to all this solemnly and then return to the water and practice, practice, practice. In the first year or so he absorbed everything the counselors could show him and by his third summer, when he was twelve, he was ready for advanced training. Only there was no one who knew enough, so he taught himself. He discovered how to breathe properly—through the mouth and never the nose; how to kick—from the hips; how to pace himself—it was like having a stop watch in his head; and how to keep in condition.

Much as he loved it, he treated swimming with respect by not overindulging, by not pushing himself to his utmost limit. He did not know his limit and did not want to know it.

His greatest fan at Camp Skylark, aside from Doc Howell himself, was Doc's niece, Meg Crane. Meg, a gangling girl with braces on her teeth and legs that were too long and bony, was a year younger than Harry. She would work with him by the hour, timing him and fixing him hot drinks.

Harry tolerated her—he had found she was persistent and would not go away even when he yelled at her. In the end, he grudgingly admitted she was okay—but that was all the approval Meg needed to idolize him all the more.

During the fall, winter, and spring months, Harry went to school in his home town. By the time he was fourteen, he was the undisputed star of his high school swimming team. It was coached part time by the mathematics instructor, who was only too glad to turn over most of the technical duties to Harry. In exchange, he arranged for Harry to enter the competition for the scholarship offered by State University to the best swimmer in the city. Harry won, for there was no one who could come close to him.

Graduation day from high school was memorable in more ways than one. On that great day Doc Howell showed up—with Meg Crane. It had involved a two-hundred-mile trip for them, and it was then that Harry realized how much he must mean to Doc. It was funny seeing Doc all dressed up—a new suit, a white shirt, and a tie that kept coming loose and edging around to the side of his neck. His gray hair was combed flat over his skull, and he kept smoothing it with his calloused hands. Meg was forever straightening his tie or buttoning his shirt.

Harry was especially happy, since his uncle had been called out of town and was unable to make the ceremonies; if it hadn't been for Doc and Meg, graduation would have been a very lonely affair.

As they walked cross-town to his uncle's house, Harry studied Meg carefully.

"Golly, but look who's growing up!"

Meg blushed. "Look yourself!"

"No, I mean it," Harry said. "No more braces—and you've got shoes on! Miracles will never cease."

Meg started to pummel him with her little fists until she remembered that she was now a young lady of sixteen and must stop. But she didn't stop blushing.

"All set for State, Harry boy?" Doc asked as they walked along the shaded streets.

"I sure am. They've got a terrific swimming team there."

"So I hear," Doc agreed slowly. "Quite a coach, that Rusty Barnes. I knew him a long time ago."

"Is he good?"

"He's quite a coach," Doc repeated. "He's turned out some winning teams." But he didn't use the word "good."

"We're going to miss you at camp from now on," Meg observed. "You'll probably be very busy with all the co-eds at State."

"Well, I understand that Coach Barnes does have his

own training camp for the team. But I'll try to get up to Skylark if I can."

Doc shook his head. "You probably won't have time. Once a boy leaves Skylark, he doesn't get much chance to come back."

"Maybe so," Harry said ruefully, "but I'll come back."

"Hmmmpf," Meg murmured.

"I mean it."

"We'll see," she said and she turned away suddenly.

Doc took Harry aside once they got to the house. He placed a friendly arm around his shoulders and looked him in the eye.

"Don't forget what you've learned at Skylark, my boy. I mean besides swimming. Heck, there wasn't much we could teach you. The rest, though, is important. Honesty and integrity. And never do anything that you'll be ashamed of afterward. Goodness knows none of us are perfect; we all make mistakes, but if you are ever in doubt about anything, just try to think how it would impress me and Meg. Will you do that, Harry?"

Harry's throat was thick. "Of course, I will, Doc. You know that."

"Good. I know it won't be easy sometimes. I also know that maybe I did you an injustice in letting you be your own coach, your own boss."

"An injustice!" Harry echoed. "What do you mean?"

"I can't explain it now. You'll see what I mean when the time comes. Anyway, you know that come what may, I'll always be available if you need help."

"Thanks, Doc. I appreciate that."

When they joined Meg again, they found she had made

some cocoa and they sat down for one last meal together.

"Now you watch your step," Meg admonished. "We'll be watching for your name in the papers."

"What papers?"

"Why, didn't Uncle Doc, tell you? We're subscribing to the *State Daily,* as of next September."

"Hey, you two are like a couple of detectives."

"We've got to keep tabs on our graduates," Doc smiled.

Presently, the conversation turned to Meg and her future.

"What's going to become of you, Meg?" Harry asked.

"Oh, I'm going to school, too—next year."

"Is that so? Which one?"

"Art School—in Philadelphia."

"Art!"

"Yes. What's wrong with that? I like it."

Doc nodded in agreement. "That's the truth. My bright young niece has developed into an artist. And a good one, too, I might add."

"Bravo," Harry shouted. "A toast to our next Rembrandt." He held his cocoa cup high in the air. Doc beamed on the blushing Meg. Their cups clinked together and they downed the cocoa.

They said good-byes not long after that—Doc and Meg had a long drive home ahead of them. They all shook hands, and as they left Harry felt that unaccountable lump in his throat again.

Doc was right, of course. Things were different at State. It was very difficult to retain his old acquaintances from high school or even from the town. His interests at college took up virtually all of his time: studying, making new friends, taking part in new activities, discovering an entirely new world. And then there was swimming.

Coach Barnes had handled the tank team for nearly twenty years. Before that he had been a professional swimmer, and there were rumors, never substantiated, that he had defeated Weismuller in one 1500-meter race. In any case he had his own methods of teaching and he was tough. He did not go by any book, or any "scientific" system—he went by his own hard-won experience, which, although it had served him well for many years, did not necessarily prove that it would be successful for everyone.

For two semesters Harry Williams went along with Coach Barnes, listening to his instructions and following his orders, genuinely interested in picking up new pointers to improve his swimming. But it was not possible. They were two individuals, two self-made swimmers, and their systems collided head-on. The personality clash was even greater.

At the start of the third semester Harry told Coach Barnes that he was going to swim in his own way, using his own style. Since he was already recognized as the best swimmer on the squad, Coach Barnes agreed.

Actually, Harry felt that Barnes, rather than instructing his boys, was trying to conquer them, to bend them to his will—to frighten them into swimming well. It occurred to Harry that Barnes was more worried about keeping his job than about molding champions. And if it hadn't been for Dorothy Bryson, he probably would have left State to go to another school—and another coach.

Harry had met Dotty in one of Professor Bryson's English classes and they had liked each other at once. If Harry had belonged to a fraternity, he would have given her his pin. He did the next best thing—he let her wear his Block *S* jacket, and from then on she was known to one and all as his girl.

Now here he was in his last year—his last few weeks actually—of college. Until this week the future had appeared to be fairly secure. After graduation he would see about getting a Master's Degree and a job teaching and coaching in a high school. Then he and Dotty would get married.

But after the events of the day—his open clash with the coach and with the professor—he realized that life is not always easy and smooth. He realized that there are many facets to it and many problems to be solved; and even then one could not be positive that everything would go well all the time.

Swimming, Harry Williams knew, was in his blood. A part of him. He wanted very much to swim—and win—in the Olympics. This year he had reached his peak; he was acknowledged by opposing teams and sports writers as one of the finest young swimmers in the country. His best four-forty time was only a few seconds off the world's record for that distance.

Oddly enough, he had reached another peak, too—his temperamental peak. He could no more plunge into the warmed water of the Fieldhouse pool and attack a world's record at a moment's notice than an actor could "try" for an Academy Award every time. Consequently, in the school's intercollegiate meets he would swim only as fast as he had to in order to win. Not since his high school freshman year had anyone slapped the end of the pool before him in the same race. His muscles, his stomach, his brain were all involved. If any one was out of kilter, he could not swim. He *would not* swim.

So it was not snobbishness or conceit that prevented Harry Williams from obeying Coach Barnes. It was a highly personal matter of his own integrity. That was why tonight, as he sat in the deep leather chair in his room, with the lights out and the heavy history book unopened on his lap, Harry Williams was intensely disturbed by the turn of the day's events.

In his own stubborn way he had alienated not only Coach Barnes but the Brysons. Especially Dotty. She had never questioned his actions before, but now she was obviously not sure whether or not he was right. And neither was he.

And what happened the next day only served to add further to his own doubts.

3

THE NEXT ISSUE of the *State Daily* carried a lead editorial written by the sports editor under the headline: *Dissension on the Tank Team?*

> Our favorite little bird tells us that Swimming Star H. Williams talked back to Boss Man Barnes yesterday, and even refused to swim the medley relay. The excuse was a charley-horse, but we know better. This confirms our own suspicion all season long that High Hat Harry is getting too big for his trunks. Well, that too-good-for-you-peasants act is wearing thin with the Athletic Department so don't be surprised if a wrist gets slapped. Williams should be put in his place by the powers that be. And fast. After all, is he part of a team or not? State doesn't like glory-grabbers. As a student in good standing, Harry Williams owes it to all of us to carry on our tradition. What say? Who is all wet—the student body or Harry Williams?

Harry did not read this until one of his fellow students in American Government pointed it out to him and then hung around until Harry finished it.

"How about that, Harry?" the fellow asked. "Is that on the level?"

Harry ran a hand over the brush of his hair and scanned the words again. "No, it isn't," he murmured. "He's got it all wrong."

"Well, where did he get it?" the other persisted.

"I don't know. Not from me."

"What are you going to do? Write a letter to the editor?"

"I don't know now. I've got to think it over."

The other boy shook his head. "This is pretty serious stuff, you know. It won't help your popularity rating on campus."

"I guess not." Harry did not want to let the boy know how much it bothered him, so he chuckled. "I imagine the sports editor was hard up for something to write about, so he picked on this. It'll blow over in a day or so."

"I doubt it," the other said.

With upward of ten thousand students enrolled in the various schools at State, it seemed impossible that any one person could be known by every other person on campus, but that day Harry Williams realized that an awful lot of people knew him—and that most of them had some sort of opinion on the fracas at the swimming pool.

When he dropped into the Corner Store for a coke, he was hailed by a bunch of co-eds who were having lunch in a booth.

"Hi, Harry," one of them said. "I see you're getting splashed."

"A little," he grinned.

A cute, dark-haired girl said, "*We* hear that the paper is going to be called the *Daily Fiction* from now on." The others giggled.

Harry resisted the temptation to give them his honest opinion of the sports editor. It would not be wise to go around making public statements until he found out exactly what was going on.

The first girl asked, "Why don't you just announce that you did have a charley-horse and that will clear it all up?"

"But I didn't," he said quietly.

The four girls exchanged glances. "But why didn't you swim in the relay then?"

"I . . . well . . . it's hard to explain . . ."

He was standing in an aisle between two rows of booths, and some other students were trying to get by. Noticing Harry and overhearing some of the conversation, they paused, and in another minute he found himself in the middle of a mob of curious men and girls.

A voice came from the crowd: "Seems to me that since Coach Barnes has been here for twenty years and you've been here only three, that should settle it."

"Yes," someone else added, "this isn't a private school just for you, Williams. What would it be like if every athlete behaved that way?"

Harry sensed the hostile mood of the crowd and he wanted to get away. It had been a mistake to talk about it in a snack-bar. But he was surrounded.

Just then he heard a familiar voice. Bud Hill.

The tall swimmer broke through the ring of curious students, forcing his way with his elbows.

"Here you are, kid. Come on, I've got us a booth." He grabbed Harry by the arm and led the way; Harry gratefully followed.

Behind them the others milled around for half a minute, talking among themselves, but now that the center of attraction was gone, there was little to hold their interest and they broke up and went their various ways.

Harry sat down opposite his roommate with a sigh of relief. "Thanks, Bud. It was getting pretty sticky there."

"Okay," the redhead grinned. "It's just that I hate to see lynchings on nice spring days. Looks like you've become an *enfant terrible.*"

"Not by choice."

"That's what you say. I'm beginning to see that all you have to do is breathe deeply in order to get into a controversy. Whether you like it or not, Williams, you are now a celebrity."

"I don't think I like it."

"Nevertheless, I think that from now on I should be your press agent. No interviews or autographs unless I approve. Got that?" he asked with mock severity.

"Yes, sir. Do you approve of a coke?"

"Indeed, I do. In fact, you've earned a double coke." He signaled a waiter and ordered two double cokes.

When the drinks came, they sipped slowly. Gradually, Harry felt the tension drain out of him.

"Well, Bud, what have you got to say about the affair? I suppose you'll suggest I go apologize to Barnes?"

"Not at all," his friend said cheerfully. "You didn't do

anything to Barnes, and I honestly do not believe that he feels you did."

"Then what is all the fuss about?"

Bud thought for a moment, his freckled brow furrowed, his pale-blue eyes narrowed to slits. "My opinion," Bud said cautiously, "is that the sports editor has it in for you. Maybe he put two and two together and decided to interview the Coach. He might have convinced Barnes that it was wrong for you to be your own boss and that it would serve you right to get chastised in public."

"What good would that do?" Harry interrupted. "Barnes and I have had an understanding all season long."

"Remember that Barnes has his contract coming up at the end of the semester, and also that he'd like to be on the Olympic coaching staff. By making you get into line, he'd be able to take full credit for developing a champion. Maybe he didn't think of this himself, but if that crazy sports editor began harping on it he probably decided to go along."

"Then they want to teach me a lesson?"

Bud grinned at him, showing a mouthful of crooked teeth.

Harry felt himself redden. "All right, but what do you think? Honestly, now."

"Me? Well, I'm a swimmer, too, and I know how you feel. I know most people haven't the foggiest notion about how it feels to be a champion—what it takes. And I'm one of them. But I can guess. I say stick to your guns."

"Resist this pressure to make me knuckle under to Barnes?"

"Yes. Sure, it may make you out as a villain for a while, but in the end you'll be a better swimmer for it. And that means the school will benefit, too."

"I don't want to sound conceited," Harry said, "but I believe that, too. However, you saw how the kids reacted. They think I'm betraying the university out of selfishness."

Bud finished his coke and then chewed some of the ice. Harry could hear his teeth crunching on it, and the sound made goose flesh rise on his forearms.

"That's the hardest part," Bud agreed. "And of course some of the guys on the team kind of think you're letting them down, but that's the way it goes."

"Am I letting them down?" Harry inquired.

"No," Bud said promptly. "So get that out of your head right now."

"It's not easy. Maybe I'm all wrong."

"You're not all wrong," Bud insisted. "It'd be wrong if, after all these years of hard work and training, you gave it all up in order to cater to a few egos on campus. Listen—ninety-nine percent of the people in the world are conformists. And they never win the medals or get the awards or reach the top. It's the individualists who amount to something. Lincoln . . . Edison . . . Bell. They did not listen to the people who called them fools. And how about Hillary and Tenzing? Could they have climbed Mt. Everest if they had been conformists? No!"

Harry blinked and smiled at his friend. It was heartwarming to hear those words from him, to hear the encouragement.

They paid for their cokes, got up, and walked out of the Corner Store, ignoring the stares cast in their direction by several of the customers. Harry knew that Bud secretly delighted in such attention.

Out on the sidewalk, they hesitated. "Where you going?" Bud asked.

"I have a class in history this afternoon and I want to go to the library first to bone up for it. I'll go down to the pool about four o'clock."

Bud yawned and stretched his long arms high into the air. Then he scratched his chest thoughtfully. "Me, I think I'll take in the movie at the Bijou. All about another planet. Want to come?"

"I'd better not," Harry said regretfully, for he really did not feel like studying today.

"You are velcome do choin me, Herr Williams," Bud intoned in a German accent, one of the many he used to amuse his friends. "Id's a goot flicker."

"Scat!" Harry laughed. "Nothing doing. Besides, here comes Dorothy. I'd rather join her."

Bud made a circular motion with his forefinger just above his temple, as if confirming his doubts as to Harry's sanity. Harry knew all this was to help get his mind off his troubles. He slapped Bud on the back, and Bud loped down the street toward the Bijou.

As usual, the sight of Dotty Bryson walking toward him, the sun shining on her auburn hair, a bounce in her step, and her mouth twitching with a tendency to smile, made Harry feel dizzy. She had on a neat, straight skirt and a sloppy-joe sweater, and she wore white woolen socks and saddle shoes on her dainty feet. Under her arm were a couple of books.

"Hello, Dotty," he said, looking down at her and taking her offered hand.

"Hello, Harry," she answered. "Wasn't that Bud?"

"Yes. He's off to study his astronomy."

"Good for him. It's about time he thought about books. Usually all he wants to do is go to the movies."

"Where are *you* going?" Harry inquired.

"I'm looking for you."

"Fine. Let's head toward the library."

They crossed the street together and went past the neat little shops, the book stores, the drug stores. Now that he was with someone else—and such a one!—Harry was not so conscious of the stares of others.

The campus lawns were wide and green and inviting. Here and there couples were seated beneath trees studying or just loafing and gazing at the sky. Overhead, the branches were laden with leaves and buds; green sprays of ivy climbed the walls of the older buildings.

"Going to practice later?" Dotty asked lightly, her eyes on her feet.

"Yeah. Four o'clock.

"Do you think it's a good idea?"

"Sure. Why not?"

"Well, what was in the *Daily* and all."

"There wasn't very much in the *Daily*," he said quietly. "Just some fellow sounding off."

"But everybody reads it."

"Evidently."

Suddenly, Dotty stopped and planted herself in front of him, looking up into his face. A tiny, vertical crease appeared between her two lovely eyes.

"Listen, Harry, you may resent this, but Dad read the article today at breakfast, and he said he agreed with it."

"A lot of people seem to agree with it," Harry answered.

"Dad is on the faculty," Dotty pointed out. "He says that most of the faculty members are siding with coach Barnes."

"I had no idea it was *that* big a battle," Harry said.

"Neither did I—until this morning," Dotty said. "That's why you just can't pretend nothing is wrong." She turned again, and they continued walking.

"You know," Dotty went on, "Dad was very upset about last night. Of course I know you didn't mean it, but after all he is in a position of responsibility at State, and he has to consider what the administration will think."

"I'm sorry about yesterday," Harry told her. "I truly am. But that was how I felt. And how I still feel. Look, I'm not some sort of mechanical toy you can wind up and make go."

"Nobody said you were!"

"But that's the implication," Harry retorted hotly. "Some people think that all a coach has to do is say *'Swim,'* and a fellow goes out and swims and beats everybody in sight. It doesn't happen that way. No more than you could pass an examination without studying beforehand."

"That's different," Dotty said defensively.

"No, it isn't. I have to study for a race and get myself adjusted to it."

"Maybe you are a *prima donna* after all," Dotty observed with a little smile.

"No, I'm not. I'm just a human being. You know yourself that swimming is not like football or basketball. It is an individual thing. In football, if a boy isn't up to his best for a game, there are ten others to help him along. In swimming, you're on your own."

"All right," she replied, her face going crimson. "But that's no reason to ignore Coach Barnes or be rude to Dad."

Harry hurled his book to the ground. "You, too! I'm trying to explain, but you just won't understand."

"Dad has already explained to me."

"Explained what?"

"That you're headline-happy!"

Almost as soon as she said the words, Dotty bit her lower lip as though trying to retract them. But they were out. "Harry . . ."

"I see," Harry said, bending to pick his book from the sidewalk. "Just because he's a big wheel on the faculty, your father has to be right—and you have to believe him."

"Oh—oh," Dotty began, and then her eyes overflowed with tears. "I was only trying to be helpful and diplomatic. And after the way I've defended you today."

"What do you mean? Defended me."

"Just that. Several girls asked me what came over you at the meet, and I told them that you weren't up to the relay and you needed the rest and all. But they only laughed. Some of them said they wouldn't speak to me again if I continued to go around with someone who has no school spirit."

"They said *that?*" Harry asked in disbelief.

"Some of them."

"That's fantastic."

"And now you act like I'm a villainess!"

"Boy, this thing sure has gotten out of hand," Harry said, shaking his head.

"That's what I've been trying to tell you," Dotty murmured tearfully, wiping at her eyes with a handkerchief.

"Heck, a guy can't even make his own decisions."

"Not with so many people involved, Harry."

"I feel trapped," he said.

"So do I, especially after what Dad said."

"What did he say?"

"That I was not to go out with you until you apologized both to him and to Coach Barnes."

"Apologize for what?" Harry almost yelled.

"Dad says that you know for what."

"But I haven't done anything yet."

"Maybe that's what's wrong," Dotty said quietly.

That was too much for Harry Williams. He lengthened his stride, and Dotty was soon far behind him. She did not run to catch up with him, and he did not look back.

4

It was not until he was on the broad concrete walk that led to the entrance of the imposing Fieldhouse later in the afternoon that Harry Williams thought about Doc Howell. The thought was disturbing. What would the old-timer think about this state of affairs? Though they had not corresponded for a long time, Harry knew that Doc would be alarmed if he knew the story.

It was one thing to be engaged in a wrangle right on the spot where you knew all the facts, but it would be a horse of another color to someone as gentle and wise as Doc Howell, a man who somehow managed to avoid making enemies but who usually could make his point. Thinking about Doc gave added weight to the issue, a weight that settled leadenly in the region of Harry's heart.

What would Doc say? Would he be disappointed?

Crucial as they were, these were questions that could not be worried about now. Others, more immediate, demanded his attention.

No one else was in the locker room, so Harry undressed quickly, stepped into the shower briefly, and then put on his trunks. He felt better this way, encased in the tight material, with his torso free from constricting outer clothing. This was the uniform by which the world could identify him. From the pool came the hollow, echoing yells of the rest of the team, punctuated by Coach Barnes' frequent whistles and bellows.

The air in the vast cavern was warm and humid. Perhaps a dozen fellows were either in the water or on the pool apron. Some in the water were using paddle boards, pushing them ahead for support so they could exercise their leg muscles and not tire their arms. A few were racing.

Coach Barnes wore an oversized, underwashed sweatsuit with a large capital *S* stitched on the front. A green eyeshade decorated his forehead; a whistle on a leather thong hung around his neck. At the moment, the whistle was between the coach's teeth and was being blown loudly.

Harry walked over to Dixon, the back-stroker, a rangy boy with terrific shoulder muscles. "How's the water?"

Dixon gave Harry a queer look, said "Okay," and plunged in. He surfaced in the middle of the pool and did not look back.

Jim Holland, the freshman sprinter, came plowing down a side lane. Harry knelt on the tile and greeted him, "Good going, fella. Your leg action's improving all the time."

Holland glanced up briefly and said, "Thanks, Harry. Thanks a lot." Then, to Harry's astonishment, the lad pushed off, putting a period to the short conversation. That was odd. Ordinarily, Holland was tickled pink to get some free advice from him.

The nearest swimmer now was Reynolds, who, with Bud Hill, made up the breast-stroking punch of the squad. But Harry didn't risk another rebuff. Something was wrong here today and he intended to find out what it was. First, though, he would get into that water—he needed to plunge in and feel its texture.

Diving, he glided to the very bottom and then leveled off, feeling the rough composition of the pool floor with his hands, following it all the way as it sloped upward. He popped to the surface just a stroke from the other end, scarcely winded by the long underwater trip.

Harry took a deep breath, about to repeat the swim.

"Williams!"

Coach Barnes' rasping voice growled resoundingly.

Automatically Harry said, "Sir!"

"On the deck."

Harry reached up, gripped the run-off rim, and hauled himself from the water in a single, fluid motion. He would have preferred to remain in the pool, for his sinews were just beginning to loosen—and the water felt so good. As he padded toward the coach, who was seated on the third row of the bleachers, Harry wondered if Barnes was going to apologize for the fracas.

The coach was busily scribbling on a clipboard that was propped on his knees. He continued to write after Harry stood before him with his hands on his hips. The swimmer shifted from one bare foot to the other. Barnes glanced up as if aware of Harry for the first time.

"Ah, Williams," he said pleasantly.

"You called me, coach?"

Rusty Barnes frowned, as though trying to remember. "Yes. Yes, I did," he mumbled absently. "I was wondering when you last did calesthenics."

"Why—yesterday. Last night, at the house. I always do them at the house so I'll have more time for swimming here."

"Hmmm. Well, I kind of thought I hadn't seen you working out lately. I don't suppose you'd mind doing some now?" The eyes in the leathery, jowled face were utterly expressionless.

Barnes wasn't talking very loudly, but most of the team had paused in its workout and was watching the pair.

"I was planning to do them later on."

"I'd prefer you did them now," said Barnes mildly. "Some push-ups, back bends, sit-ups. Oh, well, you know." He commenced writing again.

Harry was about to make a violent protest when he remembered that the others were watching. Evidently, the word about Barnes' plan had spread before his arrival, which explained the aloofness of the boys. All were straddling the fence, aware that a struggle for supremacy was taking place between the coach and the star swimmer.

Harry, however, had no desire to compete with Coach Barnes for control of this team or any other. He wanted to be left alone, and if Barnes was expecting a demonstration of insubordination, he was going to be disappointed.

Harry found an open place, spread out a towel, and proceeded to sit on it. He hooked his feet under a wall rung and started his sit-ups.

A few moments later the rest of the squad resumed its labors. The tension in the room lessened noticeably. Harry reasoned he could finish this business in a few minutes and get back into the water. He might as well humor Coach Barnes.

His body responded rapidly to the demands he made on it now—pulling up into a sitting position from a prone, slapping his thighs with his palms, touching his toes, and then back on his spine again.

Up. Slap. Touch. Back.

Once out of the corner of his eye he glimpsed Barnes watching him thoughtfully. Well, let him try to figure it out. This would prove that Harry Williams was not staging an insurrection. He merely wanted his rights. It would be insane to make an issue out of calesthenics. Actually, Barnes was correct in making the request. True, were it not for yesterday's eruption, Barnes would not have bothered—he knew, too, that nobody was in better condition than Williams.

Before long, Holland sidled near, obviously interested in talking.

"Okay, Holland," said Harry in time with his movements. "What gives?"

"We didn't want to cut you, Harry," said the sprinter, "but after the fuss, we didn't know which way to jump. Coach Barnes says you're liable to cause dissension on the team."

Dissension. That was a word from the editorial this morning. Coach Barnes wasn't being very original.

"I see. What do you think, Holland? Am I letting the team down?"

Holland looked away. "I don't know, Harry. I'm just a freshman around here."

The boy's reply disturbed Harry. He had hoped there would be an unequivocal vote of confidence. This half-and-half stuff indicated that the boys were split. Holland, as if not wanting to be caught spilling the beans, turned abruptly and trotted along the side of the pool, broke into a run, and sprang far out into the water.

Ten minutes later, Harry, feeling he'd had enough, finished his push-ups, rose to his feet, and headed for the water.

"Williams," called Barnes as he emerged from his office. "You're not finished yet."

"What's that, coach?" asked Harry as he halted in mid-stride.

"I say—you're not finished yet. You've got another hour to go."

"Hey—" Harry felt a flame of anger lick through him.

Barnes planted himself firmly near the diving board, jaw jutting, brows dark. "An hour more. I haven't seen you do calesthenics in over a week. You've got some catching up to do."

Once more the other swimmers paused in their training, and Harry wondered if he could keep a tight hold on his temper. Talk about dissension, this sort of treatment would bring about a mutiny in no time.

It hurt him to comply, but Harry snapped, "Yes, sir," and went back to the exercises. Suddenly, they were not fun, but were an arduous chore that made his stomach churn with frustration. Never in all his years as an athlete had he been forced to condition himself. He had done it automatically, just as a dancer or singer will rehearse every chance he gets. On top of that was the humility of it all—no one else was exercising now. But then, maybe that was what Barnes had wanted to achieve: to put Williams in his place and make him like it. Of course it would be a terrible error to rebel, for that would set a bad example for the others. No. He would have to take this without a word.

Up. Slap. Touch. Back.

Harry knew that all this nonsense would end if he would only repent and eat crow. But that was out of the question, for it would negate all he believed in. It had become a matter of pride with him—but not blind pride. With the most important races of his career coming up in a few weeks—the Conference and then the Nationals—he could not risk being told by Barnes which events he could enter and which he couldn't. And an apology would mean just that—once he surrendered, he would never be able to stand up to Barnes again.

At that moment Bud Hill came into the hall. He was shuffling along, jabbing out with his left hand, holding his right poised, muttering, swiping at his nose with his thumb, dodging invisible punches thrown at him, lashing out suddenly with vicious right hooks. An unseen blow rocked his head back. He shook himself, his lips curling into a sneer of hate as he drove forward, swinging his arms, pumping his fists at an imaginary opponent, building up to one cataclysmic blast that must have shattered the phantom. Breathing heavily, Bud let his arms fall to his sides as he looked down, a faint smile touching his mouth. He kicked his ghostly victim as a sign of contempt. Then he held his hands aloft in the time-honored gesture of the victorious boxer.

That was when he saw Harry toiling on the floor.

"So what's this? A new kind of joke?"

Up. Slap. Touch. Back.

"I was going to ask the same thing. Having fun?"

Bud looked mystified. "Oh, the boxing? Well, I was just getting in a few licks in case I ever get bounced from the swimming team. I'll go right to the boxing coach and let him sign me up. I've already got a string of fifteen knockouts."

"You act," gasped Harry, "as if you were the one getting knocked out."

"I do absorb my share of punishment," said Bud seriously, "but I give as good as I get."

"Hill!"

"Coach?"

"Ten laps in the pool and no remarks!"

At that Bud Hill sucked in his lower lip so far that he resembled a freckled chipmunk. He staggered to the edge of the pool, hovered for an instant, and flopped into the water like a fallen log. He stayed under until Barnes' anger had passed. Harry thought he saw a flicker of amusement on the coach's face. He stood up.

"How about having a little talk, Coach? In your office."

The big, bluff man hesitated, not wanting to look as though he were being ordered around by Harry. Finally, he loosed a massive sigh, wagged his head, took off his eyeshade, and led the way toward his office.

Sinking into the swivel chair behind his desk, Coach Barnes said, "Okay, Williams. What's on your mind?"

"That's my question, Coach. What's on yours? This business wasn't my idea. I'm not stomping on anyone's fingers. I'm not giving interviews to the papers."

"You're the cause of it all," Barnes said harshly.

"I thought we'd come to some sort of agreement, Coach."

"I know of no such agreement. I'm being paid to coach the swimming team. Not *part* of the team—*all* of it. The whole team. You've undermined my authority." He pointed in the direction of the pool where, after the disrupting influence of Bud's entrance, the team was buckling down to work again. "You know how high-strung those boys are; you know how easily they can be put off their form. First you tell me what races you'll swim, then that redhead gets funny." The finger focused on Harry. "I may not be able to bring you to heel, Williams, but I *know* I can crack the whip on Hill."

"I'm sorry about that, Coach," said Harry contritely. "Bud just has too much spirit and energy."

"Suppose some of the trustees or faculty members witnessed this behavior?"

Harry was tempted to chide Barnes for worrying too

much about the bigwigs. Instead, he admitted that it might not look too good.

"There you are," Barnes said, slapping the desk with the flat of his hand. "Those fellows have seen the way you flout my authority and they think they can be cute, too. Williams," he leaned toward Harry, "this is my job—teaching those boys out there. It's a big responsibility. Maybe in your eyes I'm not much, but most of them look up to me. And I respect them. I can't afford to throw it all away just to please one man."

"It isn't a matter of pleasing me, but as long as we're being candid I think I'm safe in saying that much of the success of the team depends upon me and my form. Do you agree?"

Coach Barnes frowned heavily. "In a small way, yes, that's true."

"Believe me," said Harry, "I've no desire to start a rivalry with you. I'm merely a student. In a few more weeks I'll be out of college looking for a coaching job myself."

Barnes nodded. "I'm glad you see my side of it, Williams. Now perhaps I can expect more cooperation from you in the future."

"As much as I can, but I can't promise that I'll enter every race and try for a record every time. I'm not built that way."

The coach lifted his huge arms into the air with exasperation. "That's what I mean. You want special consideration. And favoritism will cause resentment."

"I doubt that."

"I don't!" the coach shouted. "It has to be done my way or not at all."

Harry Williams averted his eyes and glanced at the walls of the office. The framed photographs of past State stars looked down on him. Most of them were autographed to Coach Barnes, expressing appreciation and thanks for his guidance. Inside a glass-fronted cabinet were several cups and small golden statues, awards won by teams in years gone by.

The coach followed his gaze. "Take a good look, Williams. Each one of those cups is the result of teamwork. Not lone wolves. Everyone working together—cooperating."

"Yes, I see," Harry said, and once more he wondered whether he was perhaps stupidly wrong in his actions. Just the same, that did not necessarily prove that Coach Barnes was right.

Harry stood up and rubbed his hands on his trunks. "Coach, it's unfortunate that things have turned out this way. I certainly don't want to make you look bad in front of the others. I'm sorry that it all had to be printed in the *Daily*. Makes it pretty awkward around campus for me."

Coach Barnes joined him and they walked back to the pool. The walls reverberated with the yells of the swimmers as they splashed from one end of the pool to the other.

"Then I take that to mean," mused Barnes, "that I can expect you to back me one hundred per cent from now on."

"I didn't say that, Coach."

"You forget that I can use discipline and no one will say I'm wrong."

"That won't get us anywhere—except maybe to force me off the team."

"If it has to come to that," said Barnes in a low voice, "then I'm ready for it. I want another five-year contract to coach at State. I also want to make the Olympic coaching staff. Those things are more important to me than keeping you happy."

Harry Williams bit his lower lip to keep from saying anything more. He stalked away.

Bud Hill was resting on the bench when Harry strode up angrily.

"Got a watch?"

"Sure," said Bud quickly. "Want to know what time it is?"

But Harry passed by and went over to the end of the pool and stood with his toes curled over the edge. He shook his arm muscles loose and took several deep breaths. Bud, realizing this was no time for dawdling, picked up a stopwatch from the timer's box, adjusted it, and held his thumb over the button.

Harry peered into the smooth, unrippled surface of the pool. On the bottom the painted lane markers stretched toward the distant end.

"Take your mark," said Bud. "Go!"

As the last word echoed in the air, Harry sprang, his body low and straight, and sliced the water neatly, his arms churning almost at once. His lungs were full of air that he released gradually and he scarcely took another complete breath until he had made his turn. He kicked off from the concrete, catapulting on the return trip. The anger he'd felt at the coach spurred him on, and he felt the water slide past swiftly.

At the end of two lengths he sensed that the rest of the team had left the water and that he was alone in the pool.

The pool was twenty-five yards long, which meant sixteen laps for four hundred yards. Bud Hill yelled out the number of laps he'd done each time he touched the end of the tank. The redhead had to bend close to the water to be audible. Now and then Harry caught glimpses of the others, although he couldn't hear their cries of encouragement.

This was what he liked. This was really his element and with every stroke he felt the surge of power in his body and heard the rapid-fire drumbeat of his kicking feet behind him, pushing him ahead.

He might have gone the whole sixteen lengths if there'd been someone else to push him, another swimmer plowing on his heels. His anger at the coach had ebbed; it was not enough to sustain him through the strain of a race, although it was the anger that had furnished the initial impetus.

Feeling he had reached his peak at the end of the seventh length, he decided to sprint the final twenty-five yards, and he kicked off viciously, driving hard and fast.

Suddenly, he was slapping the end of the pool for the last time right under the kneeling Bud Hill, and he hung on, gulping air. In that moment he felt the clean exhaustion that comes with having swum well.

"Terrific time!" Bud yelled. "Terrific!"

The guys were shouting and applauding, but it wasn't wild. Harry sensed they were disappointed that he hadn't continued for the full four hundred yards.

But Bud Hill, the eternal optimist, was not discouraged. He saw in the race signs of great things to come.

"Keep that up," he cried, "and you can't miss breaking the four-forty record. Olympics, here we come!"

As he hauled himself from the water, Harry found himself wishing that he were as confident.

5

Mrs. Gray was standing on the front porch of her home when Harry came up the walk. His muscles were cleanly tired and his whole body was smoothly relaxed after the workout. He grinned a greeting.

"Hello, Mrs. Gray. You're looking wonderful."

The kindly woman blushed and fiddled with her iron-gray hair. "Now, Harry Williams. After I've been working in my garden all day, I know very well I don't look well. I feel as if I've been digging ditches."

Harry placed an arm around her shoulders. She was diminutive and attractive in a crisp gingham dress. Her eyes twinkled at him.

"Well, I won't argue with a lady," Harry said. "But if you looked any prettier, you'd have the co-eds throwing tomatoes at you."

Mrs. Gray tossed her head back and laughed a deep, warm laugh. Then her face became very serious. "You are such fun, Harry. One would never think you had so much on your mind these days."

"Not so much," Harry said deprecatingly. "Others have more."

"Do you have a minute, Harry?" she asked.

"Why, sure."

She led the way to the porch swing, where they sat down side by side.

"What's up?" he asked lightly.

"First of all," Mrs. Gray murmured unhappily, "what is all this about trouble on the swimming team? You know that if there is any way I can help—you mustn't hesitate for a minute. Remember, Dr. Gray was highly thought of on campus. And I daresay that I am, too."

Harry touched the older woman's hand gently. "That's wonderful of you, Mrs. Gray. It really is. But I don't think there is any need for anything right now. I imagine it will work out somehow."

"Well, I don't want to pry," she continued, "and I won't ask any more personal questions about the matter; however, I'll feel very hurt if you don't turn to me in case of need."

"I know I can," Harry said, genuinely and deeply touched by her affection.

"The second thing," Mrs. Gray said, somewhat brighter and gayer, "is more pleasant."

"Carry on," Harry told her. "I can use some pleasantries."

"I thought so. In a way it contradicts my offer just now, but maybe it will augment it, too. My sister, the one who lives in Cleveland, has invited me out there for a couple of weeks while her husband goes to Mexico on business.

She used to come here before Dr. Gray passed on. I'll be leaving in a few days, and since my holiday will coincide with the school's vacation, I doubt if it will work much of a hardship on my tenants."

"*One* day would be a hardship," Harry said, thinking of what a mess the room would be in as the result of Bud Hill's irrepressible habits.

"Nonsense," she said, obviously pleased. "Anyway, I'm planning to go to Cleveland by train. And that means I'll be leaving my car here in town. In the garage in fact. Now, what I want you to do is to use the car just as if it were your own. Will you do that for me, Harry?"

"Oh, I couldn't do that, Mrs. Gray!"

"Of course you could. All young men like to have a car of their own to drive around in. Besides, I simply couldn't leave it all alone for a couple of weeks. The spark plugs would run down or the carburetor wouldn't rate or something."

Harry guffawed out loud. "Not quite, Mrs. Gray. But something like that."

"In any case, I *do* know it's much better for a car to be in use. Isn't that correct?"

"That's correct," Harry agreed.

"Well, then, you'll be doing me a favor by driving it."

"If you put it that way—"

"I certainly do," Mrs. Gray said firmly. "And just to be sure you get accustomed to it fast, you should use it tonight to take out Dorothy Bryson."

"Tonight?"

"Yes. Any objections?"

"No-o-o-o. . . ."

"Well, then. Here are the keys."

She tossed him a jingling ring of keys and explained what each one was for. "Now," she sighed, getting up from the swing. "I must be off to town to do some last-minute shopping. I haven't a thing to wear for Cleveland."

Harry knew that was a slight exaggeration, but he also knew that all women, young or old, always insisted they had nothing to wear. The real meaning was that they had nothing *new* to wear. Since most men he knew managed to buy about one suit every two years and maybe two new shirts every one year, the constant need for brand new clothes left him bewildered. But he was wise enough never to question a female on the subject. They had a very cold, hard logic about such things.

He was delighted at his good fortune in securing a car for a couple of weeks. He had resigned himself to a wait of a few years before he could own his own. This was like striking oil. True, it was not a sparkling brand-new Cadillac, but it was dependable and respectable-looking. And, for a little while, it was his.

He was so pleased that he forgot he had quarreled with Dotty the day before; he telephoned her at her home and, to *her* astonishment, made a date for that evening.

Bud Hill was as pleased as if the car had been left for him, and before supper he joined Harry for a warm-up spin around the town.

"Si, si," he said, "Disa isa gooda cara. Goes-a real zoom-zoom."

Harry cleared his throat with dignity. "Ahem. Well, it's not much, but *we* think it's all right for a *town* car."

Bud Hill was shaking his head as if in amazement. "Gee-a-whiz. This-a monster makes almost as-a fast as-a Signor Williams, the Human Shark."

"Lay off," Harry laughed. "This is off-duty time. No shop talk."

Bud blinked myopically. "Whatever-a you a-say, boss."

They drove around the town as if they'd never seen it before. The ivy-covered buildings on the campus never looked so good, the grass never as green, the trees never as tall. They drove by the imposing statue of the first chancellor of the university, which faced the soaring columns of the chapel. The chapel bells were ringing out six o'clock.

"Great place, isn't it, Harry?" Bud breathed with sincerity.

"Wonderful," Harry replied warmly.

All at once he was filled with awe for this institution of learning and the students and teachers that inhabited it and made it great. He was proud to be a part of it, and he hoped he would never do anything that would bring discredit upon either the school or himself.

That night Harry was so anxious to show off his new possession, temporary though it was, that he arrived at Dotty's half an hour early.

Professor Bryson admitted him and led the way into his study. There were several shelves of books along two walls. A picture-window looked out over a neatly tended garden shaded by twin maples. The professor's mahogany desk faced the window. Right now it was littered with papers and opened books. Apparently he was working on some sort of research paper.

"Come on in, Harry," the professor said. "Dorothy isn't quite ready yet. You know how girls are."

"I guess I do," Harry replied hesitantly. He was still not sure how he would get along with Professor Bryson. They had not met since that awkward moment in the parking lot. However, the older man did not appear to be holding a grudge.

"Working, sir?" Harry inquired, indicating the littered desk.

"As a matter of fact, I am. Getting ready for the spring examinations."

"I never thought of that," Harry observed. "I mean, it never occurred to me that professors had to do homework, too."

"We certainly do. I would guess that most instructors have to put in at least three hours of preparation for every class. And exam time is even busier. But we don't complain. This is our job—and I for one like it."

"May I ask what you're absorbed in at the moment? That is, if it isn't top-secret."

"Of course. It's for my Shakespeare classes. We've concentrated on *Hamlet* this semester and my questions will be on both the play and the man."

His intense brown eyes fixed on Harry steadily. As he talked, he reached for his pipe and filled it with tobacco from a soft leather pouch, tamped it carefully, and then lit it with a large, wooden match. Clouds of gray-blue smoke billowed around his head. He squinted at Harry through his spectacles and the smoke.

"Of course, you know the Melancholy Dane," the professor stated.

"I found *Hamlet* the most exciting of all Shakespeare's plays," Harry said with enthusiasm. After reading it two or three times, he had gone to see the college players put on a performance and then he'd seen the motion picture.

"You remind me of him in some ways," the professor said.

"Me?" Harry was genuinely mystified. "Heck, Hamlet was brilliant—and moody, too. He was all mixed up."

"He was a man who could not make up his mind," Professor Bryson said, his eyes intent on Harry. "In the end, his indecision killed not only him but half a dozen others as well."

"Where do I fit in?"

"Harry, sit down," the professor offered gently. Slowly, Harry sank onto the couch. "What has happened in the last few days has not been unique in man's history, certainly not in State's history. A boy, to put it briefly, has attempted to assert his individuality over the good of the mass. However he was motivated, however just his cause, those things are not important. The fact that he dare rebel against the unwritten precepts of society *is* important."

"Rebel? Society? That was not me, Professor."

"I think so," was the quick reply. "It's not that I do not comprehend your problem—I do, Harry, believe me—it's that I could not, in clear conscience, support your stand. You see, I was a swimmer once—and a good one. Some thought I could have been a great one."

"What prevented you, sir?"

Professor Bryson puffed thoughtfully on his pipe for a few moments. Harry sniffed the sweetish aroma. He himself did not smoke, but he thoroughly enjoyed the smell of fine pipe tobacco.

"Two things," the professor said. "My ambition and my love. I wanted to be a college professor and I wanted to marry Dorothy's mother. I succeeded in both, but it is unlikely that I could have done so had I insisted on being a swimming champion."

"Why, Professor?" Harry asked. "That's not so unreasonable."

"For me it was. I had to make up my mind which were the most important. I knew I could probably achieve two of my choices—but not all three. One had to be sacrificed."

"Swimming," Harry said simply.

Professor Bryson nodded.

"I was not aware that I was in a similar dilemma," Harry said.

"You are, though."

"How do you mean?"

The professor held up three fingers. He bent the first one down. "Swimming." He bent the second one. "Education." He bent the third. "Dorothy."

Harry bobbed his head slowly. "Mmmm. Maybe so,

but I don't feel torn. I simply want to do all three and I think I can."

The older man loomed over him heavily. "But at what a price, boy! At what a price! You are altogether too absorbed in just one aspect of living and are neglecting the others. You have been deliberately throwing away some other pleasant aspects, you know, for the sake of winning races that no one will remember a year from now. Don't you see—you have to make up your mind. As Hamlet put it: *'To be, or not to be; that is the question. . . .'* "

"I think I see, sir," Harry said. "You are more or less suggesting that I ease up on swimming and pay more attention to my studies—and to Dorothy."

"That's about the size of it," the professor said flatly.

"Then you don't believe that the swimming is worth that much effort and concentration?"

"Not as much as you are putting into it—to the exclusion of your friends and superiors. No man can get very far alone. He needs the company of others—he needs a *team* behind him."

"Let me ask you a question, Professor," Harry said. "Please understand that I do not intend to be rude or fresh, but would it be right for me to turn my back on the thing in my life that means so much to me, the one part where I can make, in a small way, my mark on the world?"

"Well, now—"

"For instance, suppose swimming is just as vital to me

as your becoming a college professor was to you. What would you say then?"

"That's unfair, Harry," Professor Bryson snapped. "One is just an avocation, the other is a means of livelihood."

"Why did you want to teach, if I may ask, sir?"

"So that I could be of some help to my fellow man," the professor answered promptly.

"Well, I feel the same way about swimming," Harry said. "I think that I can show the way for youngsters who aspire to great things—to records, if you will—and perhaps I can even serve as a model for some of them. It is even possible that what someone may learn from me about the water may save his life. That is my way of serving my fellow man."

The older man's pipe had gone out. He fished in his pockets for another match, dug one out, and struck it on the sole of his shoe.

"Williams," he said, "you are a mighty stubborn young fellow. If there were more time, I know I would be able to convince you of your misplaced confidence."

"No one ever convinced Hamlet, though, did they?" Harry grinned.

"It cost him his life," the professor noted again.

"And made him immortal," Harry said triumphantly.

Dorothy Bryson chose this moment to break in on the two men. She skipped to the middle of the study, stopped, and spun around on her toes. Her skirt flared prettily around her legs; her shining hair swirled attractively. "What a topic," she chirped. "Hamlet, indeed. Why not Falstaff? At least he was funny. How do I look?"

Both men broke off their argument and gazed with approval at the lovely vision. Harry had forgotten the quarrel they had had and could now think only of how beautiful she was and how fond he was of her.

He felt her father's glance shift from Dotty to him, as if to say, "Isn't *she* worth sacrificing everything for!"

For a brief instant he thought that the older man might have a point.

They bade the professor good-bye, promising to be back early. Dotty stood on tiptoe and kissed her father's leathery cheek. Then she took Harry's arm and they went out into the twilight and left the professor to his work.

"My Golden Coach!" Dotty cried at the sight of Mrs. Gray's very modest car.

"With one hundred and ten horses at your service, Madam. Will you enter?"

"I will, kind sir," she murmured, and hiking her skirt slightly, stepped into the front seat. "It's like sitting on the feathers of a thousand hummingbirds," Dotty whispered.

"Plucked them just for you," Harry said as he got in. He started the motor, let out the clutch, and they roared away in a thickening fog of exhaust.

Word of Harry's remarkable performance in the pool had spread like wildfire around the campus, and that evening when they went to The Blue Parrot, the college hangout, both he and Dotty were greeted cordially by all except a few die-hards. The Blue Parrot featured a loud jukebox and a spacious dance floor and the vociferous antics of the Campus Comedians, fellows who would do anything anywhere for a laugh. Until he had begun to room with Harry, Bud Hill was known as the Clown Prince of these jokers. Harry had persuaded him to leave off such doings and make way for the sophomores.

Harry and Dotty were lucky enough to get a table for two in a remote corner where they had privacy and still could see everything that was going on. When some of the younger students exploded onto the dance floor it was better than watching a Martin and Lewis movie.

Watching them, Harry felt immeasurably older and more mature—the fate of the senior who is highly conscious of the responsibility that awaits him after graduation. For a moment he had a pang of regret that he was no longer a freshman or sophomore with little to worry about for the next couple of years. But he knew that was a juvenile thought; he should be happy to be making plans for his future.

And speaking of plans . . .

Dotty must have read his mind, for suddenly she blurted, "Have you any definite plans for the summer, Harry? We haven't had a chance to talk or anything lately."

"It all depends," he said, eying the frantic dancers on the floor. "Depends on how I make out in the All-Conference meet next week. If I'm any good, I'll want to swim in the Nationals and then maybe I should train all summer for the Olympics."

"Won't it cost a lot of money?"

"I guess so," he said ruefully. "I'll have to see about some sort of job to keep me going. Unless I can find someone interested enough in me to subsidize me a little."

Dotty was methodically destroying a paper straw between her fingers.

"What's wrong, honey? Did I say anything?"

"You *didn't* say anything, that's what's wrong."

"Huh?"

"You haven't even mentioned me," she said in a choked voice.

"But I'm automatically including you."

"How?"

"Well, I'll keep in touch and all that. And if I can get a job right here in town, I'll take it. You know that."

"But you aren't talking about *long-range* plans. What about us?"

"Golly, you know darned well that I won't do anything without you—only . . ."

"Only what?"

"Well, only that I've really got to concentrate on the Olympics if I expect even to qualify."

"The Olympics come first then?"

"Not exactly. It will only be for a couple of months and after that you and I can really begin to map out our future."

"I have to wait then?"

"For a little while," Harry said.

"Is that fair?" Dotty queried. Her lower lip was sticking out in a pretty pout; her eyes were downcast. The straw was just a crumple of paper now.

"But this can't be news to you," Harry persisted. "You've known my ambitions for a long time. I'm good enough for the Olympics, and it would be a terrific honor to make them. I can't turn my back on my one big opportunity."

Dotty sighed and looked up in time to see one of her girl friends approaching the table. Harry recognized her: Sally Dougherty, a flighty, bubbly little blonde who seemed to have a different beau every other week.

"Dorothy!" Sally cried, "you are a *doll.* And so is Harry." Harry nodded and smiled and then shook hands with the embarrassed-looking youth who had followed in Sally's wake.

"See!" Sally cried, holding out her left hand.

The third finger looked as if it were on fire. A diamond as big as a grape glittered and flamed as Sally fluttered her hand this way and that.

"Oh, wonderful," Dotty said, but with little enthusiasm in her voice. "I heard about it this evening. All the best to you and Cyril."

Cyril had rather prominent teeth and wore horn-rimmed glasses; he drove a convertible that was almost but not quite as long as a freight car.

"I know you'll both be very happy," Dorothy said a little sadly.

And then Sally was on her way, preceded by the blinding flash of her engagement ring and continuous little cries of delight. Poor Cyril brought up the rear in solitude. This was Sally's night and she was making the most of it.

Harry was amazed to see that Dotty was staring after Sally with open envy.

"Hey, what gives—" he blurted out and then he knew. "Oh–oh! I think it has finally sunk into this melon of a brain."

"Don't they make a lovely couple?" sighed Dotty dreamily.

"Sally and the Ring?"

"That's no way to talk. You can tell they are very much in love."

"They sure are," Harry said, shielding his eyes as though the light from the huge diamond were blinding him. "Why didn't you say that that was what bothered you?"

"It's hardly up to a girl to say," Dotty said primly.

"Well, how is a guy supposed to know?"

"It's spring, isn't it? And we are going steady, aren't we?"

"Sure, we are, but—"

"But nothing—all you think about is that old swimming pool and one-fifties or nine-eighties or whatever it is you're always talking about."

Harry was about to make a crushing retort in defense of his sport. Then he paused. It was getting to be a habit for members of the Bryson family to take pot shots at his devotion to swimming. Coincidence wasn't the answer; the comments had a pattern. For a moment he was undecided which topic to pursue: the matter of rings in the spring, or the one that touched on his avocation. He felt confident that he could steer her thoughts from talk of engagements and elopements and marriages to less romantic but, to him, equally vital subjects.

"Dotty," Harry said, pressing her hand, "Dotty, I haven't asked you about this before, but apparently my swimming has a great effect on your attitude toward us. We have to talk about it, and I hope you'll be frank with me. I will be with you."

"What do you mean, Harry?"

"I mean that unless we have it out now, we're going to run into a peck of trouble before long."

Dotty traced an invisible design on the table top. "Yes?"

"Do you agree with your father about me?"

"You mean about the swimming and all?"

"Yes."

She tried to smile at him, but it didn't come off very well. "I suppose I do sound kind of catty sometimes."

"Sometimes," he replied gently.

"Maybe it *is* Dad's influence—and maybe it's merely my way of being jealous. It'd be different if there were a real person, another girl. Then I could stand up and *fight.* But it's hard to fight something a man has to *do.*"

"You're jealous of my swimming?"

"Well, I certainly recognize it as my rival."

"But it isn't." Harry felt suddenly that Dotty was going to ask him to choose between the water and her.

"Dad thought it was coming between him and my mother years ago."

"He told you that?"

"Not in so many words, but I have seen his face when

we go to swimming meets. It's as if he wanted to be in the pool himself, splashing away."

"Has it occurred to you, Dotty," murmured Harry, "that your father might have a few sour grapes on his vine?"

"I thought of that," admitted Dotty, "but you see, he remembers that he almost lost Mother because of his swimming. He doesn't want that to happen to me."

"It won't," Harry promised.

Dotty pressed her face into his shoulder and whispered fervently, "I hope not, darling. I hope not." He couldn't see her eyes but he guessed they were wet.

"Is it possible that in the final analysis the choice won't be mine, between swimming and you, but rather that it will be yours, between your father and me?"

"You've twisted my words," she protested.

"Maybe I just straightened them out."

Thus far Dotty had not raised her voice or used harsh words, but her message came through to Harry—it was a veiled ultimatum that he'd better start thinking of diamond rings rather than swimming meets.

What were the alternatives? One alternative was the possibility that Dotty might tire of waiting and might even meet another Cyril. The idea sent a tremor of panic through him, and he tried to push it away. But the more he tried, the larger it grew.

The worst part of it was that she had a good case—such a problem had arisen in her own family and, as a precedent, she had her father's example of how to cope with it. In the end, if she had to choose, family ties would probably make her choice go against him.

That was the risk he would run if he allowed Dotty to make the final selection. And yet he was not prepared to do the selecting himself. Whether she knew it or not, Dotty Bryson, by speaking her mind, by being frank, had dropped him smack into the middle of a pool—full of quicksand.

6

JIM HOLLAND broke his arm the day before the All-Conference meet was slated to begin at State Fieldhouse. Apparently Holland had taken his title as "The Sprinter" too seriously, for he broke one of Coach Barnes' cardinal rules—"no running on the apron of the pool."

All week long tension had built up in the members of the host team as they practiced several hours a day. Sports writers had labeled them as slight favorites over the six other conference squads, and that added to the pressure. It was tentatively agreed that Holland would enter the shorter races due to his speed in the 50-yard and the 100-yard distances; Harry Williams would do the 440- and the 1500-meter races.

Knowing the distances he would have to do, Harry mentally prepared himself for them, building up his stamina, conserving his energy for the long pull. He was glad that Barnes would leave him alone and not insist on his being the pool work horse. Besides, Holland was coming along nicely, very nicely.

Meanwhile, the rest of the team were settling down and readying themselves for a tough meet. Even Bud Hill cut out his role of court jester, and although the laughs were few and far between, an air of confidence pervaded the Fieldhouse and spread out over the campus. No longer was there any talk of "dissension" on the team. No more angry accusations were hurled at Harry Williams.

Then Holland broke his arm. He had been lolling at the far end of the pool, resting after a particularly good sprint, when Coach Barnes blew his whistle for the next practice race, and, anxious and eager, he had sprung to his feet and trotted toward the starting line under the diving-board structure. Inadvertently, he had stepped on a wet spot and slipped. He tried to hurl himself into the water, but he missed and his elbow struck the concrete.

Wincing with pain, Holland was led to the infirmary where the doctor set his arm and put it in a cast.

The team was as stunned as Holland, and their mood changed quickly from one of exuberance to one of impenetrable gloom.

"Golly," Bud Hill mumbled, "what will happen to us now?"

He spoke for the whole team. . . .

On Saturday, University City took on a festival look. Out-of-state licenses were plentiful on the cars; a dozen buses were parked near the Fieldhouse—the focal point of all the activity. Extra policemen were put on traffic duty in the campus area.

Inside the Fieldhouse itself, the stands around the pool

were jammed. Many spectators were standing wherever there was foot space. An excited hum swept through the audience, and now and then various blocks of fans sent up cheers for their particular teams and heroes. Each race was swum to the accompaniment of shouts and cries and exhortations to victory.

Harry Williams had acquitted himself rather well in the 1500-meter race, just nosing out last year's champ by five or six yards. It was not record time, but it was close to it. Then he had a three-hour rest before the afternoon races. He knew he would be ready for the 440 and was prepared to put out his best effort; he would have to if he expected to defeat the stars from the other schools.

But things were not going as well for the rest of the team. The competition today was a good deal stiffer than it had been with Tech a week before. However, State had managed to build up sufficient points to remain in a virtual three-way tie with Cranford and Hollis. As the afternoon wore on, it became clear that the meet would be decided in the final three races: the 100-yard sprint, the medley relay, and the 440. Since everyone had all but conceded the 440 to Harry Williams, State would only have to pick up a couple of seconds and thirds in the other races to walk off with top honors.

While the last of the divers were doing their stuff, Harry sat calmly on the end of the bench. Bud Hill was not so calm. He was going to swim the breast stroke in the relay and was not too keen on it.

"Heck, I don't think I'm a swimmer at all. I should have stuck to bird watching."

"Don't worry," Harry said. "You'll knock them dead."

"I won't, I won't," Bud jittered. "I'll get a cramp and I'll drown—in front of all these people."

"At ease. There's nothing to it. Don't forget the Cranford and Hollis guys are just as nervous."

Bud held up hands that trembled like leaves in a hurricane. "Yeah?"

Harry laughed.

"Oh," Bud wailed, "why did Holland have to break that limb? Why couldn't he have waited until tomorrow? With him in the 100 and you in the 440, we would have it cinched and I could do the dog paddle in the relay and it wouldn't matter."

Bud could make sense sometimes. If Holland were available, things would be much simpler. He could guarantee a second at least and with luck could have won.

"Williams."

At the whispered mention of his name, Harry glanced up. Coach Barnes pointed his finger and then crooked it—a sign he wanted to talk in private. Wondering what was on the coach's mind at this point, Harry got up, walked over the apron, and made his way through the crowd of official timers and judges. On the way he winked broadly at Dotty, who blew him a kiss.

In the comparative quiet of the locker room, Coach Barnes sank heavily to a bench that was littered with wet towels.

"We're in a fix, Harry," he said.

"I know. But don't worry, Coach. The boys will make it."

"They *have* to make it," Barnes said, looking up at Harry. "I've just heard that if we win the meet today, I will be offered a chance to join the Olympic coaching staff."

"No kidding," Harry said. "That's fine."

"It won't be fine unless we do it, Harry. Unless *you* do it."

"What do you mean, Coach? I feel pretty good. I think I can take that 440 with no trouble at all. And with the Cranford fellow pushing me, I might even make a record."

"It's not that," Barnes mumbled. "Even if we take the 440, we can lose the meet if we get blanked in the relay and the 100."

"What are the chances of being blanked?"

"They're good. Too good. Holland . . ."

He didn't have to finish the sentence. Harry knew how bitterly he regretted the loss of the flashy freshman.

"Well . . ."

"Harry," Barnes said fiercely. "You'll have to enter both the relay and the 100."

Harry blinked his eyes. "But coach, I'm all set for the 440. This is the day. I can feel it."

"Forget the 440, Harry. With you in the other two, we're just about certain to win."

"I thought you promised last week that I could pick my own races."

"I didn't break Jim Holland's arm."

Ignoring the aching knot of disappointment in his stomach, Harry said, "Okay, Coach. Tell me what you want me to do."

It was almost worth the sacrifice to see the way Barnes' lined face lighted up with surprise and gratitude.

At the announcement that Harry Williams would not swim in the 440-yard race, a growling roar went up from the crowd. After his great practice race earlier, they had begun to anticipate seeing a record being broken in the pool and were keyed up to watch Williams do it. Just as in the meet with Tech, they felt they were being cheated. But this time it was for an entirely different reason, and Harry Williams was quietly certain that no sports writer would ever squeeze the true story out of Coach Barnes.

Unable to respond to Bud Hill's persistent questions, Harry watched as the Cranford boy took an early lead in the 440 and built it up gradually until it was unbeatable. No one else was around to press him, so he more or less coasted to victory in ten seconds over Harry's best time. Harry tried not to think about what a race it could have been with him in it and with such a splendid swimmer as the Cranford boy as his competition. Well, now it was history.

Winning the 440 gave the Cranford team a lead in points; all they had to do now was to win one of the last two events and the meet cup would be theirs.

For the first time in his career as a swimmer, Harry Williams felt like a "team man." He was determined that State should win. Afterward . . . well, he would think about that afterward.

Harry walked over to an open locker and leaned against the door, feeling the metal cold against his skin. He closed his eyes. So it had come to this after all. Once more he was being flayed with the whip of decision. Dotty was right when she had said that he had no right to expect to make decisions easily when so many other people were involved.

Now, here was the whole future, not only of the team's reputation, but of Coach Barnes' fate, laid in his lap. He felt his heart beating fast. Today might have been the day to make his name a household word the country over—if he had raced in the 440. He knew he was not fast enough in the 100 to crack any marks. And, dependent as he would be on his slower colleagues, there would be no question of a record-breaking medley relay.

If only he did not *care* so much; if only he could be like Bud Hill or some of the others. Then it would not matter which race he swam or what his time was.

Which of Shakespeare's characters had been described as the one who "loved not wisely, but too well"?

Coach Barnes remained on the bench, slumping, dejection written on his features. Harry felt a wave of sympathy for Barnes, who had toiled for twenty years for this chance at the Olympics; and now it was almost within his grasp . . . and no way of telling if such a chance would be repeated.

One look at Barnes and Harry knew he could not refuse the man's request. He would obey. . . .

Then it was time for the 100-yard sprint. Harry Williams did not feel geared for that distance, but no one else had the remotest chance of winning it for State. He joined the other competitors at the end of the pool and, with them, tensed at the starter's: "Take your marks . . . Get set . . ." Harry began to lean into it. The gun cracked and he sprang far and low into the water.

Even before he touched the far end of the pool after the first twenty-five yards, he knew he could not take first place. Hollis had a man who seemed equipped with fins and who had trained specifically for the sprint. So Harry's best bet was to aim for second, to nose out the Cranford man and rack up second-place points.

Over the crashing roar of the crowd Harry made out the singular voice of Bud Hill:

"Go-go, Williams–chop-chop. Makee winner . . ."

Only with a very great effort did Harry Williams prevent himself from expending every last ounce of energy in this sprint–there was still the relay and he had to save something for that. It was not very much fun to be able to see another's feet ahead of him and he felt as if those fluttering heels were kicking his solar plexus.

In the very next lane he could see the contorted features of the Cranford swimmer–they were abreast of one another. Harry released a precious bit of his reserve energy and increased his arm beat; he slapped the end of the pool at the fifty-yard mark, doubled his knees, and pushed off viciously. It was enough to give him a lead of a few feet on the Cranford boy. All he had to do was hold it. The Hollis man was thrusting through the water like a surfaced sub, quite out of reach, with a lead that could not be beaten in the few yards remaining. Naturally, the Cranford rooters were exhorting their man to a superhuman effort in order to gain those valuable second-place points that would all but wreck State's hopes.

Williams jounced off the pool wall for the last time, two or three seconds behind Hollis. He could hear the strained gasps of Cranford in the next lane. Williams pumped his arms faster and harder pulling himself through the liquid; he spat water, snorted, and gasped. But he knew he was going to make it and when he finally did slap the end wall, he got as much of a cheer as the winning boy from Hollis. A second after him came the frustrated and surprised Cranford man.

Harry hauled himself out of the water, ignoring the numerous hands that offered to help; pushed past the people who wanted to congratulate him; past the smiling Coach Barnes; even past Bud Hill, who was leading mass yells. He went straight into the deserted locker room.

Harry did not come out again until the medley relay was announced. Still he did not speak to anyone. He was not in the mood for chit-chat and he wanted only to get the day over with now. He had turned off his brain and was now little more than a swimming machine. He was no longer thinking about the 440 or anything but doing anchor for the relay.

Probably no one in the entire auditorium was aware of the most significant part of the race he had just swum: it was the first time in years that Harry Williams had not won. . . .

The names were announced for the medley relay: Dixon

as back-stroker, Shaw as butterfly breast-stroker, Hill as orthodox breast-stroke, and Williams as free-style.

Harry glanced at the scoreboard.

Seven teams were listed, but only the first three meant anything. Only Hollis, Cranford, and State were entering the relay.

The scoreboard looked like this:

HOLLIS	39½
CRANFORD	41
STATE	37

Through a special method of scoring there would be a total of twelve points at stake in the relay—eight for first place, three for second, and one for third.

The most uninformed spectator in the audience saw plainly that State would have to take first place to win the meet. In fact, whichever team took first place in this final event would trot off with top honors.

The tension was almost unbearable as the three back-strokers dropped into the water; braced against the rim of the pool; and looked up at the official starter, who held his pistol high. Then the blank was fired and the swimmers sprang off and plowed their way backward through the water.

Harry Williams leaned against the tiled wall near the Cranford and Hollis 100-yard men. He glanced sideways at the Hollis man who was still heaving slightly from the exertion of winning the last sprint. He looked tired—a little too tired to be in top form for the anchor leg of the relay. Harry kneaded his muscles with his large hands.

He did not look at the audience, although he was fairly certain Dotty Bryson would be trying to catch his eye.

In the pool the back-strokers were keeping pretty even with each other, sending sprays of water high into the air. Each swimmer had to put in four pool-lengths—one-hundred yards. Oddly enough, they managed to stay within a length of one another all the way, so that when the first leg was completed, the butterfly breast-strokers all hit the water within a second or two of each other.

To Harry, this stroke was one of the most arduous of all, for it involved circular motions with the arms that lifted the torso half out of the water, and the accompanying froth and spray virtually obliterated the swimmer from view. Each time they came up they had to gulp huge draughts of air and then plunge back below the surface. Yet, for all its awkward appearance, the stroke was a fast one.

While Shaw was considered a good butterfly man, he was up against two others who were really specialists and he began to fall back. When he finally hit the end of the pool, Bud Hill, the orthodox breast-stroker, had nearly half a pool-length to make up.

Harry's heart was beating rapidly as he watched his friend take off. If only Bud could keep the *status quo,* there would be a chance. Not much of a chance, but a chance.

This was a more quiet race for most of the swimming was done beneath the surface of the water. Bud did the fantastic by going the entire initial twenty-five yards without coming up once for air. The careful eye could see that he had not lost any distance. Then his freckled face was gulping air and again he went under, looking like a fishy shadow flitting along the pool bottom. The Hollis and Cranford men, Harry noticed, were coming to the surface more often than Bud—that meant they were tiring, that their lung capacities were not as great as the crazy red-head's.

Harry heard himself yelling, too, as the three men went into the last lap. He was happy to see that Bud actually picked up several yards on his opponents. However, it was certain that he, Harry, would start with a sizable handicap, perhaps ten yards. Ten yards in a 100-yard race is a good chunk to give to flashy opponents.

He tensed as first the Cranford free-styler sprang into the water and then the Hollis man. He waited until Bud Hill was within arm's reach and even as Bud's hand was groping for the wall, Harry was catapulting himself into the air. The split-second timing worked, for the hand hit the wall an instant before Harry hit the water. If it had been the other way around, he would have been dis-qualified.

Then he was nothing but arms and legs and there was only water. Almost at once he realized that despite the 100-yard race of a half an hour before, he still had plenty of power left. If only the other two did not feel the same way. Just before he reached the end of the first lap, he saw the other two coming back toward him. If he started to think about how far behind he was, he might get dis-couraged, so he merely swam against the clock.

The only way he knew he was making headway was by

the cheers of the crowd, which seemed to be watching only him. As he came to the half-way point Bud Hill was there, telling him to keep with it, to get going . . .

"Chop-chop," Bud screamed.

The Hollis boy was first to tire. Harry expected this. The lad had burned himself out in the earlier race, and presently Harry was abreast of him and then passing him. Now, only five yards ahead, was the Cranford man—still going strong. But the lead had been cut in half.

Harry's arms were like pistons, pumping up and down. He did not catch up with the Cranford man until they were twenty feet from the finish. For a couple of seconds they stayed together, head to head, stroke for stroke, kick for kick. And then, abruptly, Harry was alone.

There was no one to either side, no one ahead of him. His famed kick had propelled him into the lead. Then there was no time to think of anything except the beckoning hands of Bud Hill and the feel of the concrete beneath his palm. The striking of it by the Cranford man was so close that it seemed like an echo of his.

The crowd exploded with cheers.

The next few minutes were utterly fantastic. Nothing made any sense. Grown men danced around in circles, pounding one another's backs. Girls screamed in endless shrieks, cheering and laughing at the same time. Bud Hill had slumped limply and hung over one of the diving-board railings. Coach Barnes was busy shaking hands with several very officious-looking men.

In the chaos, Harry himself was forgotten and he quickly slipped through the mob, feeling his heart still going like a trip hammer. On the way to the locker room he met the Cranford man, a good-looking boy with a ready smile. They shook hands solemnly.

Harry knew that this was his hour, but he didn't want it. He wanted nothing but to be alone. He did not even want to see Dotty. He knew what it would be like—everyone would congratulate him on his decision to become a team man. But that was just *not* true. What he had done, he had done because he had been forced into it. He had simply been a swimming machine operated by Barnes. There was no satisfaction looking back at a second place in a 100-yard sprint and a first place in a relay that could not have been won, really, were it not for Hill's performance. It was not his doing. And if the Hollis man had not killed himself in the first race, they might have won.

No, he wanted no glory, no cheers. Nothing. He had to get out.

He could hear the crowd chanting his name in the stands and the announcer saying, "Wait a minute, folks, and Williams will be right out!"

It was not true.

Harry dressed quickly, not even bothering to brush his hair or tie his tie. The Cranford man, still bent over in after-race exhaustion, watched disinterestedly.

"Where are you going?" he asked.

"Away. You take the bows, okay?"

"I'm taking them now," the Cranford swimmer said. He groaned.

"Good race, boy," Harry said. "And I mean it. I really do. So long."

He knew now where he was going and he managed to get out by the fire exit of the locker room just before the other door opened to admit an ecstatic mob of people.

Outside, the streets were empty of everything except parked cars and buses and, at the corner, a lonely traffic officer. Harry found Mrs. Gray's car parked where he had left it. He trotted to it, got in, started it, and then pulled out of the space.

When he reached the corner the traffic policeman waved and said, "Who won the meet?"

"State," Harry said and then he was on the avenue that would take him out onto the north-south highway.

7

IT TOOK A LONG TIME before the terrific tension built up during the races left Harry Williams' mind and body. It took almost as long for his stomach to settle again.

All the while he drove the car steadily northward. Twilight came; and then night, black as pitch. And still he drove. He stopped only to eat some supper—with three cups of coffee—and then he was on the way again.

He liked the sense of speed and humming power that was the car; he felt as though he were aloft in a plane skimming over a sleeping world. Gradually the traffic thinned out and gradually the urban areas fell behind. The hills came first and then the curves, and the car was climbing hour by hour. He left one state behind and entered another. Ultimately, sleepiness began to overcome him. It had been a terrifically long and eventful day.

He pulled the car off onto a shoulder, under some pines, and after checking to see that he was in no danger of being struck by other vehicles in the darkness, he climbed into the back seat, drew a blanket around himself, and went to sleep.

The sun, bright and insistent, boring through the pine-needled branches, awoke him. He had parked next to a brook, so he scrambled through the undergrowth, doffed his shirt, and splashed water on his face and shoulders. It was so cold that it made his fingers ache.

Refreshed, he returned to the car and resumed his journey.

Fortunately, the car did not have a radio, so he could not be tempted to tune in to any news or sports programs.

He saw that he was now in the middle of the mountains and all around him the leaves and bushes were shining with the wetness of morning dew. Slight patches of fog and haze frequently settled over the road, making him slow down; then the car would move through the patches and disperse the moist air and make it scatter in feathery swirls.

The road was narrow and twisty as it wound through forests of pine, balsam, evergreen, and birch. From time to time, he would catch a breathtaking glimpse of a strikingly blue lake, peaceful and unmarred in the pure rays of the new sun. Or perhaps a solitary farmhouse with smoke rising placidly from its chimney.

It was such a pleasant ride that he didn't even stop for breakfast. He merely kept on driving into a region that grew more and more familiar as the miles went by.

According to the dashboard clock it was not yet seven when he finally arrived at a dirt road that jutted off the main highway. A weather-beaten sign fashioned out of birch logs and branches read: *Camp Skylark—Two Miles.*

The woods and fields were coming alive now, and he could hear the sounds of birds and small animals and insects. The chirping made a kind of morning symphony that was very soothing to his ears. He studied the road ahead for signs of recent tire marks. There were some. The car entered an aisle of pines whose branches interlaced overhead, forming a cool and dark tunnel, rich with the aroma of fresh pine needles.

Presently, at a curve in the narrow road, he saw Skylark Lake, glittering in the near distance like a handful of blue sapphires scattered in a valley. A minute later he saw the first buildings of the camp itself, and then he was passing through a rough wooden gateway that had another *Camp Skylark* sign overhead.

Harry stopped the car and got out, stretching his legs. He inhaled deeply of the fresh, clean mountain air. This was more like it!

From the chimney of the Main House came a telltale curl of smoke, but Harry did not go there first. He headed down the path between the two dormitory buildings, walked out onto the boat landing, and then turned around and looked back. There were some ten buildings in the camp area proper—the Main House, dorms, a dining-hall, recreation hall, boathouse, storehouse, and a couple of utility structures. Very neat and compact. It was like coming home.

Before his eyes, that were still a little sandy from his abbreviated night's sleep, the lake spread far out into the thinning mist, clear and cool and inviting. Harry did not feel like resisting the temptation any longer. Very quickly he stripped down, stepped out of his loafers and socks, sprinted to the end of the dock, and dove in at a full run.

The bitter coldness of the water was a shock at first as he dove deeply and ran his hands along the sandy bottom. Then he arched for the surface and the air was warm on his face; he knew that presently he would be accustomed to the cold water.

It was wonderful, absolutely the greatest. After spending eight or ten hours behind the wheel—with only a few hours of cramped sleep—his body simply cried out for this kind of exercise. He splashed about in the water, doubling up and going under, feeling very free and weightless and enjoying the sense of life and energy that came tingling back into his bones. By golly, it was almost worth the entire trip just for these few magical moments in the lake.

Funny, but he did not feel at all like racing or plowing hard through the water, as if it were some kind of enemy to be overcome. He was content just to be in it, like any duffer who needed an inner tube to hold him up. He treaded water easily, moving his hands and feet slowly, and slowly revolved his head so that he could take in the panoramic view offered by the mountains far off on the horizon. He stared long at the mountains that seemed to be beckoning him to hidden and mysterious adventure, dark and unknown, and yet thrilling. He could never look at mountains without having that sensation.

Nearer, lining the shore like tall sentinels, were the trees, silhouetted against the clear blue sky. From them he could hear the call of the whip-poor-will, the nightingale, and the skylark. Not very far away was what sounded like a flock of ducks, perhaps roosting in the trees.

It was almost too much to bear. But what was even more unbearable was the smell that was tantalizing his nostrils. The rich, smoky smell of bacon frying and coffee brewing. By sniffing hard he could even get the aroma of toast on the still morning air. He put them all together and they spelled breakfast.

All at once he realized he was famished and, without any further dawdling in Lake Skylark, he struck out for the dock, hauled himself out of the water, and slipped into his khaki trousers. He paused a moment, trying to decide whether or not to put on the rest of his things, and then said aloud, "To heck with it—this is the country."

Bare-chested and bare-footed, he loped the length of the dock, feeling the icy-cold air against his moist skin; then he was on the grass and trotting toward the Main House—the source of those splendid odors.

Harry Williams pulled open the screen kitchen door. There, bent over the stove, a skillet in one hand, a spatula in the other, was Doc Howell.

At the sight of his old friend Harry felt a surge of warmth go through him. It had been a long time; a very long time. Doc was wearing a T-shirt that had been stitched and sewn so many times it looked like a quilt, a pair of blue jeans that had faded to almost white, and battered old moccasins.

Harry conjured up his last sight of Doc—on Graduation Day—when Doc was turned out like a Beau Brummel.

Doc had been uncomfortable that day—today he looked as smooth and at ease as an old bedroom slipper.

The stove was wide and broad and black. On one gas burner was the huge coffee pot, on another was the skillet that held a whole flock of frying eggs. Over an open charcoal fire rested a grill with several slices of bread toasting.

Harry glanced at the table—it was set carelessly and was decorated with a plate that held a huge, creamy slab of butter and a pitcher of thick, creamy milk. His mouth watered at the sight of them.

"Well, don't stand there and let the flies in," Doc Howell said without looking up. "Come on in."

Harry let the screen door slam behind him. "Good morning," he said.

"Good morning—get that toast, will you, before it burns!"

Harry moved with alacrity, speared the browned bread with a fork, and dropped the toast on a plate.

"Butter it, man, butter it!"

Harry obeyed and spread the slices with butter.

"Gangway!" Doc was saying as he backed away from the stove and began sliding the eggs out of the pan and onto the two plates that sat on the checked tablecloth.

With a loud "Whew!" Doc finally set the equipment down and looked Harry in the eye. He wiped his hands on an apron and said, "Good to see you, Harry boy. Let's eat."

For the next few minutes Harry concentrated solely on eating. His appetite had been whetted by the crisp mountain air, and the food was as hearty and delicious as he had remembered it from four years before.

Doc was friendly and exuberant, and it was wonderful to be sitting here with him just like old times. Studying him, Harry saw that Doc did not really look four years older. If anything, he looked younger. A little smile played about his lips as he ate.

What Harry liked most, though, was that Doc had not besieged him with questions, asking what he was doing here and why. None of that. The two of them had sat down to breakfast as if it were the most normal and usual thing in the world.

"You're up early," Harry said around a chunk of toast. "Got insomnia?"

"I'll insomnia you," Doc muttered. "Been up for an hour. Every morning at six—until camp starts. Then it will be five."

"Going to be a big season this year?"

"Big enough."

"Fine," Harry said. "Happy to hear it. Surprised, too. After I left I was pretty sure that everything around here would collapse."

Doc shook his head slowly. "No. As a matter of fact, it was right after you left that we started to operate in the black."

"Well, I knew there were *some* changes. Of course, I can understand if you never really approach the old days as far as fun and brilliance and intelligent conversation are concerned."

"Well," said his old friend, "things are kind of lonesome—until one of those bears lumbers down out of the woods. *Then* we don't miss you at all."

They looked at each other for a few seconds and then, simultaneously, their mouths twitched and broke into broad grins.

"Doc, you are a wonder," Harry cried, reaching over and clapping the bony shoulder with his hand. "It's really great to see you again!"

"Same here, boy," Doc said. "More coffee?"

"You said it!" Harry said happily.

Doc got up stiffly and shuffled to the stove, where he tilted the heavy pot over the cups.

"The place looks wonderful," Harry told him. "You too."

"Thanks, Harry. I might say the same about you."

"Hey," said a feminine voice, "save something for me!"

Harry was so surprised that he spun around, knocking a spoon to the floor.

There, at the doorway leading into the rest of the house, stood a girl. She was tall and slender and had brunette hair tied into a becoming pony tail. She wore no lipstick or make-up mainly because her peaches-and-cream complexion did not require any. She had on a checked woolen shirt and Bermuda shorts and sandals.

Harry felt his face flushing. He had not expected a girl to be around. A girl? No. A *woman.* And a very pretty one at that.

"Excuse me," he said. "I didn't know anyone else was here." He looked at Doc, flustered.

Doc shrugged. "Oh, I thought you two had met. Harry, this is my niece, Meg Crane. Meg, this is Harry Williams."

"Meg!"

The girl tossed him a dazzling smile, lowering her lashes briefly. Then she made a very slight curtsy.

"Charmed, I'm sure."

Harry couldn't believe his eyes. "Meg?"

"That's my name," Meg said.

"But—but—you don't look the same!"

"You mean, where are the braces and the knobby knees and the freckles and skinned elbows? They're gone."

"But you're still here."

"Yes, I am, and I'm famished. Let's eat."

As they sat down opposite one another, Harry thought he had never seen any girl prettier than Meg Crane.

8

PROBABLY THE MOST remarkable part of the breakfast was that neither Meg nor Doc asked Harry what he was doing at Skylark. It was as if only four days had passed instead of four years, and they accepted him calmly, refraining from plying him with questions. For that reason Harry did not inquire into *Meg's* reason for being here.

The conversation concerned the sparklingly clear weather, the daily egg yield of the hens in the chicken coop, and the work ahead. All the while, Harry kept staring at Meg Crane, who seemed in many ways to be a stranger. No. Not a stranger. A *new* girl. She was indeed pretty and she possessed considerable poise—particularly in contrast with the old days of her adolescence.

However, although Meg appeared animated and happy, Harry detected a somber note. Her mouth might laugh—but not her eyes.

At the same time, it occurred to him that he must also present a curious figure. He was hardly the life of the party, for always, just below the surface, was a heavy feeling over his flight from the university. He knew he was not enough of an actor to conceal his consternation. But Meg and Doc were good enough actors to pretend not to notice.

After breakfast Meg excused herself to return to her room on the upper floor, and Harry fell to with Doc in doing the dishes and cleaning up the kitchen. As he was drying the frying pan, he saw a small smile tugging at the corners of Doc's dry mouth.

"What's so funny, Doc?"

"Funny?" Doc repeated, white eyebrows uplifted in surprise. But now he couldn't carry it off—the smile broke into a chuckle. "Well, I guess it is funny to an old duffer like me—seeing the look on your face when Meg walked in."

"I didn't laugh," Harry reminded.

"Your eyes about popped out," Doc said. "You reacted like a kid spotting a movie star."

Harry concentrated on the heavy iron skillet. "I wasn't that bad," he protested. "The truth was I didn't know anyone else was around. I thought you were alone."

Doc shook his head, still grinning to himself. "That's *your* story." Then he came closer to Harry and whispered conspiratorially, "The fact is—I gaped when I first saw her grown up, too!"

For a moment the two men stared at one another, and then Harry broke into laughter. "Okay, okay. You win. So I was really bowled over. Meg is certainly one of the prettiest girls I've ever seen. I don't think Pygmalion was any more astonished after he finished the statue of Galatea."

Doc cleared his throat noisily. "It's that good old Howell blood that did it. My sister wasn't much of a cook, but she sure could raise beautiful daughters."

For a time they did not speak, each occupied with his own thoughts. Harry was bursting with questions about Meg, but he did not dare ask them. Doc Howell, phlegmatic and patient, would consider such inquisitiveness rude. After spending most of his life in the outdoors, living the slow but rich existence of a man who loves and respects Nature, he was not inclined to haste. He knew that, of all things, there was plenty of time.

And Harry Williams, as a guest, abided by Doc's unwritten and unspoken rules. Questions of a personal nature could wait. Now was the time for queries of a different sort.

"What's got to be done today?" he asked as he put away the last of the silverware and wiped his hands on the towel. "I'm rarin' to go."

Doc led the way out onto the porch which overlooked the lake. "The polite thing for me to say, of course, is that you are a visitor, that it's not right for you to work." His gray eyes twinkled. "But I've never yet been accused of being polite, so I'll be more than happy to let you use your young muscles."

"Where do I start?"

"With the canoes. They have to be looked over carefully for cracks and leaks. Probably need some patching.

Can't let any of my kids paddle around in unsafe canoes. Right?"

"Right!"

"And then," Doc said, squinting into the sun, "the float can be launched again. Got to be anchored, too."

"Consider it done," Harry said.

"Hmmm. That lake ice sure raised hob with our dock, too. But nothing a hammer and boards and nails can't fix."

"Hammering Harry they call me!"

"After that while you're resting between jobs," Doc said slowly, "you might try your hand at the ax. Gets cold some nights here, and the kids like to build lots of fires. And they'll need firewood."

At this Harry could not repress a groan.

Doc's face remained still. "Now, then, this afternoon . . ."

"Wait a minute!" Harry yelped. "If all this was yet to be done, and if there was no one else around—how did you expect to get it all accomplished in time for camp opening?"

Doc hit Harry on the shoulder. "Why, I was just saving it all for you, Harry boy."

"For me? Why you didn't even know I was coming up here."

A crafty smile spread over Doc's leathery features. "Ah, but you're wrong there, Harry. I *did* know you were coming."

"You did! How?"

But Doc had gone back into the house and the interview

was ended. Harry stared after his old friend for a while and then, still mystified, headed for the boathouse and the first of his Herculean labors.

Around mid-morning, after he had gotten the canoes out of the boathouse and floated them for signs of leaks, and was sitting on an up-ended log splitting kindling with a hatchet, Harry saw Meg Crane approaching from the big house with a pitcher in one hand and some paper cups in the other.

"Hello, there, Paul Bunyan," she cried gaily. "How about some fuel?"

Harry drew his forearm across his sweating brow and said, "Hi, yourself. What do you have there?"

"Lemonade—straight from the lemon."

"Just what I need. Fill 'er up."

Meg poured from the pitcher into a paper cup and handed it to him. Harry took it and swallowed the liquid gratefully. It was just tart enough.

Meg looked at the sizable stack of wood. "My, but you've been a busy little bee this morning. I'm amazed."

"Amazed? How come? I have all my arms and legs—plus my full growth. Did you expect less?"

"I expected that all that soft college life had ruined you."

For a moment Harry thought she was serious, but then he caught the unmistakable twitch of one of her facial muscles and realized she was needling him gently. She had not changed so much after all. Right now she was watching him out of amused eyes—eyes that were dark and lustrous. Her hair was tied back, but loose curls tossed in the breeze. She was neatly formed and moved with the smooth grace of a thoroughbred.

"It's wonderful to see you again Meg," he said sincerely.

"Thanks, Harry," Meg said softly. "That goes for me, too. Now, can I pitch in with you?"

"Oh, I don't think so," Harry replied. "Wood-chopping is hardly for a girl, but I do have to get the float in the water . . ."

"Let's do it!"

Harry was only too happy to leave the woodpile. They walked down to the lake front. The float was a solidly constructed affair, with a diving board and a ladder, and was mounted on empty oil drums. It had been hauled out of the water the previous fall and secured to the upper end of a pair of short railroad tracks that led down to the water. The task was to release the structure, get it into the lake again, and maneuver it out beyond the end of the dock so it could be anchored there. It was too much for one person to handle, and Harry was glad of Meg's offer of help, even though he was not sure how much she could be depended upon.

But he had forgotten that she, too, had spent her childhood at Camp Skylark and was as efficient as any boy when it came to odd jobs. While he was still on the ground examining the ropes and oil drums attached to the float, Meg nimbly climbed the ladder and attacked the knots with deft fingers. Two of the ropes were looped around the trunks of nearby trees.

"See that one," she said, pointing. Harry looked and

quickly saw that the rope was affixed in such a way that it would serve as a kind of clothesline. The one on the other tree was the same. Meg scrambled down from the platform and showed Harry how to manipulate the rope. Each of them would hold one rope and by playing it out slowly the float would slide down the tracks of its own weight, with the ropes serving as brakes—if the holders were strong enough.

Before she attended to her rope, Meg went back to the boathouse and in a minute reappeared with a can of oil. She poured the oil on each of the rusty tracks.

All the while Harry watched speechlessly. If it had been any other girl, he would have felt sheepish for not taking charge. Somehow, it seemed quite all right that Meg should know precisely what to do.

At last everything was ready. At Meg's command Harry unknotted his rope. Immediately he felt the powerful tug of the float. He glanced at Meg; her slim body was tense as she gripped her rope.

"Easy now," she warned. "Ready. Let 'er go."

Harry gingerly allowed the rope to slide through his hands. With a great creaking and cracking sound, the float began to go down the oiled tracks. Harry felt the terrific strain on his muscles and wondered how long Meg could hold on. There was no need to worry, for Meg was wholly capable of doing her share. Foot by foot, the float went down the tracks toward the water. The great danger, of course, was that it might go down too fast and smash into a million splinters on the shallow shore.

Like a tired giant, the float neared the water, held back

only by the pair of taut ropes. To Harry it was like holding onto a truck that was trying to break away in third gear. He forgot about Meg and concentrated on his end.

Presently the float was slipping into the water, still on the tracks that plunged ten feet deeper.

"Let go!" Meg cried suddenly.

Harry obeyed. At the same instant Meg released her grip on the rope and the float, suddenly free, shot into the water, dipped alarmingly, and bobbed up and down. Sprays of water shot high into the air, and Harry feared that the float was wrecked.

But no. There it was on the surface of the lake, rocking gently, supported by the huge oil drums.

Harry looked at Meg. The pretty girl was rubbing her slender hands together and breathing deeply. She leaned against a tree for a few seconds, eyes closed.

"Oh, Harry," she breathed, "I just couldn't hold on a second longer. I'm sorry."

"Sorry! Holy cats, that was terrific. Talk about surprises!"

"You had to take most of the weight."

"Nonsense. You did the job of a wrestler. And the size of you! As a matter of fact, I'd hate to tell you how close *I* was to letting go."

Meg smiled prettily. "That's sweet of you, Harry, but I don't believe it. Anyway, I'm glad it's over."

"But it isn't . . ."

"Oh?"

"Now it has to be anchored before it floats away."

"I almost forgot."

"But don't you bother," Harry told her. "I'll get into my trunks and do it in no time."

"We started together," Meg said firmly, "and we'll finish together."

With that she sprinted up the lawn toward the house. Harry stared after her, shaking his head in admiration.

Twenty minutes later Harry, wearing boxer swimming trunks, watched Meg as she skipped down the hill again. She had on a black lastex bathing suit and was tucking her hair into a rubber cap. Meg's figure was as smooth and supple as a young doe's.

"How was the water this morning?" she asked.

"Cold."

"Well, the sun should have warmed it by now. Ready?"

"Ready."

With no further word, Meg went to the end of the dock, curled her toes over the edge, lifted her arms, and sprang into the water. Her dive was like the slice of a knife; she went under and then came up and headed for the bobbing float in an easy, effortless crawl. Harry followed.

The rest of the job was relatively simple. They had to guide the big float to the location of cable anchors that had been dug into the lake bottom years before. The upper ends of the cables were held free of the bottom by cans filled with air. It was necessary to free the cans and then hook the float cables to the water cables, and that would be that.

There was sufficient buoyancy in the oil drums under the float to permit Harry and Meg to move it through the water by pushing against the vertical braces and kicking with their feet. This was the one phase of the work in which Harry could assert his authority. But when he glanced over at Meg and saw her determined features and the way she strained and the way her long legs flailed the water, he knew he could not bring himself to show off. It was an unfair match—and yet there was Meg putting everything she had into the task, as though it were some kind of race with a fantastic prize at the end.

Therefore, instead of trying to prove how adept he was in the water, Harry eased up and exerted no more force than he had to, to keep up. As it was, he found it necessary to kick pretty hard owing to Meg's unladylike efforts. She packed a lot of strength in her whipcord body.

When the float was in position, Harry yelled, "Keep it in place. I'm going under to get the cables."

He took a huge gulp of air and dove under the surface. The water was clear and pure, and he easily spotted the cans that held the ends of the cables. Then he found the cables dangling from the underside of the float. Unscrewing the cans, he hooked the cables together. Off to one side, at the edge of the float, he saw what looked like Meg's headless torso treading water. He came up into the air pocket between the oil drums, took another breath, and went under again to finish the job.

"That's that," he called when he came up for the last time. His voice sounded strangely hollow under the float.

"I don't know how we got along without you," Meg replied in her musical voice. Then she was swimming easily back to the dock. Harry joined her as she hauled herself up and sat with her feet slapping the water.

Meg looked flushed and happy, droplets glistening on her face and shoulders.

"Fun, wasn't it?" she said.

"Sure was," Harry agreed. "First real work I've done in a long time. I liked it."

"You don't know what this will mean to Doc—getting most of these chores out of the way. He couldn't have done them himself."

"I don't mind. Is that why you're here now?"

The moment he voiced the question, he wished he hadn't. The sparkle left Meg's features as if a cloud had covered the sun. She turned away from him and got to her feet.

"I think it's time for lunch," she said in a tight voice.

"Yes," Harry said stiffly. "Yes. Let's eat."

The delightful closeness of a few minutes before was gone now. She might have been a stranger. Harry felt like an absolute fool—a blabber-mouthed fool—and he seriously doubted if Meg would be inclined to be friendly with him any more.

Just the same, he could not help but be curious about why Meg was at Skylark.

9

THE DAY BEFORE, immediately following the All-Conference meet that had been won almost single-handedly by Harry Williams, there was considerable chaos in the university's Fieldhouse. Pandemonium was king and the excited crowd—backers of both winners and losers—milled about in the daze that comes after a thrilling sporting event. In the course of the frenetic minutes after the completion of the relay, at least four fully clothed students somehow got themselves pushed into the pool, where they splashed about happily. Even Coach Rusty Barnes wound up in the water, dropped there by the enthusiastic members of the tank team.

Photographers' flash bulbs were popping like strings of exploding firecrackers, recording the incredible scene for those who were unlucky enough not to be present. Reporters scrambled about trying to get interviews from the coach and the swimmers and the trustees and just about anybody within earshot. A series of organized cheers echoed through the vast hall. Bud Hill, the indefatigable, had mounted the diving board, where he improvised a hula dance of victory that was cut short only by the loss of his balance and the sight of his twisting body as it hurtled into the pool.

As he fell, the audience heard his cry, in the high-pitched whining voice of a British cockney, *"There'll always be an England!"*

With such confusion it was no wonder that Harry Williams' absence was not noticed for a long time.

The fact was that everybody thought he was somewhere else. When the mass of newspaper people and officials burst into the locker room just a split second after he had left by the other exit, they looked about frantically for him. Not finding him, they decided he must be out in the Hall and returned there. Other people, like Dotty Bryson and Bud Hill, not seeing him in the pool area, assumed Harry was in the locker room or otherwise occupied.

Finally, after almost a full hour of excitement, the crowd thinned out and made its way home. The exhausted swimmers dressed and left. Bud Hill spent a few minutes looking for Harry, but then decided that perhaps he had been taken in tow by some officials. Consequently, Bud joined a group that was heading for Miller's Ice Cream Bar. Dotty Bryson left with her father, full of disappointment that Harry had not sought her out after the relay. But Professor Bryson consoled her by saying that at such times a boy did not have much time for girls.

Professor Bryson was in high spirits, certain that he

had been vindicated in his stand against Harry's try for individuality.

Coach Barnes did not look for Harry at all. He was too busy talking with Olympic observers and university trustees about plans for his future.

Bud Hill got back to the Gray house around nine o'clock that night. The exuberance of victory had worn off, and now he was very tired. But he was not so tired as to ignore the hard fact of Harry's absence. It was an absence emphasized by the number of telephone messages left on the downstairs desk. Calls from the newspapers, the athletic department, and from Dotty Bryson. All unanswered. Besides, their room was locked and unlighted.

There was no doubt in Bud Hill's mind now—Harry Williams was definitely behaving oddly. . . .

From downstairs he heard the insistent ringing of the phone. Thinking that it might be Harry, he descended two steps at time. Probably the joker had run out of gas on some highway and was looking for help.

It was Dotty Bryson. "Hello, Bud," she said worriedly. "Is Harry there?"

For an instant Bud debated whether or not she should know. Then he said, "No, he isn't, Dotty. I thought he might be with you."

"Well, he isn't. I haven't seen him since the meet."

"I haven't either. But I'm sure he must be with one of the newspaper reporters or the swimming officials. He's the star of the day, you know." His attempt to sound light-hearted was an utter failure.

"I don't understand it," Dotty said sadly. "This just isn't like him. I know we quarreled, but it wasn't too serious. Dad is anxious to see him, too."

"So am I. But don't worry, Dotty," Bud assured her falsely, "he'll show up soon. And when he does I'll tell him to buzz you right away."

"I wish you'd do that, Bud."

"I will. Better yet, I promise to have him on your doorstep first thing in the morning."

He heard her tinkling laugh. "Bud—you're the greatest."

They said good-bye and hung up.

Bud was really in a quandary now. If Harry had not even phoned Dotty, something was wrong. The worst part was that he, Bud Hill, Harry's great and good and faithful friend, had not the slightest notion of Harry's whereabouts. How was he expected to hold off a whole city full of people who wanted to congratulate the hero of the day? Harry should have given him a clue at least. He did not know whether he should simply lie outright and protect Harry, or if he should admit to one and all that he was just as mystified.

Tired and torn as he was, Bud knew that no matter what happened or what did not happen, he should crack a book or two. Harry was lucky—his spring exams were over. Lucky . . . A strange thought entered Bud's mind—suppose something serious had happened to Harry. Why, this very minute he might be in pain somewhere, lying under the wreckage of Mrs. Gray's car. Or maybe the Hollis student body was playing a prank and had kidnaped him. Oh, that was absurd, Bud told himself. Harry was a big boy, and it would take more than a car or a bunch of Hollis guys to subdue him. He would appear eventually.

Bud went to his desk and stared down at the accumulation of papers and notebooks and textbooks. It was a mess, just a mess. He glanced at the bed. Back at the books. That bed looked very tempting. One of his hands strayed to the buttons of his shirt.

No! By golly, he would get to work and study. With great reluctance, and hoping against hope that some minor miracle would occur to prevent him from studying, Bud Hill sat down at his desk and reached for the nearest book. It was Plato's *Republic,* a deceptively thin tome that had broken better men than Bud Hill over the past hundreds of years.

Bud opened the book and the letter fell out.

He recognized Harry's handwriting immediately and assumed that Harry had been glancing through Plato and had inadvertently left a piece of doodling paper between the pages. Then he saw his own name printed in capitals: HIS MOST SERENE HIGHNESS CASPAR BUD HILL. Underneath were the words TOP SECRET AND CONFIDENTIAL.

Bud opened the envelope, withdrew a sheet of paper, and read:

Dear Bud:

First of all, don't fret your head about me. I'm okay. I'm off to do a little thinking, a little reconstructing, something that's been long overdue. You'll understand that I couldn't ask you to come along. Or anyone, not even Dotty.

Secondly, I must ask a favor. In order to let your mind be at ease, and in case of dire emergency, I will tell you that I am going back to Camp Skylark for a while. I hope you will be able to keep this information from everybody else, and yet at the same time calm them down in case they make too big a fuss. I trust you can be counted on to handle Dotty, too.

Of course, I am writing this *before* the Meet but I am fairly certain of the outcome. We'll win, but that does not necessarily mean *I* will win. I think you will understand what I mean by that.

I'll appreciate whatever you can do for me—and I'll someday try to repay you. Above all, don't worry, hit the books, and bend a kind thought toward me.

Harry

P.S. I was sure that with your exam coming up, you'd be bound to open Plato at last.

Never had Bud felt closer to Harry Williams than now, when Harry was hundreds of miles away. He envisioned the tall, lean young man with the sand-colored hair bending over the desk to write the letter. His handsome features would have been furrowed with concentration as he tried to tell just enough, but not too much.

Bud suddenly felt relaxed and happy. As he thought over the letter, however, he felt pensive. Uncertain, confused, Harry had apparently felt he had no choice but to cut himself off from the present and return, in a way, to the past.

After the letter poor Plato was out of luck. Bud could

no more have studied that ancient Greek philosopher than he could have won an argument with Socrates. What he did do was to dig out some maps and pore over them to find the location of Camp Skylark in the Adirondack Mountains of New York State. The lake itself was marked by a minute dot of blue. Bud circled the lake with his pencil and mentally noted the route numbers of the highways that led from the university to the camp. There were several different ones, so he traced the most direct route with a pencil.

He did not know why he did this, but at the time it seemed quite logical.

In the days that followed Bud Hill achieved a certain anonymous fame through the newspapers and over the airwaves as "a usually reliable source close to Williams."

This "source" was quoted as saying ". . . that Swimmer Williams had long planned for a badly needed vacation and merely jumped the gun—a tactic he has never been accused of during a race. It is said that Williams is in seclusion to prepare for the arduous Nationals two weeks hence. . . ."

That last element Bud had introduced to lend more authenticity to his story. In any case, the circulation of the information caused the campus to calm down.

Only Dotty Bryson guessed who the "source" was and, after persistent questioning, finally got Bud to admit it.

"Okay, so it's me," he said, as they walked together across the quad. "But don't tell anybody."

"I won't. But you will let me know if you hear from him, won't you?" Dotty pleaded. Seeing her this way, perturbed and motherly, Bud thought she was never more attractive or more appealing. That Harry certainly had himself a fine girl.

"He did mention me, in his letter, I mean?" Dotty asked.

"Yes, he did."

"What did he say?" Dotty asked eagerly, clutching Bud's sleeve.

"Some rather nice things," Bud smiled. "Among them was the admonition that you shouldn't worry—and that I should see that you were okay."

"I should be angry with him," Dotty said, "for going off that way without letting me know, but somehow I think he had to do it that way."

"I agree," Bud said.

"However, I do hope he won't stay away long. Lots of things are happening."

"What kind of things?"

"Well, Coach Barnes came to visit Dad late last night."

This was news to Bud. His ears perked up. "Oh?"

"Oh, is right. They talked for a long time."

"What about?"

"You seem to assume that I listened."

"Well?" Bud said with a grin.

Dotty's pretty lips curved into a shy smile. "I guess I'm a real woman—either a secret is too good to keep or else it's not worth keeping. I did manage to overhear a few words—when they were talking loudly."

"The suspense is killing me. . . ."

"I heard Coach Barnes mention the Nationals and that Harry had to swim in them and Dad agreed. It seems that the coach was worried that Harry might not show up for those races, and he wanted to be sure that Harry came." Dotty turned her soft brown eyes on Bud. "Is that justified?"

"I don't know," Bud said slowly. "I just don't know. Harry is a very complex guy. I know the All-Conference meet took a lot out of him—physically and mentally."

"Anyhow," Dotty went on, "Dad told Coach Barnes not to get upset about it, that he could guarantee that Harry would appear for the Nationals."

"Guarantee?" Bud repeated. They had arrived at the library and paused on the lower steps. Several students nodded and said hello as they passed. Both of them were well aware that as Harry Williams' closest friends, they were subject to curious looks. But right now Bud was not so impressed with the fame. He was afraid of the implication in the word "guarantee."

"That's what he said," Dotty replied. "And he sounded as if he meant it. Knowing my father, I think he did."

"I don't know how that's possible," Bud murmured. "Unless some pressure can be brought to bear on Harry."

"What kind of pressure?"

"Scholarship pressure," Bud said.

"Dad wouldn't do a thing like that!" Dotty gasped.

Bud was inclined to think differently about what Professor Bryson would or wouldn't do, but he could hardly share his suspicions with Dotty.

"No, I guess not," he said cheerfully. "Anyway, we'll probably be seeing Harry any day now."

"I hope so," Dotty said. "What do you suppose he's doing?"

"Him? Up in the woods?" Bud laughed. "Probably living in a tent, doing his own cooking—making like a hermit and wishing he were right back here with us."

10

HARRY WILLIAMS had never been a believer in "love at first sight." That sort of thing, he felt, was strictly for the movies or for high school sophomores. His relationship with Dotty Bryson had begun casually, and it had taken him something like four months before he kissed her; and a few more months to recognize love.

Ever since that day—the day he knew himself to be in love with Professor Bryson's very pretty daughter—Harry had, in effect, turned off his radar; no longer was he tuned into the wave lengths of other girls. For him, Dotty was enough to keep him occupied for several decades to come. Also, even if another girl did appeal to him, he considered himself quite capable of ignoring the appeal and shrugging it off.

After lunch, Doc relented and told Harry that Skylark couldn't be built in a day and that he should take it easy. This was Meg Crane's cue to invite Harry to accompany her to the town of Bencove to do some shopping.

Harry felt a faint pang of disloyalty to Dotty at the realization that he really wanted to go. He quickly snuffed out that pang—after all, a guy couldn't be expected to shut out the whole world, could he?

The misunderstanding of a few hours before had passed with no further reference, and Meg was once more bubbling over with good spirits, a quiet smile playing about her unpainted mouth. She led the way to the camp car—a 1937 Ford pick-up truck, roofless, almost bodyless, and certainly graceless. The tires were smooth, one headlight was missing, and the seats consisted of a plank with a pair of bed pillows on it.

Harry stared at the monster dubiously; he was a little uncertain about this machine. He need not have worried. Meg, clad in plaid shirt and blue jeans, took charge. She got behind the wheel, turned on the ignition, tried the starter. She expressed no dismay that the engine did not turn over, but got out, went to the front end, cranked, and then, with the motor kicking, coughing, and sputtering, raced back behind the wheel, hit the accelerator, let out the ancient clutch, and with a delighted laugh at Harry's dumbfounded face, sped out of the camp in a cloud of smoke.

The road into town was fairly busy for that time of day—all told they passed, or were passed by, two automobiles, three wagons, two bicycles, a tractor, a manure-spreader, and a truck hauling a house trailer. At each one Meg would wave and show her flashing smile. Finally, Harry got the idea and joined in. It was kind of daring to yell and wave to utter strangers—only somehow on this road nobody seemed like a stranger.

"You like this kind of life, don't you, Meg?" he said presently.

Her head bobbed. "Yep. I've missed it. I'm glad to be back."

"Been back long?" Harry asked tentatively.

"One day."

"One day! You mean you came yesterday?"

"Yes. Didn't Doc tell you?"

"No. He didn't tell me anything. Nobody told me anything." He blinked his puzzlement. "But I don't get it. *Yesterday*. Where did you come from? I had the idea you'd been here a long time. Look at the way you say hello to those people."

"Well, this was my life for a long time, Harry," Meg said as she expertly wheeled the Ford around a small herd of cows that was ambling casually on the right of way. "I came up from Philadelphia by plane. Landed at the airport near Plattsburgh and Doc came over and picked me up." She smiled suddenly. "Goodness, it was good to see him again."

"I'll bet he felt the same way," Harry observed.

A faint pink tinge spread over Meg's features. "Sometimes I wish I would never have to leave Skylark."

Thinking of the mess he had made of his educational and athletic careers, Harry said, "I agree." He leaned back in the seat, propped his feet up on the dashboard, and laced his fingers behind his head. "I had no idea how much I really missed the place until I saw it in the mist this morning." He glanced at Meg. "And until I saw you walk into the kitchen."

"Take it easy on my poor vanity," Meg laughed. "I doubt if you lost too much sleep during those semesters at State. From what I heard, State has the best looking co-eds in that part of the country."

"That's what I'd heard, too," Harry grinned. "But Philly doesn't do too badly."

To his own astonishment, he found it very enjoyable to compliment Meg. Enjoyable and genuine, too. The praise flowed easily to his lips, and that it flustered Meg pleased him no end. For all her capabilities and efficient mannerisms, she was still more than a little feminine.

"Isn't it true that you are going with a very nice girl?" Meg asked.

"How did you know?" Harry shot back.

"I didn't," said Meg, "until you answered my question. What's she like?"

"Dotty Bryson is quite a girl," he said. "She's small, neat, and she can make guys whistle—but not make passes. That kind."

"Good for you," Meg said warmly. "You deserve a fine girl. Now, don't object—it's true. And if you like her, I'm sure she must be a peach."

The road was winding through arched branches of trees and it was cool and fragrant in the shade they cast. Meg, Harry noted, drove with nonchalant expertness, her long slender fingers light on the wheel. Another ten minutes and they would be in Bencove.

"And you," Harry began, "isn't there someone who thinks the same of you?"

Meg didn't answer immediately. Her lower lip came out ever so slightly and her left eyebrow went up a fraction and stayed there. "Yes," she said slowly, "there is someone like that. However, I doubt if right this minute he is referring to me as a fine girl."

"You're kidding," Harry said.

"No, I'm not kidding. I wish I were. I'm not quite the same knobby-kneed girl you knew four years ago, Harry. A lot has happened. It may be denied in some quarters, but I've grown up. Or at least I've grown older." She hesitated, almost frowning. "That, in general, is why I'm here now, I suppose."

Harry, about to drop a crack or semi-humorous remark, held his tongue. Meg was profoundly disturbed. It was a tribute to her upbringing and her innate strength that she hadn't unburdened herself sooner. Therefore, he had no compulsion to pry into her secrets; yet he would like to offer what he could in the way of advice or support or consolation.

Meg took her eyes from the empty road long enough to throw him a searching glance. Then she looked back, a vertical crease between her dark eyes.

"Perhaps I've grown old in age but not in wisdom, Harry. I always looked up to you as a very wise man. It might be you *could* tell me what's happening to me—and if I'm wrong."

Harry knew that if he were absolutely candid, he would tell her then and there that he was scarcely the guy to be playing King Solomon. As a matter of fact, he was in desperate need of a Solomon himself.

"You've got my curiosity up," Harry said. "It beats me how you could have any sort of trouble at all—or that anyone would have difficulty liking you."

It was funny talking to Meg like this, when half a dozen years ago he had had little other than a "Get outta here" for her. But she had been miraculously transformed from a gawky child to a serious-minded young lady, and Harry didn't feel at all sheepish about treating her as an equal.

They passed through the outskirts of Bencove, past the lumber mill next to the river, the massive piles of bare new planks waiting on the siding to be taken away. Then they went by a new housing development in a section that had been a swamp; a couple of gas stations; a drive-in movie; and, presently, they came to the town itself.

The best way to describe Bencove is to say it resembled a muscular youth who had grown too fast for his clothing and was on the verge of bursting out at the seams. However, he was still a youth, unsophisticated and unspoiled, and merely in need of a little more leg room. It was modern and ancient at once; urban and suburban; sassy and modest. Lumbering, farming, and winter sports were its major industries and major interests.

Some of this information Harry remembered from the old days; some Meg passed on to him in the manner of a guide giving a spiel to the tourists.

"And there," Meg went on, pointing at a neat white frame bungalow that looked like a model house, "there is the mayor's office, which right now is in the middle of a very big squabble."

"What about?"

"Oh, whether or not Bencove should concentrate on being a year-round resort, with visitors all the time, or be kept the way it is."

"Who's fighting?"

"The mayor, who is all for what he calls Progress, with a capital *P*. He wants to hire a big public relations firm and make Bencove into another Sun Valley or Palm Springs or Lake Placid or something. On the other side are lots of the older families who say they prefer to keep Bencove the way it is, instead of getting all tangled up in neon signs, penny arcades, and picnics on the courthouse lawn." Meg at this point spun the wheel sharply into an angled parking place and switched off the ignition. The silence was almost deafening to Harry. His body was still trembling from the egg-beater motion of the springs.

"Of course, the mayor's argument is that with more tourists there will be more income for the townspeople."

"He kind of wraps it up in a neat little bundle, doesn't he?"

Meg turned her lovely face full on him, approvingly. "I think you and I share the same feelings about His Honor, the Mayor."

"What's his name anyway?" Harry asked. "So's I'll remember not to vote for him."

"Wells. Norm Wells."

Harry cleared his throat meaningfully. "I'll have to

make a note of that and have my boys pay him a little visit. Ahem."

"Who're your boys?" Meg whispered.

"They're led by a strangler named Killer Hill."

"He sounds sweet."

"He's a doll," Harry snarled.

Meg, pretending to shiver, came very close to him. Automatically, as he would have done with Dotty, Harry put out his arm and placed it tenderly around her shoulders. For a long moment they remained that way, not speaking. Then Meg drew away, not looking at him, blinking, touching her hair with her fingers.

Harry's face felt flushed and he wanted to say something to Meg, but nothing seemed quite right. He could not apologize, for actually nothing had happened. It would be a mistake to draw her attention to a thing she probably hadn't even noticed.

It had been a long time since Harry had done any major shopping. He'd forgotten how much fun it could be. Or was it fun just because he was with Meg? That was a very interesting question, and the answer might be even more interesting.

They loaded up at the supermarket with milk, butter, coffee, bread, beefsteak, potatoes, oranges, and bananas. Here and there, Harry's eye would be caught by an attractive box of cereal or a chunk of yellow cheese and he would pop it into the wire cart. Meg picked up two avocados, admitting that the rich, delicious fruit was very high in calories, but even higher in taste, and she was sorry but she just had to have them. Harry, feeling oddly like a husband, permitted her to indulge her whim. He trailed her about the store like a puppy on a leash, quite impressed with her poise and confidence.

Afterward, they stopped at the hardware store for a quantity of tools and supplies that made Harry groan in anguish; at the drugstore for bandages and medicines against emergencies; at the news store for a pile of magazines, newspapers, and books.

When at last Meg announced that her buying spree was at an end, Harry gaped at the tottering load in the back end of the pick-up truck and inquired, "Expecting to be snowed in this summer?"

"Unless my memory has been riddled by termites," Meg said primly, "methinks your appetite will force us to refill this vehicle within three days."

This indictment was enough to seal Harry's lips from further comment. He was glad to be leaving the town now. He was rather anxious to be alone with Meg, to talk with her, to look at her, to investigate her curiously fresh mind and personality.

But they were delayed.

A broad-shouldered, deep-chested man, with black hair combed straight back from a high forehead, called to Meg from the other side of the street and dodged a couple of cars to cross over.

Just before he arrived within earshot, Meg murmured, "Norman Wells."

Harry had a few seconds to study the mayor of Bencove as he approached on sturdy, determined legs. He wore a gray-flannel suit, striped tie, and a fixed, factory-made smile.

Meg made the introductions in an even tone, trying not to notice that Wells was staring rudely at her. Harry didn't have to be told that the mayor was a bachelor and that he had a fond eye for Meg Crane.

"And how is Doc?" Wells inquired cheerfully. "Haven't seen him in weeks. Been meaning to get out to his beat-up old camp and have a chat with him. Maybe I will this week."

"A chat about what, Norm?" Meg asked.

"This and that," the mayor laughed. He glanced pretentiously over his shoulder and went on, "I have a proposition that might just interest Doc Howell. It could mean a nice piece of change for him—not to say prestige."

"That's kind of you, Norm," Meg replied. "Doc won't sleep until you tell him."

"It won't be long now," the mayor promised and then, calling in a loud voice, angled across the street again to greet another passerby. Midway he paused long enough to wave a farewell to Meg and Harry.

Meg turned to Harry. "Sometimes I think Norm takes his job seriously."

"Do you?"

"Does anyone? Doc says the only way Norm Wells got elected was because no one else cared about the job."

Harry frowned. "From the sound of him, though, he seems to be a very busy fellow with a great deal on his mind."

"A fair assumption."

"Is that good?"

"I'm not sure. And I know that Doc doesn't care for the man." Meg lifted her slim shoulders and dropped them. "But Bencove isn't my town. Is it yours?" She looked at Harry.

"No," Harry said slowly, "Just the same it bothers me to see a man like that in a position of authority and power."

They climbed back into the truck but—what with the clatter of the crank, which Harry manipulated this time, and the rattle of the engine, and the grumble of the chassis—there was little time for talk or observations about the celebrities of Bencove.

11

THE TRIP BACK TO CAMP was uneventful and the conversation directed largely at the political situation in Bencove. Consequently, Harry couldn't get Meg to explain in detail about the cause of her unhappiness. Anyway, it was unlikely that Meg would bring up the subject herself. She probably felt she'd already said too much.

For the remainder of the afternoon Harry worked with Doc, making badly needed repairs to the dock and some of the buildings. It took Harry a little while to get back into the swing of things; but backed by Doc's quiet competence, he was soon wielding a hammer and saw like a veteran. There was something about Doc that filled him with confidence and security. Here was a man who was not out to "prove" anything or change anything or promote anything. He had found his niche and was dedicated to filling it—and to making youngsters into well-adjusted, happy adults.

Harry suddenly realized the tremendous responsibility

that rested on Doc's slightly stooped shoulders. He had in his hands a terrible force for good or evil and if he had assumed the role of an important, officious man, it would almost be understandable.

When Harry mentioned this to Doc, the leathery old man smiled.

"Well, Harry," Doc said, carefully laying down his hammer, "most fellows who wind up acting like little tin gods probably know all the answers. Me, well, I don't believe that I've covered all the ground there is to cover—why, I'm learning as much from these kids every summer as they're learning from me." He chuckled softly. "The idea of *me* being important!"

Harry studied his old friend, more certain than ever that he *was* important and that his influence was still felt, after many years, by the hundreds of men who'd come to Camp Skylark as boys.

"How you getting on with Meg?" Doc asked in a very blatant attempt to change the subject.

"Grand. She's a wonderful girl. Why didn't you ever let me know that she was turning into another Miss America?"

"I didn't know myself. It happened all at once, almost over night. When she flew in the other day, why, she had to kiss me on the cheek before I recognized her." He rubbed his face thoughtfully. "All dressed up and poised. Like a lady, all right."

"I hope everything's okay with her," Harry offered as he pounded away on a ten-penny nail. He didn't want to appear *too* nosy.

"She's a pretty level-headed girl," Doc said and that ended the topic as far as he was concerned.

Harry might have been completely frustrated in his attempt to do something for Meg had he not come upon her after supper, at twilight, just after the sun had gone down. She was perched on a stool facing an easel. In her left hand was a palette. In her right hand was a brush that flicked from paint to canvas, capturing the multicolored sky on the horizon. Harry did not approach her immediately but stayed a few steps away, looking over Meg's shoulder at the picture that was slowly coming into existence before his eyes.

There was a soft grace diffused through the picture, betraying a high degree of excellence and meticulousness. He was no art critic but he knew this was good. Contrary to what he had expected of painters, Meg worked rapidly and in a few minutes—minutes that encompassed the most brilliant period of the sunset itself—she got everything down on the canvas.

It was just one more of the series of surprises the girl held for him. She was very complex, with an infinite variety of talents, not the least of which was to look perfectly enchanting while quite absorbed in her work. It occurred to Harry that while the sunset was a good subject for a painting, an even better one would be a painting of Meg painting. The last fading light of day danced off the sheen of her hair and the planes of her face, etching this vision of her forever in his memory.

At last she rose from the chair, gave a final dab with

her brush, and then slowly backed off. Her unseeing steps carried her directly into Harry.

"Oh!"

"It's me," Harry said softly.

"I'm—sorry. I didn't know anyone . . ."

"That's all right. I should apologize. It's not very polite to stare at people unannounced."

"Have you been here long?"

"Since the second pine tree."

At first she was bewildered and then looked at her canvas. The sun itself was framed by a pair of elongated, stark pines.

"This," she began, "this is just a rough sketch . . ."

"No, it isn't. It's a very professional piece of work. And artistic, too. I may not be much of an artist myself, but I can tell good art when I see it. And this is good."

"This particular piece was just an exercise."

Harry shook his head. "I doubt it. There is more to that canvas than the paint on it. Emotion. Sadness. Is it effrontery to suggest there is something symbolic in your doing a sun*set* and not a sun*rise?*"

"Harry Williams!" Her eyes flashed in the twilight. "You must be a clairvoyant. For a swimmer you seem to be quite perceptive. You have hidden depths."

"Ha! Look who's talking! It's like having twenty people in the camp instead of just three."

Meg strolled back to the easel and regarded it dubiously.

"Wait. Don't throw it away. Let me keep it."

"Really?"

"Of course. Then in a few years when you're famous I can sell it, if I have to, and make a small fortune."

"It'll be mighty small," Meg warned. "But you can have it if you want."

"You'll sign it, won't you?"

"Of course. Will you give me an autograph?"

"It's a deal. You can peddle my autograph and I'll peddle your paintings and between the two we ought to make a very good living. Of course, I know I'm getting the best bargain because I can never improve on my signature while you are bound to improve on your art."

"That," Meg said in an oddly tight voice, "is open to debate."

She repacked her paraphernalia, Harry seized the chair, and together they walked up the steep lawn in the darkness that had descended like the lowering of a black curtain. Harry had no intention of returning to the house immediately. Now was the time to have that heart-to-heart chat with Meg.

"Ever since we met this morning," Harry said, "you've teased me with clues about what is going on with you. I can tell you are trying to make a big decision. Now, you don't have to tell me about it if you don't want to, but it's possible that someone with an objective viewpoint could get right to the crux of the matter in no time at all."

"Could be," Meg murmured as she set her stuff down and sat on the middle step of the porch. Her arms laced around her long legs. "Could be." She turned to look at him. "You're right, Harry. I'm trying to make up my mind—and it's no fun."

"Is there someone else involved?"

"Isn't there always? But at least you're rational."

Meg's voice modulated with the sounds of the evening, the chirp of crickets, the sighing of the wind in the trees, the myriad orchestral noises. Her voice came from deep in her throat, and Harry felt very special that she was singling him out for attention.

"Rational?" he repeated. "I don't know about that."

"Well, more rational than Ken is."

"Ken?"

"Ken Varden. Those two words sum up my entire problem."

"That's not very complicated."

"Don't let it fool you, because it is indeed a confusing thing. What I'm attempting to decide now will affect me for the rest of my life."

There was a temptation in Harry to say, "Me, too," but this was Meg's story, not his. Courtesy demanded that he hear her out—then if he wanted to bore her with his tale, he could.

"Actually," she went on in a soft voice, "I suppose it is simple. Art *versus* Love sort of thing that you see in the movies. Career *versus* Marriage. Will Marriage Spoil a Beautiful Friendship? I wish I knew. I really do."

"I don't understand. Doesn't this Ken like your art?"

"Oh, yes, he likes it—just the way it is."

"You mean—?"

"I mean that he is satisfied with my art right now and would like it never to change—never to get better. In other words, Ken thinks I've had enough art instruction to last me a lifetime and that I should not think about Paris or Rome."

"What does he want you to think about?"

"Philadelphia and marriage and a family and a home."

"I get it—he thinks that a woman's place is at the sink and over the hot stove? That's rather medieval, isn't it?"

"Well, in some ways perhaps Ken is archaic. He's older than I am by five or six years. He's been in the service and has a very good job as an account executive in his father's advertising agency. Some of the girls on campus consider him the best catch of the year."

"Do you consider him a catch?"

"Not at all. I'm not a fisherwoman. I'm just in love with him, that's all."

Harry felt a pang of disappointment. A very peculiar reaction. What made him think that Meg should be in love with *him?* What colossal conceit.

"What are you going to do?" he asked.

"That's what I don't know. That's why I had to get away and come up to Skylark and think things out. In Philadelphia I was always under Ken's pressure to say yes or no. It so happens that I'm not built that way. I can't open and close the doors of my life so simply. He wants a final decision—either I set a date to marry him and start planning for marriage, or I go to Europe with my paint brushes and forget about him."

"He won't settle for both, say for marriage after the European tour?"

"That's the issue in a nutshell," Meg sighed. The moon, peeking from between the fingerlike branches, shone softly on her face, accentuating its beauty. A silvery strip of moonlight lay shimmering on the rippling waters of Lake Skylark.

"Couldn't he go with you?" Harry suggested.

"Now, Harry," Meg said quickly. Then, "No. Right now he's in a crucial period of his own career. He has to make a name for himself aside from his father's, and he can't take too much time off. No, I have to search my own soul and have the courage to make the decision and stick to it."

"You like to paint, don't you?"

"It's the most important thing in my life," Meg replied simply.

"You've had encouragement?"

"Lots. The head of the school said I could be one of the best dozen painters in the country—eventually. A few critics have indicated it would be a loss if I were to give it up. I've won four blue ribbons in exhibition and goodness knows how many medals and things."

"I can believe it."

"Yet, I'm not sufficiently sure of myself to sacrifice my own emotions and private life to my art. It would be tragic to throw up everything for a year or two in France —only to find at the end that I was a flash in the pan and that my talent was transitory. And I certainly would not be the first prodigy to flop in the big time." One of her hands rested firmly on Harry's bare forearm. "The truth is, I'm afraid to decide. I'm afraid of alienating Ken—and I'm afraid of ignoring what I deeply feel is right. I don't want to be one of those people who are always talking about the portrait they could have painted or the novel they could have written if they'd only had the time or money or something."

"Or the races they could have won," Harry said.

"What did you say?"

"If."

They got up from the step and moved inside the porch screens. A chill was in the air now and Harry for the first time was conscious of how tired he was.

"So there, Harry, you have my problem—lock, stock, and easel."

"It's no snap."

"If you can make head or tail of it, I'd appreciate any suggestions. Of course, it's probably all very silly to you, and a year from now, after I've married Ken and am all settled down, I won't even be able to remember worrying about it."

Harry detected a plaintive tone in her voice, as though she were trying hard to treat a serious problem lightly.

"I would be a real dope to dispense neat solutions right away. Let me think about it and maybe in the morning we can hash it over again."

"That's all right with me," Meg said. "I'll be here then. I'll be here until I know what I'm going to do."

For a moment they faced one another at the bottom of the staircase, their hands touching, their eyes fixed. Harry heard a thick roaring in his ears and felt an enormous pressure on the back of his head that aimed it at Meg's face. But he resisted the roar and the pressure and turned away. He was not certain, but he thought a shadow of disappointment fell briefly over Meg's features.

"Good night, Harry boy," she whispered huskily, and then turned and ran up the stairs.

Harry watched her go. After a while he slowly made his way to his own room on the ground floor. Meg was certainly in a dilemma. There seemed to be no sure exit, no way of coming out of this, without losing something that was very important. It wasn't fair. People, especially people as lovely as Meg Crane, should not have to try to find their way out such mazes. He made up his mind that he would help her, somehow.

It was not until he was in bed that it occurred to him that his own trouble was really insignificant when compared to Meg's.

12

FOR THE NEXT DAY or so there was little time for the exchange of confidences. The clean-up and fix-up schedule set by Doc was a Spartan one and demanded everyone's full attention. Actually the three of them were doing the work of ten; but no one complained, and the very arduousness of their labors drew them closer together. With the wall of Meg's inner torment breached, Harry relaxed more in her presence; and she, too, behaved as if a weight had been lifted from her girlish shoulders.

Doc, patient and understanding, did not press either of them. Perhaps his long years of living with younger people had equipped him with an antenna that enabled him to understand exact moods and to treat them accordingly. While he never considered Camp Skylark as a haven for the ill, he recognized that strenuous work could be as effective as a religious retreat. So he bided his time.

One morning at breakfast Doc told Harry that they ought to plot out a trail for the campers. During the long winter nights Doc had already mapped out a camping and hiking itinerary, drawing on his experience in the woods he knew so well; but now it was vital to go over the ground itself. The hard winter had wrought changes on the face of the forest and before he could send out any groups he had to know precisely what they might run into in the way of hazards and obstacles.

Meg put up a lunch that Harry stashed away in his knapsack, and with Doc taking the point, they struck off into the thickly wooded area north of the camp. They had not taken a hundred steps when they were utterly isolated from the camp and any sign of civilization. Were it not for Doc's unerring sense of direction—plus the compass strapped to his wrist—Harry knew they could be lost in no time. Every two hundred yards Harry blazed a tree with his hatchet to mark the way.

They moved easily, Harry feeling very fresh and strong, capable of going on for miles and miles. Overhead the birch and pines and oak branches played patty-cake in the mountain wind. Now and then they came to an open space and would pause while Doc made notations on his map; then they would skirt by, keeping in the shade of the trees that ringed the area. This caused them to lengthen the distance, but the object of the hike was as much to show the youngsters *how* to march as to instill in them a sense of safety. No Indian file or infantry patrol would cross an open field when it could avoid it. Open fields were subject to easy surveillance and therefore were dangerous. Doc Howell had more than once cited to Harry the letters he had received from his prewar campers who had remembered well their hiking lessons while they were on actual missions in the South Pacific or France or Italy.

Of course, Skylark was not a military camp, but Doc saw no reason why the boys shouldn't be prepared anyway. Conceivably, the training they got at Skylark could one day save a life or two. That alone was worth it to Doc to spend this day in the forest.

The sun was high and hot in the bright-blue sky, and Harry began to sweat. His limbs felt oiled and his muscles loose. The pack was not heavy and served as a slight pressure to push him forward.

At one point, after a particularly stiff climb, they reached the summit of a rocky hill. Doc called a halt, and they turned and looked at the vast spread of trees and mountains laid out before them. Lake Skylark was like a chip of green glass several miles off. Harry uncorked his canteen and gratefully swallowed the cool water. Doc joined him. Harry did not dare mention it, but Doc's stamina impressed him. The man was over sixty, and yet he was as lean and springy as a sapling.

"Nice, eh?" Doc observed laconically.

"Nice," Harry agreed.

Then they were off again, angling down into the depths of the forest, blazing tree trunks and ticking off landmarks. Harry could not remember when he had felt quite so good or quite so free. Yes, he could remember the last time he was on such a hike—years before. Ahead of him he saw how sweat had seeped through Doc's shirt, making it stick to his back. Although he was certain of his own strength, he did not know what Doc's limit was.

He hesitated to suggest an end, for he did not want to appear weak; but it was possible that Doc was feeling tired.

The sun reached its noon height and began to slide into the western portion of the sky and still Doc continued, effortlessly and smoothly. At length hunger forced Harry to suggest a rest. Or was it hunger? One of them had to give in, had to wave the white flag. Were his companion as young, Harry would have been willing to continue the silent, friendly duel all day and night before asking for quarter. Maybe Doc felt he had to prove himself to Harry? In any case Harry saw no sense in pushing Doc to the extreme. It was a long way back to camp.

"Don't you ever get hungry?" he gasped.

Doc paused on the trail ahead, next to an outcropping of rock from which a silvery stream of water flowed. He studied Harry closely; it was no effort for Harry to look exhausted.

"I'm not in shape for this kind of thing," Harry explained. "If it were water, it would be a different thing."

Then Doc said an odd thing: "Would it?"

"Let's eat," Harry said.

Out of the corner of his eye Harry noticed that Doc's chest was heaving deeply; the strain was beginning to show on his leathery face. But he had been willing to go on until he dropped. It did not matter to Harry what Doc thought about him at this moment—whether he was soft and out of condition. What mattered was that they had stopped before Doc had reached the end of his rope.

They ate the fried chicken Meg had fixed that morning, washing it down with mountain spring water, and then each unpeeled and ate an orange. For dessert they devoured two chocolate bars apiece.

Stuffed and content, they lay back against a boulder that had been planed smooth by some forgotten glacier and stared up at the patches of sky they could see through the branches. Between them was the intangible bond that arises between two people who have endured hardship together, the kind of camaraderie he had known with the members of the swimming team after an especially hard meet.

"I haven't felt quite so bushed since my last 1500-meter race," Harry said. "You certainly lead a rugged pace, Doctor Howell."

"Have to," Doc replied. "Endurance has won more than one battle. A man is cheating if he takes the easy way out, if he doesn't put all he's got into a mission."

"You taught me that ten years ago, Doc, and it still holds."

"I hope so. I'd hate to think that some boy failed on a job because I'd failed to make him realize it pays always to do your best."

"You'd never have to worry about that," Harry laughed.

"I'm not so sure," Doc said. He got up and squinted into the sun. "I'm not so sure," he repeated distantly. He didn't look at Harry, but the boy felt as if he were being examined under a moral microscope. Odd, how such an impression could be gained in the midst of the immensity of nature, the endless forest, the massive mountains.

For a time neither spoke, and then, at last, Doc asked

the question that Harry knew had been between them for three days.

"What happened at State?"

"How do you know anything happened?"

"The same way I knew you were coming up here."

Harry frowned up at the taut figure. "You're way ahead of me, Doc. As usual."

"There's no mystery about it, Harry. I subscribe to the *Daily*. I've subscribed to it for a good many semesters now."

"Of course," Harry said slowly. "Of course. You've known everything about me all along."

"Well," Doc smiled. "Not everything. It didn't print your private life."

"It could have," Harry chuckled. "So you read about the scrape after the Tech meet?"

"It took me about three minutes to figure out you'd be heading up this way before long. A fellow can't take too many punches like that without running for a neutral corner."

"But this isn't neutral," Harry said hopefully.

"That," said Doc, "remains to be seen."

Harry was disturbed by this reply. Of all people, he had expected Doc without question to back him and right down the line. Doc seemed to read his mind.

"Maybe that sounds as if I'm letting you down, Harry boy. Not at all. I'm perfectly willing to back one of my boys on a matter that indicates serious reflection on his part—but not on an impulsive, thoughtless act. I'd like to hear from all the precincts before I start counting votes."

"So you're withholding judgment on me until I plead my case."

"I'm not that bad," Doc laughed.

"That depends," Harry said. "Shall we start back while I unload my dread secrets?"

"Okay."

Without the food, Harry's knapsack was much lighter and the straps did not bite into his shoulders as before. The way back would be largely downhill and therefore they should make good time.

Doc took the point again, consulted his wrist compass, and they were off. Harry followed by half a dozen paces. "On the bare face of it," he began, "I may look pretty silly. But I felt I had no choice. I had been forced into an untenable position by Rusty Barnes and I had to fight back in the only way I could."

Up ahead Doc grunted noncommittally.

Bit by bit, Harry unfolded the story of Williams *versus* the State swimming team. He explained how he had trained himself to a fine edge, to the very limit for a potential record, each time he went into the tank. This was the culmination of ten years of water work. Then in a few short hours Coach Barnes had jeopardized his entire program—for the sake of making an impression on some visiting brass.

At this point, Harry explained, he had rebelled. He had not learned to swim for the sake of Rusty Barnes' career as a coach. Nor had he learned so that State could add another digit to its win column.

"Why did you learn?" Doc interrupted.

"Why—why, because it was the thing that meant the most to me. Some fellows like law, some like medicine, some like baseball. I have to swim. And I feel that someday I can transmit some of my knowledge to other kids, as you've done to me."

"Okay. Go on."

They moved in step easily, just a little tired, their muscles aching slightly. It was nice to be going home.

Harry repeated the events of the All-Conference meet and how Barnes had gotten him to enter three events he was not ready for. There had been no chance to try for a 440 record that day—and there might never be again.

"In other words," Doc said over his shoulder. "Rusty asked you to swim for the team."

"That's putting it too simply, Doc. It was for his sake too."

"But as far as the general public was concerned, you pulled out the victory by some competent team swimming. As I get it, your swimming at that meet was not overpowering—but it was brilliant. You didn't out*swim* the other teams so much as out*wit* them."

"I guess you could say that."

"I guess I will say that. All right, carry on. So far you're mad as a hatter because you won a swimming meet."

"Wait a second, Doc Howell," Harry protested. "You're putting words into my mouth."

"How would you say it then?"

"I feel that I betrayed my own concept of what an athlete should be by swimming the kind of races I didn't believe in. Had I been allowed to swim my kind of race there would have been at least one world record set—I'll swear to that. . . ."

"And a meet lost."

"Maybe so, but the record-holder would have been a State man. A Barnes-coached tanker. It was a trading of one kind of glory for another."

"It would have been the trading of a single man for a whole team."

"Come again?"

"The others—they trained and sacrificed a lot, didn't they? Had you gone on to your record, only you would have made the headlines next day. Not the State team. Just Harry Williams." Doc stopped in the middle of the trail and peered back at him quizzically.

Harry felt as though he were bound in vines. Every way he had turned, Doc had tied him up in verbal knots. Doc had misinterpreted the whole situation down at the university. They just couldn't talk properly while hiking. However, Doc had no intention of letting him off the hook so easily.

"So everybody knew you were an individual champ before the meet. Now they know you are also a team champ. So that's bad?"

"So it doesn't matter to me, Doc. Years ago I started out right there." Harry pointed a long arm at the green chip that was the lake far below. "I intended to go to the top. I got sidetracked." He shrugged. "And now I'll never make the top."

"Who says?"

"I say."

"Sour grapes?"

"No. I'm just fed up with misdirected effort. Rusty Barnes doesn't own me. State doesn't own me."

"Who does own you?"

"Nobody. Well, maybe I do."

"A dubious thrill, that. So you won't get to be Mr. Number One and therefore you won't play any more. No Nationals. No Olympics."

"No," Harry muttered, his eyes on the rocky ground that fell away beneath his feet.

"I see. I guess that'll show them."

"Show who?"

"Oh, the people of the United States and all the other countries in the world, too."

"I'm not mad at them."

"But you should be," Doc chided. "After all, it's their system. They make the rules by which we live and play and swim."

"That's exaggerating, Doc."

"Call it anything you like—the point is that Harry Williams is not going to swim because one man, Rusty Barnes, got him annoyed. Looks like that Barnes is a bigger man than I ever gave him credit for."

Harry shook his head in puzzlement. "Something's cockeyed here. This isn't the way my story started out."

"But it's the way it's finishing. By the way, when are the Nationals?"

"A week from today."

"I only asked out of curiosity. You're not going, of course. But I thought I might follow Bud Hill's progress in the sports pages."

"Hill! He couldn't make the Nationals."

"Why not? Barnes won't have anyone else to send. He won't be able to send his best man, so he'll send his next best. That's just horse sense."

"You're trying to talk me into something, Doc Howell, and I'm not listening. You've got my side of it all mixed up. It's like trying to swim with forty pounds of lead on my feet."

"All right," Doc said. "I'll forget it—if you will. It's no skin off my nose. And this summer when the kids come we can say that their trail was blazed by a lad who was *almost* champion of the world."

"Lay off."

"A week, eh," Doc muttered and began to step up the pace.

Camp was still two miles off when Doc stepped on a smooth stone half-hidden by the underbrush. With a wild cry, he threw his hands into the air and fell forward heavily. The bushes crackled with his weight, and he disappeared.

Quickly Harry plunged ahead. Doc had rolled several yards downhill and had come to rest against the trunk of a sturdy oak. Groaning, he struggled to get to his feet, but he collapsed at once, reaching for his left leg.

Harry knelt beside him. "What is it, Doc? Where are you hurt?"

Grimacing, Doc pointed to his knee. His teeth bit into his lower lip. From his throat came anguished moans of pain. Harry knew that sixty-year-old bones were far more brittle than younger ones and a break or even a strain was proportionately more severe.

"Can you stand at all?"

"I don't think so. The blasted thing is on fire."

"I don't like it. You'll need medical attention right away." Harry slit Doc's trousers with his jackknife and peered at the knee. It was faintly discolored. He touched it with his fingers, and Doc squirmed and yelled. It didn't look too bad, but you could never tell with a knee.

"I could try a splint," he murmured, "but even then you couldn't walk."

Doc leaned back against the tree, his eyes closed, his lips tight. He did not speak.

"Or I could go back to camp and get help—only a stretcher could never get through the undergrowth."

"Do *something,*" Doc hissed. "This thing is killing me."

There was only one thing to do. Carry him.

"The only chance is piggyback, Doc. Think you can make it?"

"Can you?"

"Can I? I have to. Let's go."

He slipped out of the knapsack and hung it by the straps from a lower limb. Then he got Doc's off and hung it up, too. With great delicacy he maneuvered so that Doc could crawl onto his back. The first time, Doc was just about up when he uttered a piercing yell and crumpled to the ground, dragging Harry with him. For a few minutes they were a tangle in a patch of young raspberry bushes. Harry felt the thorns pricking him no matter how he tried to get to his feet. Doc was very awkward; his arms and elbows kept getting into Harry's spine.

At last, Harry got to his feet again. He looked down at Doc, who was lying on his back, his right leg out flat, his left leg straight up in the air.

"Danged thing!" Doc cried. "Can't you watch your step, Harry? You're clumsy as an ox."

"Okay," Harry said heavily. Doc's weight was deceiving. Hiking, he had appeared to be skinny and boneless. Now all at once he was as heavy as half a ton of wet cement.

They tried again, and this time, with much grunting and groaning and whined suggestions on the part of Doc, they made it. Doc was mounted, his arms wrapped around Harry's neck, his legs supported by Harry's well-sinewed arms.

They started off down the trail again. Harry was forced to keep his head down to watch his precarious step, so Doc acted as navigator. With well-aimed punches and nudges, he warned his beast of burden of obstacles and bad places on the track. Still Harry managed to blunder into more than one briar patch. Each time he stumbled Doc berated him with agonized cries and entreaties to be more careful.

They came to a stream that bisected the path. It was

only about three feet deep but it was very fast. The water rushed by angrily. On the way up, they had negotiated it rather simply by hopping across on the boulders. Now it looked as wide as the Hellespont to Harry. He wanted to rest but Doc whined, "My knee. Have mercy, Harry boy. I'm an old man."

A rush of impatient words rose to Harry's lips, but he held them back. He should not be harsh with Doc—not in these circumstances. He could hardly be blamed for his state of mind.

"We can only try it," Harry said, getting a tighter grip on Doc's legs. "Game?"

"If you are."

Harry took a tentative step onto the nearest boulder. Doc's hands gripped his neck like a vulture's talons. "Don't get nervous, boy. We'll make it. We'll make it!"

He was shrieking into Harry's ear and clutching his windpipe at the same time. One hand spread over Harry's face until he couldn't see anything but calloused fingers.

"Doc! Please! My eyes!"

"I'm sorry, Harry. But keep going. You're doing okay."

Harry took another step, balancing gingerly. Doc seemed to have tripled in weight since Harry had picked him up. Just below his probing foot the mountain torrent rushed past like a miniature Niagara. Foam obliterated the next boulder, and he could only guess. His toe tried for purchase, made it, and then he hauled himself onto it with both feet and teetered there with his human load.

"Good boy! Almost there," Doc gasped. "Another step."

Harry's foot went out to the next stone, a stone that was slippery with moss. At that moment Doc's weight shifted higher and Harry's two legs strained to hold, a foot on each rock. He couldn't get enough momentum to pull one foot after the other.

"That's it," Doc coached. "Give 'er the gun."

With a superhuman effort, Harry shoved. At the same instant Doc rose high on his back, almost to Harry's shoulders. But the moss defeated them in the end. Harry felt himself falling and then Doc was gone. Harry strove for balance, lost it, toppled into the stream, and went under.

The water wasn't very deep, but Harry had to scramble to keep from being washed many yards downstream. His hands closed on a low branch and hung on. Spitting and spluttering, he came to the surface, numb with terror at what might have happened to the half-crippled Doc.

He needn't have worried. There on the opposite shore, propped up on one elbow, was Doc Howell, solemnly watching Harry's watery struggles.

"Are you okay?" Doc called calmly.

"I . . . think . . . so."

"Can I give you a hand?"

"No. I can make it."

Somehow, he fought his way to the bank and pulled himself, dripping, onto the grass.

"Thank God you're all right," he said when he got his breath.

"You're a very brave man, Harry Williams."

At the moment Harry Williams was a very wet and tired and miserable man, but he didn't want Doc to know it. There was still a mile to go. So, sopping wet and muscle-weary, he lifted Doc again and lurched onward to Camp Skylark. They finally staggered out of the forest and onto the gravel path that led to the Main House. Meg Crane was waiting on the porch, eyes wide.

"What's wrong?"

"Doc," Harry gasped. "Knee. Get some hot water. Hurry."

With these words, Harry slowly crumpled to the ground. Meg reached out and half-caught her uncle. Harry lay there a few seconds, sucking air back into his flattened lungs. When he opened his eyes next, the first thing he saw was Doc Howell—vertical. The leathery old timer was walking slowly in a circle, supported very lightly by Meg, flexing and bending his left knee.

"Not bad," he was saying. "Not bad, at all. I think I'll live." Then his cool gray eyes fell on Harry. "But I'm not sure about my two-legged mule. You'd better see to him, Florence Nightingale."

Harry wasn't sure, but just before Doc limped away and up the steps, he could have sworn that Doc's right eye closed in what was unmistakably a wink.

13

AFTER ANOTHER full day's work, the biggest tasks of readying the camp for summer were finished. What remained now were minor, though necessary, jobs that could be handled during the remaining six weeks.

Late one afternoon, Meg announced that she had to go into Bencove to get a shampoo and manicure and asked if anyone wanted to go into town with her.

Doc, dozing in a hammock slung between two trees, mumbled, "You two small-fry go—just be back in time for my supper." A straw hat shaded his eyes from the afternoon sun.

Meg looked at him and shook her head in mock despair.

"Look at him. Before we came here a few days ago, Doc had to do everything himself and made no complaint. Now, he's spoiled rotten."

"Don't misunderstand me," Doc sighed. "I *like* peeling potatoes and washing dishes and all that—but I know you like it better and I always like to be courteous to young ladies. 'Sides, everybody knows a woman's place is in the kitchen—not going into the big city to get all prettied up." He lifted the straw hat and peered out craftily. "That is, unless she's got herself an extra special reason for getting prettied up . . ."

"Oh, Doc!" Meg cried, blushing furiously. "Go back to sleep."

A smile appeared on the thin lips and an obnoxious snore issued from his flared nostrils.

Harry seized Meg's hand and tugged her away. She started for the pick-up truck, but he would have none of it.

"We go first class today, my lass. My car."

Meg tried to look chagrined, but it didn't come off, and she happily agreed to let Harry drive. As the car swung around and went past the hammock, a voice yelled, "See if they've got any bargains in splints at the dime store!"

Harry blew the horn as his only form of rebuttal. Doc's cackling laugh followed them down the road.

They reached Bencove in time for Meg's appointment; Harry dropped her off and went on to the market with a small shopping list. Within ten minutes he had finished what he had to do. There was still another three-quarters of an hour before Meg would be out of the beauty shop, so he strolled along the main street. He wore a white T-shirt, khaki pants, and loafers. He felt fresh and neat and good. He knew that after four years few of the townspeople would recognize him, and in fact few did, so he took his time and window-shopped in the secure anonymity of a stranger in a familiar town.

One place he wanted to see was Parker's General Store which, eight or ten years before, had been a Mecca for everyone who lived on the lake. There had been the old cracker barrels, the open jars of cookies, the canisters of figs, and flour in cloth sacks, and the cured hams hanging from hooks in the ceiling. In the center of the store was the inevitable potbellied stove, with the floor around it worn thin from a half-century of group discussions. Harry remembered that in the summer the front porch of Parker's store was a gathering place for the local politicians, pundits, and philosophers.

Parker's General Store was a two-story frame structure flanked by elms, right opposite City Park. At the curb was an ancient iron jockey, whose metal hand was outstretched to receive the reins of horses long since gone. The interior of the store was cool and dark and fragrant with the scent of spices, tobacco, coffee, and candy.

Progress, of course, had by-passed Parker's as a source of groceries. But Parker's old clientele continued to patronize the store, if only to talk and argue and pass the time of day. A few old-faithfuls whittled, a few more played cards; others would read the newspapers and comment pro and con.

By and large, it was a stimulating atmosphere. Here you could find out anything about anybody; this was the center of controversy and the origin of countless ideas, schemes, and political careers—the finish of political careers, too.

The store's porch was, in effect, a town meeting, and anyone at all was free to sit down on a step or in a vacant chair and take part in the conversation—or simply mind his own business. As Harry walked up the street, he saw there was a sizable throng gathered in front of the store. His natural curiosity hurried his step.

It took him a few minutes to decipher the train of the talk. A couple of men were arguing politics—which of course was not unique—but it intrigued Harry because he heard the name of Mayor Norm Wells mentioned several times—and not in altogether complimentary terms.

"My good sir," a young man was telling a tall, lanky farmer in overalls, "my good sir, you are simply standing still in the inexorable path of progress. This is the twentieth century—not the eighteenth. What is your name, anyway?" he inquired, with a malicious grin on his face, "Rip Van Winkle?"

The throng chuckled at the sally, and the young man sucked in his plump cheeks with pleasure. The tall farmer blinked his eyes and shuffled his feet on the planks of the porch. "Wal, ah don't know about progress, young fella, but I do know what's happened to them other towns what went touristy."

"What *did* happen?" the young man asked with a great show of courtesy.

"Wal . . ." the farmer stammered, "they got plenty of them neon lights and wild people drivin' around nights crazy and crashin' cars. An' taxes went up and lots of people lost their houses 'cause new roads was built. Stuff like that."

"In other words, everybody had more money and therefore lived in better, more modern homes." The young man shrugged and gazed vacantly at the crowd. "Doesn't sound very catastrophic to me."

Harry nudged the man next to him and asked who the talker was.

"That's Norm Wells' assistant. College boy. Norm got him up here to work out a plan to get some vacation money into Bencove."

"College boy, you say?"

"Yep," was the answer. "But you can't trust them over-educated kids these days. Got all sorts of new-fangled ideas about making everything streamlined and chrome-plated."

"Right," drawled Harry. "What's the argument all about?"

"The tall fella says he won't vote for a man like Wells who is trying to commercialize Bencove. Primary's next week, you know. So the mayor's assistant is defending Norm."

A middle-aged woman, overhearing their conversation, came between them. "The young fella thinks the merchants can do a hundred thousand dollars' worth of business in a year if the tourists come."

"That's impressive, all right," Harry observed cautiously.

"Depends on how you look at it," the woman muttered.

Harry realized quickly that these people were very chary about revealing their true feelings—especially before a stranger. And like it or not, he was a stranger.

On the top step, the young man gazed around expansively, as if daring anyone else to enter into an argument with him. Several of the old-timers, those who frequented Parker's, tried to slip back into the crowd. They were not inclined to make fools of themselves in public. The young man smiled a smile that made his eyes disappear.

"See what I mean?" he said smoothly. "None of you have any real, sound reasons to keep Bencove a hick town—except that it's too tough to change. Or at least that's what you think. It's not true. Look here." He held up a hand and tapped the forefinger. "A developer will come in here and put up the money to install a ski tow up Bald Mountain. Another one will build a hotel for the guests. For warm-weather sports, you can get an experienced man to chop down all the trees around Lake Skylark and build up the area with cabañas and tourist cabins."

He shook his head back and forth. "Golly, you'll have more money than you'll know what to do with. Pretty soon you'll have your own radio and TV station and you'll all be driving big cars."

The throng began to talk in low voices, some nodding their heads. Whatever resistance had faced the mayor's assistant earlier was melting before this implacable and attractive logic.

"Wait a minute there."

It was with astonishment that Harry heard his own voice. Fifty heads swiveled and a hundred eyes stared at him.

On the porch, the young man raised his eyebrows. "Yes, sir. What is it?"

"Just a question or two," Harry said, drawing out the

words so as to disguise the fact he was not a native. "Is this new development your idea or the mayor's?"

"Why do you ask that?" the other parried.

"Well, I would like to know if the idea came from the inside or the outside. Is it a kind of demand by the people of Bencove or by some other people who'd like to make some easy money?"

"I don't know what you're driving at, but the idea was both mine and the mayor's."

"How much are you getting out of it? Ten per cent, say, from each of the developers and contractors you invite in?"

A hush fell over the crowd, and the mayor's assistant slowly descended the steps. A path opened for him that led to Harry. As the man walked through the human aisle, it closed behind him and presently he and Harry were in the circle, facing one another like a pair of wary dogs. Harry's heart was beating like a piston, his mouth was dry.

The man was two inches shorter than Harry, but outweighed him by a good twenty pounds. Up close, his friendly cherubic face was smooth and hard.

"That's very dangerous talk in public, sir," the heavy man said quietly. "Are you sure you don't want to apologize?"

"What did I say?" Harry asked.

"You accused me of being a thief and a grafter."

"You misunderstand. I *asked* if you were."

A titter rippled through the audience. The man's face reddened. "I don't know who you are," he snapped, poking at Harry's chest with a finger, "but you're looking for trouble. Lots of trouble. I think these good people will vouch for my integrity. What about yours?"

Harry was on the spot. Maybe he had gone too far without adequate preparation. Yet he could not retreat. And he did not want to retreat.

"What's your hurry about making Bencove into a boom town, Plumpy?" There were some outright guffaws at the nickname. "Bencove has gotten along all right for the last hundred years. If there are changes to be made—let the Bencovers make them."

"I can see you *are* a hillbilly. For your information, mister, Norm Wells and I are going to wake up this town and put it on the map." He dropped his gaze to Harry's shoes and then slowly raised it again, insolently, until his eyes were focussed on Harry's upper lip. "On your way, boy, and I promise not to press charges of slander."

"Oh, I'll go on my way—but one more question first."

"What's that?" Plumpy said calmly, certain he had vanquished another heckler.

"You haven't answered my original question yet—are you getting a kick-back or not?"

There was a concerted gasp from the throng. The air crackled with tension. Every eye was on Plumpy. Plumpy broke the tension. He swung his right fist at Harry's chin. The blow jarred Harry backward and into the arms of the bystanders.

The punch cleared his head, and when Plumpy came on again, he was ready. He dodged the fist, caught it on his forearm, and slammed his left against the other's jaw.

Plumpy's mouth fell open in surprise and shock, and his guard dropped. Harry measured him for the finisher.

That was when he heard his name called in a high feminine voice. He held the punch and looked around. Meg Crane was pushing her way through the mob, her lovely face set in lines of determination.

"Harry! Leave that poor man alone." Hands on hips, lips tight, she made a very fierce picture. She glared at the sheepish crowd. "Shame on you for letting Harry hit that creature. Don't you know he's a professional boxer?"

Harry looked shyly at the ground.

"Come along before that little fat man gets hurt."

Taking him by the hand, Meg led Harry through the mob that parted respectfully to let them pass. Murmurs of admiration followed them down the street. Harry chanced a look over his shoulder and saw that Plumpy was sitting on the ground, rubbing his jaw and looking as if he had just been rescued from a gruesome fate. As everyone drifted away from the scene of battle, he picked himself up, dusted off his suit, smoothed his hair, and hurried back to the mayor's bungalow.

Meg's fingers closed meaningfully on Harry's. He returned the pressure. Out of the side of her mouth, she said, "You were wonderful, Slugger. That little idiot deserved all he got."

"Huh?"

"I heard it all, but when the shooting started I figured I'd better call a halt. Dope! You could have wrecked the good impression you'd made if you'd gone too far. They would have begun to feel sorry for him. This way, he just looks kind of silly."

They got into the car—Meg driving—and rapidly left Bencove behind them.

"Thanks, Meg," Harry said.

"Forget it." She paused. "You know, I'm kind of sorry I didn't let you finish it. What a mess it would've been!"

"Yeah." Harry agreed ruefully.

"Well. Maybe next time."

"Gee whiz, boss—honest?"

"If you're good and promise to eat your raw meat."

"On the hoof."

"There's a good boy."

Harry stared at Meg's smooth unblemished cheek, noticing how it twitched with the beginnings of a smile. Her newly coiffed hair was very pert and becoming.

"You know what," he said gently.

"No—what?"

"You are quite a woman."

Harry stretched toward her and placed his lips against the delicate expanse of cheek. Meg said nothing—she merely touched the place with her fingertips.

"Trying to rub it off?" he asked.

"No—"

"Meg . . ."

"Harry, no. Don't say anything. Please."

"But I must."

"Please, Harry! *Please!*"

Her eyes glinted with tears.

"I'm . . . sorry."

"Don't say that. Don't." She blinked and tears trickled down on either side of her tiny nose. She kept driving.

"What shall I say?"

"Nothing," she sobbed, "say nothing . . ."

14

AT SUPPER THAT NIGHT Harry asked Doc what he thought of the political uproar in Bencove.

Doc paused in his concentrated attack on an ear of yellow corn. "Not much to think about—nobody else wants to be mayor bad enough to beat out Norm Wells. So it's his job, I reckon."

"The catch is, though, that with Wells the town also gets his wise-guy assistant."

"That's unfortunate. It truly is. From what I hear of him, that young fella is a smarty. Now, I like a smart man, but I don't like a smarty."

"Isn't there some way we can get rid of him?"

"We?" Doc repeated with uplifted brows. "We? Don't tell me you've signed up as a citizen of our fair town?"

Harry looked at Meg, who laughed smugly. "I'd say so, Doc. He was doing some rather high-powered campaigning this afternoon."

"It wasn't that, " Harry defended, flustered. "That guy

just annoyed me with his ridiculous talk. Like a dictator condescending to talk with his underlings."

Meg turned to Doc. "Seriously—things don't look terribly good in Bencove what with the possibility of city slickers moving in and that jerky assistant to the mayor. Can't the townspeople do anything about it, Doc?"

"For one thing," Doc said, mopping up gravy with a remnant of bread, "the Bencove folks have never had trouble before and therefore aren't equipped to organize any sort of resistance. They have faith that nobody wants to cheat them."

"I think they're in for an awakening," Harry murmured.

"Could be. Still, if they don't like the way things are, they can turn the rascals out and elect someone they trust."

"Why don't they?"

"Probably because Wells and his assistant are at least offering something substantial—money. Nobody else has even bothered to offer a free weather report."

"What should another candidate offer?" Meg asked.

"I'd say he could offer stability. Tell the voters that these changes are coming all right, but that they should be regulated and tested. In other words, they should go slow on such a transformation. Otherwise, they'll regret it within six months—and then won't be able to do a thing about it."

Both Harry and Meg pricked up their ears. They'd not known that Doc had any theories on city politics at all. This was news.

"You see," Doc went on, warming up to his subject, "you

see, when a city gets a face-lifting, there has to be careful planning. And the authorities have to look ahead, years ahead, so that our kids won't grow up in a community that's bogged down with long-term debts, high taxes, and a bad reputation. Expansion is all well and good, but it has to be intelligent expansion. For example, it'd be insane to send in a lot of bulldozers and raze the lake front and build a bunch of hot-dog stands and tell everybody to have a good time. A smart committee would know how to develop the lake without turning it into another Coney Island—and without losing one tree."

He stopped and looked at the others. "Say—I'm going on here as if I knew what I was talking about."

"But you do," Harry insisted. "This is all very interesting to me."

"I bet it'd be even more interesting to the voters of Bencove," Meg said.

"Well, this doesn't mean anything," Doc told them. "I'm just sounding off on a few pet ideas."

"Keep sounding—we like it."

For the next hour or so, the dirty dishes were forgotten as the three remained at the table and Doc discussed in detail how the town should cope not only with the over-ambitious mayor and his stooge but with its future. By the time Doc finished, Harry had absorbed what amounted to a semester course in City Planning and Administration. Yet Doc Howell had never taken a college course. The secret was, then, that his own clear-headed thinking led him to the proper and inevitable conclusions. Harry found himself wishing Doc had been at Parker's store today—he would have put Plumpy in his place with his tongue, and not his fists.

Later, as he was saying good night to Meg at the foot of the stairs, Harry said, "It's too bad that Doc isn't running in the primaries—he could probably lick the pants off Norm Wells."

"Who says he *isn't* running in the primaries?" Meg responded cryptically; then she went up the stairs and left Harry standing there scratching his head.

The morning brought the postman and the postman brought the mail. Lots of it. Two letters each for Meg and Harry and a stack of bills for Doc to let him know that others were thinking of him constantly.

Harry and Meg wandered away to examine their letters privately. Walking down toward the dock, Harry looked at the envelopes. The handwriting he saw was familiar as the faces of Bud Hill and Dotty Bryson—one rough and jittery, the other neat and delicate. A sharp twinge of guilt lanced through him as he fingered Dotty's letter. He was so wrapped up in Meg, so enthralled with her, that he could not genuinely work up flaming enthusiasm for whatever Dotty might have to say. That, of course, was doing her an injustice; nevertheless, he opened Bud's letter first. He read:

Dear Barracuda:

Your departure has caused the greatest sensation since the Count of Monte Cristo escaped from the Chateau d'If in a potato sack. Needless to say, Ye Olde Conspirator Bud Hill is doing his best to perpetuate the fraud. This is my moment of glory—I may qualify as a tub-thumper after this hitch as a press agent. A couple of items of interest: 1) Spring exams—*veni, vidi, vici.* 2) A person of female gender has been playing Inquiring Reporter as to your whereabouts, activities, and intentions. It is common knowledge in these parts that This Person is slightly deranged and not accountable for her taste in men. I mean boys. Sad to relate, her very presence, the scent of her perfume (*Midnight Madness*) loosened my tongue and I squealed.

Item 3) is less amusing. Both Professor Bryson and Coach Barnes have paid me special visits and like The Girl have asked me what your plans are. However, I have a vague impression that their reasons are less romantic. They both send their fondest regards and say that unless you swim for State in the Nationals next week, they will arrange for you never to teach or coach in any high school or college in the country. Delightful couple—where did you ever find them, my dear?

Well, that's enough of hilarity for now. I'll write again when I get some more laughs to cheer you up. See you sooner than you think.

Bud

Harry reread the part about Professor Bryson and Coach Barnes. A cold fury grew in him until he could scarcely contain himself; he picked up a rock and hurled it as far as he could. It rose in an arc against the sky and then dropped swiftly into the lake, where it splashed and sank from sight. It made him feel so satisfied that he threw another and another, throwing until his arm tired.

At length he slit open Dotty's letter and unfolded the single sheet.

Darling Harry:

Although I promised Bud I wouldn't betray his confidence, I cannot help but write you. I was so worried and I'm still worried, but I'm relieved to know that you're with a good friend. Of course, I've missed you and I can't wait to see you, but perhaps this sojourn has been good for you. Dad asks about you frequently, but I tell him I have no idea where you are. I think he's anxious to see you. (Almost as anxious as I!) Anyhow, I know that what you decide will be best for you. For *us,* darling. Just remember that I have faith in you and that you are in my dreams every night. With much love and many kisses,

Dotty

This was the closest thing to a love letter he'd ever received, and he read it over with relish. He was absorbed in it when Meg approached, dangling a letter from her hand.

"How did you do?" she said dazedly.

"With what?"

"Mail."

His had been a strange combination—a love letter from Dotty, a warning letter from Bud.

"To tell the truth, I don't know how I did do. I have mixed emotions over my mail. My friend, Bud Hill, writes that I'm in a peck of trouble back at school."

"Me too," Meg smiled. "Only it's probably a little different. My *billet doux* was from Ken Varden—he, too, refers to school, but in a somewhat derogatory way."

"Oh, he's still singing that same tune?"

"He's singing the whole chorus. It's entitled *Make Up Your Mind or I'll Make It Up for You.*"

A few days ago Harry would have treated this bit of news objectively and would have tried to seek out a reasonable solution for both Meg and Ken. That was a few days ago. Now, today, Ken Varden's written demands to Meg infuriated him. How dare that insufferable snob dictate to her? Who did he think he was?

"As a sort of fiancé, I suppose he does have a few rights," Meg mused. "Nevertheless, it's humiliating to be talked to like a child."

"I gather he doesn't know you very well."

Harry looked at her composed face, the sweetly curved cheek—that he had once kissed—the lovely eyes and soft mouth. He knew he would always remember how she looked, no matter what happened in the future.

"Why don't you just ignore him?" Harry suggested. "Maybe he'll cool off."

"I can't ignore him."

"Why not? You're up here and he's down there with a 'thousand miles' between you."

"One reason I can't ignore him is because he's coming up to Skylark day after tomorrow."

"What!"

"That's what his letter says." A wan smile passed over her face. "There aren't many places I can run to from here, are there?"

"He can't do that!"

"But he can. He's got his own airplane; he can even land nearby—the airport isn't far away. Looks as if I'm going to have to make a decision whether I want to or not."

"That's absurd. You're free. You don't have to answer to him. You can do as you please. Tell him to go fly a kite."

Meg shook her head and sank onto the grass where she embraced her knees and leaned forward to study the water. Harry stared at her wistfully. Seldom had a girl been more appealing to him. Much as he did not like Varden, he could hardly blame the guy for shooting the works over Meg.

"Free," Meg murmured. "Are any of us free, Harry? Are any of us able to do exactly as we want to do and nothing else?" She looked up at him quizzically. "Are you free?"

"Yes," he blurted quickly, and Meg looked at him. "Well, maybe not altogether free," he amended, "but almost free."

"That's as close as any of us ever get to complete freedom, Harry. That's as close as any of us *want* to get. Wouldn't it be a terrible world if we could do just as we pleased, with no obligations, no responsibilities? If a man didn't have to work at a job and a woman didn't have to raise a family and keep house? If I didn't have to paint—if you didn't have to swim?"

That struck home, and Harry suddenly realized what Meg was talking about—not only about her relationship with Ken Varden, but about his, Harry's, relationship with the university.

"You've got a decision, too," Meg told him. "And it's at least as serious as mine—and probably a lot more important, because more people care about it. Do you feel absolutely free to choose your path?" She reached up and placed a hand on his arm. "Forgive me, Harry. I don't mean to be harsh. I just had to remind you that, although I appreciate your sentiments in not wanting somebody to order me about as Ken is doing, you are hardly in a position to serve as an example."

"You're right, of course," he conceded. "And I asked for that. No, I can hardly offer advice, at least the kind you would take. I know I should mend my own fences first."

"What *are* you going to do?"

"Nothing."

"Do you mean that?"

"Yes, I mean it. We're talking about freedom now and I'll show you that I am free."

"It may be an empty gesture."

"Better that than to be intimidated by a selfish coach."

"That's oversimplifying it, I imagine. Now, as I see it, you actually do love swimming and you won't swim for this coach *because* you love swimming. You're letting him, in effect, dictate to you."

"You've got it all backwards—he's not stopping me."

Her neat brows knitted together. "Golly, but if it weren't for him, you would swim. Right?"

Harry's brain was spinning. "Yes, but—"

She shrugged. "So he's stopping you."

Harry clapped his forehead. "Female logic," he exclaimed.

"Simple arithmetic," Meg corrected. With a quick thrust of her legs, she unfolded herself from the grass and stood up. "The only catch is that while it seems to you that you are being very noble and sacrificial about the Nationals, very few people will know it."

"What do you mean?"

"Let me put it this way. Remember Bishop Berkley's conundrum? If a tree falls in the forest and there is no ear to hear it, is there any sound? If you deliberately sacrifice your swimming career in an effort to highlight Coach Barnes' ungentlemanly behavior—and nobody knows about it, is it a sacrifice or an error?"

"You don't understand."

"If I don't understand, Harry," Meg said softly, "lots of other people won't either."

For a moment they faced each other across eighteen inches of space and then, very tenderly, Meg framed his face with her two hands and kissed him gently.

"There," she whispered huskily.

Automatically, his arms slipped around her shoulders and he drew her close to him; they remained in an embrace for a full minute.

"We've got to help each other, Harry."

"I know," he said. "I know."

But for the present he was content to forget their problems and to stay just as he was.

15

HARRY MIGHT HAVE been keener on pressing home his argument with Meg had she been more reasonable about the swimming thing. By "reasonable" he meant that she should meekly accept his decision and admire him for his sturdy stand on his principles. Although he felt that the wisest thing for Meg to do would be to write Varden a letter and brush him off completely, he knew that if he insisted on that tactic, Meg would eventually work it around to some sort of trade—that she might follow his advice, if he followed hers.

Of course, being a girl she could hardly be expected to fully comprehend all the angles and nuances of the issues. It did not occur to him that he might not know all the answers about matters of the heart. He was able to deceive himself in this way by devoting no thought whatsoever to the dilemma that existed between himself and Dotty Bryson.

Harry knew one could not deal with Meg Crane rationally—she had a shrewd merchant's sense of barter, and he was not prepared to meet her terms yet. So, he decided airily, she would have to do without his wise advice.

He also reasoned that if he refrained from picking on her about being dominated by Ken Varden, she would cease that nonsense about his swimming in the Nationals a week hence. But, in the end, he did barter with her.

The day grew hotter by the hour, and along about noon Meg suggested they try out one of the new birchbark canoes. This struck Harry as being an intelligent idea, and while Meg whipped up a lunch, Harry secured some fishing poles and a can of worms for bait.

Under Doc's approving eye, they skimmed out from the dock, Meg in the bow, Harry in the stern, and headed for the middle of the lake. Meg was wearing her black Lastex swimming suit, and Harry wore his trunks. The high, hot sun beat down on their bodies and, as far as Harry was concerned, loosened his muscles and made him feel very powerful. Each time he plunged the paddle into the water, the fragile canoe spurted ahead, lifting slightly. Now and then Meg would cry out in mock terror, and Harry would show off even more by trying the harder with the next stroke. It was distinct pleasure for him to watch the play of her arms and back as she handled her paddle.

Harry was honest enough to ask himself if what he felt toward Meg was really love or whether he was merely substituting the girl he was with for the girl he wasn't with. Or it might even be a throw-back to his youth, to the days when he and Meg had grown up together and had enjoyed such memorable times. Whatever it was, he was fairly sure that his feeling toward her was not reciprocated. Meg, to all outward appearances, was quite wrapped up in Ken Varden. So Harry understood that her problem was to choose, not between Varden and Williams, but between Varden and art.

After three quarters of an hour of paddling they reached a point on the lake that was at least a mile from the nearest land. Harry slumped in his seat and called for food and drink. Meg quickly tossed him a ham sandwich and a bottle of coke. The coke was not very cold, but it was a thirst quencher and tasted good as it trickled down Harry's parched throat.

"I've been trying to figure you out," Meg said around a bite of ham and bread. "You're an enigma."

"How so?"

"This swimming thing, for instance. Doc and I have always followed the results of your races and each time we expected to see that you'd cracked a world record. But it never happened. How come?"

"For probably the same reason that you haven't yet painted a *Mona Lisa.* You have to work up to it, you have to have the inspiration. Well, I need the pressure, the incentive."

"It's different with me," Meg said. "I'm just another hack. I know there are thousands of painters better than I'll ever be. But you—everybody who knows you is convinced you're a champion, Harry, that you've got the stuff in you. Why hasn't it come out?"

"Why hasn't yours come out?" he retorted defensively.

"Because very few painters are famous in their youth, or even their lifetime. Usually, they get famous only after they've died. But with an athlete, especially a swimmer, it has to be within a certain few years of his life. If he by-passes those years, he'll never have the chance again. Isn't that right?"

"I suppose you've got a point; but if you're trying to talk me into helping out that ungrateful coach again, you're mistaken. I've done my share and I'm through."

"I see," Meg said slowly, reaching for a chunk of cheese and nibbling at it. "You feel you don't owe anyone anything in the way of loyalty?"

"I've already paid—with that All-Conference meet, when I swam *their* races and when I didn't swim my own."

"Would you've liked it better if you were the only State man in the pool against all the other schools?"

"What kind of dopey question is that?"

"It's not dopey. So far you've indicated that you only tolerate the others on the team because of your big heart, that you could whip the entire conference alone."

"I didn't say that," Harry said morosely.

"It adds up to that. Sounds to me as if you were beginning to believe those press clippings—the Human Fish, the Shark, and all that. It's really weird, since you don't hold one world record. There must be a dozen boys in the country faster than you. Then how come you act so great all the time? You're only better than a few fellows who go to State. Now, *you* may know you are the best swimmer in the United States, but that's like that tree falling in the forest."

Harry had to admit to himself that Meg was making sense. She was not concentrating, as had others, on the personality clash between himself and Barnes and Bryson. For her, what mattered most was the swimming itself.

"I agree with you to some extent, but in order for a man to swim or run or dive or anything nowadays, he has to chain himself to the coaching system—he is not permitted to flex his own muscles, choose his own time, and be as good as he can. He is not a free agent. He can not express his true self."

"If he's strong enough, he can do all those things. First he has to prove that he is not warped by outsiders and that he can become a champion *despite,* not because of, other people." She paused and trailed her hand in the water. "Of course, all those points you raise are wonderful excuses for not bothering to try hard. . . ."

"Do you believe that's what I'm doing?"

"Not yet," Meg said quietly. "Not yet."

Regardless of the future, Harry wanted Meg to think well of him. And right at this instant he sensed that her loyalty was wavering.

"Hey, look," he said waspishly, "we're going in circles. Talking about my swimming all the time. It isn't that important, Meg. What happens to me doesn't matter to anybody."

"But you're wrong."

"What do you mean?"

"It matters to Doc—and to me. You seem to forget that

we knew you before you could *spell* water. Of all the thousands of boys Doc's seen in his lifetime, you are the one he had the highest hopes for. You were the one who was going to succeed where he, as a swimmer, had failed."

Harry lowered his head and busied himself with the fishing poles and hooks. His ears rang with Meg's quiet but penetrating words. In all this, he'd just about forgotten what Doc thought—mainly because Doc was so darned diplomatic and subtle that you had the idea he was thinking whatever you thought.

"Queer, isn't it?" he said to Meg as he handed her a baited pole and watched her drop the line into the water. "We came out here to see if there was some way you could keep your love and your art, and we wind up wrangling about me. I feel like I've got a bull's-eye painted on my back."

"You've got a question mark painted on your back," Meg corrected. "I'm trying to erase it."

"The Artist and the Athlete. Where will they be ten years from now? I know—the Artist will be hanging in the Louvre, and the Athlete will be hanging from a lamppost."

"Right where he belongs," she said in a choked voice. "Why don't you shut up sometimes?"

For once Harry obeyed her and faced the opposite end of the canoe and let his line sink into the water. Now and then a lake trout or bass would glide underneath the craft, utterly ignoring the squirming worm on the hook. Harry didn't really mind. He didn't feel like preventing a fish from swimming about freely in the deep. The sun was hotter than ever. He could feel the redness on his uncovered back. The water looked cool and inviting. He could resist no longer.

Standing up carefully, Harry announced, "I'm going in for a few minutes. Watch it."

With great care he eased himself over the side. The light canoe tipped sharply, but with Meg subjecting it to counterpressure, there was no danger of swamping. When he let go, the craft jounced up and down on the surface until Meg steadied it with the paddle.

"How's the water?" she called.

"Great. Just terrific."

His body came alive in the embrace of the lake, as though he had been away from it too long. He took a breath and dove deeply, angling for the bottom. Here and there he felt the bitter cold water of an underwater spring. Exhilarated, he practiced his fish-tail stroke, a kind of breast-stroke in which the swimmer keeps both legs together and kicks with a kind of up-and-down wriggle, while his two arms are pulling him through the water. Harry knew it was an exciting stroke to watch, and it enabled him to make fast time.

Harry practiced it now, under water, because it gave him such a weightless sensation, as though he were flying through the air, soaring above a green and shimmering world. Gradually, he swooped up to the surface and broke out into the sunlight. It took a moment for his pupils to get accustomed to the brightness. When they did, he looked around for the canoe. Then he saw it—Meg had been paddling and was about two hundred yards away.

"Hey," he yelled across the water. "Your anchor's dragging. Come on back."

Meg watched him from the stern of the craft. The paddle in her hands was poised over the water. Harry swam toward the canoe in powerful, punching strokes. The water parted to allow him to pass. He had swum what he guessed to be a good hundred yards when he looked up again. The canoe was still about two hundred yards off. He must be going blind. His judgment of distances wasn't that bad. But maybe the glittering sun made things appear closer than they were.

So he plowed on, not so hard now, for the sprint was out of him. Just pumping. Steadily. Rhythmically. Confidently. The water flowed past his eyes and nostrils and mouth, fast and foamy. He felt strong enough to go on forever.

When he paused once again, he saw that he had gained on the canoe. He also saw that Meg was paddling away from him slowly, watching him over her shoulder.

"What gives?" he laughed. "Cut the teasing."

"I'm not teasing," she said calmly, dipping the paddle into the water again. The sun caught on the streaming droplets and made them gleam like diamonds.

"Well, stop the boat."

"No, Harry," Meg said, "I won't stop it."

"Big joke. Come on, Meg."

"It's no joke. If you want to get back to camp, you'll have to swim."

"Why?"

"Because I want to see if you can do it."

"Oh, I see." A knot of anger tightened his stomach muscles. "Who do you think you are?"

"That doesn't matter. I want to find out *what* you are."

As he talked, Harry had quietly been gaining on the canoe and now he was within ten yards of it. Then suddenly he swung into a speedy free-style and powered his way through the narrowing waters that separated him from Meg.

However, he misjudged Meg. She had grown up, as he had, on the lake. At birth she did not have a silver spoon in her mouth—just a pine paddle. Harry was less than three strokes from the stern when Meg suddenly dug frantically into the water, propelling the craft in a great leap. It was close. Harry's grasping fingers scratched the taut birchbark, but before he could launch himself high enough, Meg's paddle hit the water again in a prodigious effort.

As Harry raised his eyes the canoe sped out of reach. "You mean it," he shouted.

"I mean it." She held up her free hand. In it was a watch. "If you've got the guts, I'll clock you. If you haven't, then I'll just paddle on in and take a nap. Which will it be?"

Immersed as he was up to his neck, it was difficult to project an attitude of fury without appearing ridiculous. He comforted himself with the knowledge that as soon as he got on land he could explode in proper fashion. Until then he would accept no pity or favors from her . . .

"Listen, you. You'd better start paddling until you reach shore and when you get there you'd better start running, because I'm going to wallop you like you've never had it before. And *that's* no joke."

Just before he started to swim again, he caught a glimpse of her lovely face in the sunlight. Unless he was myopic, a swift, joyful smile touched her mouth and then vanished.

Harry swam. At the same time, Meg paddled, stroking easily and steadily. Now and then, as he came up for breath, he could just see the site of the camp, the very top of the Main House chimney standing out red against the background of dark pines. It looked a very long way off. Much different from pool walls only twenty-five yards apart.

"It's a full mile," Meg yelled when his head was clear. The stopwatch was slung around her neck on a leather thong. Apparently, she'd smuggled it aboard.

Harry swam, pushed at first by the pulse of anger at anyone who would behave like this, who would pull such a cheap, kid trick. He'd show her. He'd really show her. His arms slashed the water with smooth, steady strokes. His body, well rested and well fed over the past few days, responded magnificently to the demands he made on it. He had not yet begun to tap the immense reserves of strength he knew resided within him.

The lake was calm and the water slightly cold—just right for swimming. And as he swam he felt he was leaving behind a used skin, an outer coating that had begun to crust on his skeleton. Never had he felt so clean and good in the water. Once again, for perhaps the thousandth time, he had a fleeting impression of what it must be like to be a fish, to know the unspeakable freedom of movement and freedom from gravity that only fish can know. Then the vision melted away, and he was just Harry Williams swimming in Lake Skylark—and loving it.

So he swam. And Meg paddled.

Through it all, through the ebbing tide of his anger and the whole grotesque scene Harry was always conscious of the stopwatch that dangled around Meg's neck.

Meg was not talking time, but she was talking distance. She announced the three-quarters mark and then, a few minutes later, the half-mile mark. Then the quarter-mile mark—the four-forty mark. Four hundred and forty yards to go—Williams' Way, someone had once called it.

Now, at last, Harry called forth the hidden reserves from the vault of his body and pushed into the attack. This was no poor kid from Tech, no swimmer from Hollis—this was Harry Williams swimming against the stiffest competition he'd ever faced: Harry Williams.

By now even Meg was excited. She'd been noting the times on the side of the canoe with her lipstick. What she saw there now must have shocked her. The shore was very close, the trees looming high above the beach and the dock. Smoke trailed up faintly from the chimney. Suddenly, to his own astonishment, Harry realized he was abreast of Meg and the canoe, that she had ceased paddling and was now simply yelling at the top of her lungs.

An odd sensation was coming over Harry as he drew nearer to the beach. It was one of strain, a feeling he'd rarely experienced before. He had drawn on his power, his youth, and his know-how as he had always done—in great, gulping quantities. For the first time in his memory he sensed that he was nearing the limit. A giddy fear raced through him, a fear that his stamina would run out before the water ran out. He'd seen it happen often enough to others—but never to himself . . .

He gauged there were a hundred yards left and he pumped arms that had grown strangely heavy, kicked legs that were like fat logs.

Then it was fifty yards . . . twenty-five—and his strength was rapidly dwindling.

All at once his hands were digging into sand and he could go no farther. He had reached the beach.

Beyond the wheezing bellows of his own lungs he could hear Meg's shrieks of triumph.

16

Harry Williams did not know how long he lay there, half in the water, half out, his chest thumping resoundingly against the sand. On his back the sun felt warm and soft. His mouth was dry, with the metallic taste that comes from overexertion.

Meg crouched beside him, running her hand through his hair, kneading his shoulder muscles.

"Harry, Harry, Harry," she kept saying over and over, in a kind of prayer of thankfulness.

At last, with strength and breath returning, he lurched to his feet, spread his arms and legs, and stretched. His torso was as taut as an archer's bow.

"You did it, Harry," Meg murmured, with admiration alive in her eyes.

"No. *You* did it." He tilted her head with a finger under the chin. "I couldn't have done it without you."

He went over to the canoe and, peering closely at the birchbark, made out the figures Meg had scrawled there.

Of course, the distances were approximate, but even allowing twenty yards either way, the times were impressive for the first quarters. What interested him most was the time for the last four hundred and forty yards.

"It's not there," Meg said swiftly. "I didn't have time to scratch it on." Excitement bubbled in her voice.

"Then you don't have any idea what it was."

"I do. I have a pretty good idea."

"Oh." He wanted terribly to be casual about it because deep down inside he sensed it would be significant. He had swum as hard as he could. If the effort wasn't reflected accordingly in the time, he was licked. "What was it?"

"Four minutes forty seconds."

Harry made a quick calculation, allowing some fifteen seconds for push-offs from pool ends. "Four minutes *what?*"

"Forty. And I know what it means. If you can swim that fast in a lake, you can break the world's record in a pool." Her voice quavered and cracked.

"That's incredible. Impossible. No, by golly, it isn't impossible. Unless your distances were way off."

"I wasn't off. Maybe you've forgotten, but years ago a quarter-mile course was measured. Look." She took Harry by the arm and turned him around, pointing. "That bent pine, the one struck by lightning long ago. Well, when you're exactly a quarter of a mile from the dock, you look over that pine and you line it up with that enormous boulder on the mountain behind it. It's a matter of triangulation. Elementary, my dear Watson."

"On the level?"

"On the water."

"The watch," he suggested. "Sure it's running properly?"

"Like a clock."

"Meg—this—this is just ridiculous!"

"Yes. That's the wonderful part of it. Can't we celebrate?"

"I know a way to start—now that I've got my breath back."

"How?"

He showed her. His two arms encircled her slender form, drew it to him, and they kissed. The embrace swiftly became one of fond affection instead of mere "celebration."

It was Meg who thought of Doc first.

"Queer," she said abruptly, pulling away from Harry, "why isn't Doc out here for the festivities? Surely he must have heard the yelling."

"He's probably taking a nap," Harry said.

"No. He never takes a nap at this hour. See, there's smoke rising from the chimney. That means he's up and around. But why isn't he out here?"

Harry cleared his throat and hid a smile behind his hand. "You know men—they're more discreet than women give them credit for."

But there was no talking Meg out of it. Consternation showed on her face as she moved up onto the beach. She still clung to Harry's hand.

"Harry—I don't like it."

She walked faster and faster until she was trotting, and then she broke into a run. Alarmed now himself, Harry ran after her. However, he was scarcely in any condition for a footrace and he quickly lost ground. As a result, Meg was first to reach the steps and bound up them and onto the porch. She disappeared through the screened door.

Two seconds later Harry heard the scream. He forgot his exhaustion and flew the rest of the way. Through the screen door he could see Doc Howell crumpled in a heap in the middle of the porch.

The scream that Meg was making was not the joyous kind she'd been making a little while earlier.

17

"HEART ATTACK."

The two words uttered by Dr. Lee hung in the room like a pair of heavy balloons. Tall and spare, with shoulders stooped from long years of bending over patients, and eyes full of compassion, Dr. Lee regarded Meg and Harry with sympathy.

"But not a serious one," he said as he took off his glasses and wiped them absently on his sleeve. "Fortunately, my friend Doc Howell has the constitution of a bull. The organ is merely starting to wear out. They all do eventually."

"Will he be all right?" Meg asked hoarsely. "Tell us the truth."

"Of course," Dr. Lee smiled. "Your uncle is too cantankerous to die so young."

"Can we see him now, sir?" Harry inquired.

"I'd suggested you wait a while, children. He's asleep. By all means, don't worry." He patted Meg's cheek. "My dear child, calm down. If Doc were in any danger, I'd tell you."

"Coffee, Doctor?" Harry offered.

"By all means. Lead me to it."

They sat down in the kitchen and spoke in strangely hushed voices. It didn't seem right that Doc—sturdy, eternal, rugged Doc—should be subject to the frailties of other men.

"What caused the attack, sir?" Harry said, stirring his coffee. "Doc never complained about his heart before."

"That doesn't mean that he hasn't had trouble before," Dr. Lee pointed out. "Doc and I are old friends. We keep in close touch with one another, mainly because we're of the same age. Consequently, I'm rather familiar with our mutual ailments. You may have noticed that he's not been as active in past years."

"No," Harry said slowly. "I didn't get that impression . . ."

"Are you sure?"

"Well, now that you mention it, he did assign some of the tougher jobs, but I thought that was just to toughen me up."

"How about the hike?" Meg put in.

"Why, Doc was the leader all the way!"

"*All* the way?"

"Sure—oh, no. Except the last couple of miles. Say. Do you mean? . . ."

"You carried him home," Meg said softly.

Dr. Lee shrugged. "That sounds like Doc. He'd rather make a fool of himself than extract any pity from you."

He chuckled. "Yes, he's always had something of the Tom Sawyer in him—working the angles so that others would feel it a privilege to whitewash his particular fence of the moment."

"If I'd only known—"

"Ah, my boy, if you'd known, you'd have pampered the pants off him—and he'd have hated that."

"But what was it that finally caused this attack?" Harry asked. "Surely he wasn't exerting himself on the porch."

"That's hard to say," Dr. Lee replied. "Things may have caught up with him. Or, possibly, he got overexcited about something."

"Harry!" Meg cried. "He was watching! Of course. He saw every stroke you made. Every yard of the way. He knew. He knew!"

"And that did it?" Harry asked incredulously.

"Hmmm." The doctor was bewildered. "Swimming were you? I don't know how that could exert anybody except the swimmer."

"You don't understand," Meg said quickly. "Doc's been worried about Harry—even if Harry didn't know it. He was afraid that Harry had come up to camp simply to turn his back on his whole career. I know he didn't sleep well at night because of it."

"You didn't tell me."

"You were hardly in a mood to be told anything." She turned back to Dr. Lee. "Anyhow, this afternoon Harry swam from the middle of the lake to the dock faster than anybody in the world could do it. Honestly." Her hazel eyes rested fondly on Harry. "I don't know what got into him, but whatever it was, he simply exploded. Very likely, the explosion caught Doc off guard—if he was watching, he saw what was happening." She lifted her slim shoulders and dropped them. "If you think that overexcitement could have brought on a heart attack, then I assure you, Harry's performance could have caused it. In fact, I'm glad *I* don't have a weak heart."

"Very complete diagnosis, young lady," Dr. Lee said approvingly. "Ever thought of going into psychology?"

"Just *child* psychology," Meg replied and stuck out her tongue at Harry.

"I feel like a guinea pig," he murmured. "Doc handling me with kid gloves; Meg ambushing me into swimming like a madman. It's more like infant psychology."

Meg's attention didn't stray away from Doc very long. "Doctor, what's going to happen to him now? Should he be moved or what? When can he get up?"

"One at a time," Dr. Lee laughed. "Nothing much is going to happen to him. This was a very mild attack and if he'd had the proper medicine on hand, there would have been no fuss at all." He sipped from his cup thoughtfully. "Secondly, as for moving—oh, I should say that in a week or so we can see about getting him back on his feet and taking some exercise."

"So soon?" asked Harry.

"Nowadays we advise having patients up and around as soon as possible. Lying in bed, not the ailment, is what makes them weak. In fact, any kind of indolence, in mind or body, has an eroding effect." Harry felt Meg's swift glance on him. "In short, Doc can, in a few days, resume normal living—within necessary limitations. No heavy labor, no exertion, no more shocks from champion swimmers. After all, there is a slight scar on the heart and it has to heal the same as any wound."

"Don't worry about shocks from me. I won't make a swim like that again."

"That's what you think!" Meg turned on him with feminine fury. "You're going to practice and practice and practice. You're not going to take it easy just because of this. Doc would really be hurt, then."

"What's this all about?" Dr. Lee asked. "A game?"

"Some game! Next week the swimming Nationals are taking place—and Harry Williams is merely going to win every medal and cup they've got."

"Meg . . ."

"Don't 'Meg' me. Those are orders. Right, Doctor?"

"You're the nurse here, Miss Crane. You do as you see fit."

A thought struck Harry. "What about the camp, sir? How is it going to get into shape if Doc can't work at it? Meg and I are still in school. This is a kind of vacation. We have to be back in another ten days."

Dr. Lee shook his head. "I'm certainly sorry about that. However, I don't see how it's possible for Doc to take complete charge just yet."

"We'll worry about that later," Meg said firmly.

But a silence fell over the kitchen and everyone began to think and worry about it now. The gloom was interrupted by the ringing of the telephone. Meg jumped to answer it before it would waken Doc.

"Yes. Yes. He's here. Just a moment, please. It's for you, Doctor."

Dr. Lee loosed a huge sigh, unfolded his length from the chair, and ambled over to the phone. "This is Dr. Lee," he said. He listened silently for a half a minute and then said, "I see. I see. All right. I'm on my way." He hung up. A tired smile touched his face.

"Trouble?"

"In a manner of speaking. Mrs. Dawson on the other side of the lake is just about to have her baby. Mr. Dawson sounds as if the world's about to blow up."

Dr. Lee peered around for his black satchel. Harry found it and handed it to him. He liked its strong medicinal smell.

"Life goes on," the doctor murmured. He placed a protective hand on Meg's shoulder. "You've done marvelously, Miss Crane. I'm proud of you, as, I'm sure, this young man must be."

"I am," Harry said.

"I'm sure it's a two-way street," Dr. Lee observed. They walked with him across the porch and out to the driveway where he had parked his car. It was dark. The moon was just appearing over the tops of the trees. "I'll stop in and see Doc first thing in the morning. Meanwhile, you two get some rest." He shook Harry's hand. "And good luck to you, Harry—not that you'll need it, of course. Talented people never need luck."

They said good night and watched the headlights of Dr. Lee's car cut a yellow path through the trees.

After a while they turned and walked hand in hand

back to the house. It seemed very natural that they should be together, that they should hold hands, that they should not speak.

The day had been a long day, a full one, and tiredness seeped into Harry's bones. Now that Doc was out of danger, the let-down made him feel limp and sleepy. Looking at Meg, he saw that she probably felt the same way. Of all the people he knew in the world, he couldn't think of anyone who could have matched Meg these last few days. She lifted tired eyes up to his. Very slowly and deliberately, Harry put his arms around her.

At that precise instant a pair of headlights, swinging out of the trees, caught them full in its glare. They did not move apart, but remained, half-embracing, where they were.

"It must be Dr. Lee," Harry said. "Maybe he's forgotten something."

The car came directly toward them, still pinpointing them in its headlights. Shielding his eyes, Harry went down the steps and out to the lawn.

"That you, Dr. Lee? Anything wrong?"

There was no answer. Abruptly, the headlights went out, and Harry heard the opening and closing of a door, then measured footsteps on the gravel path.

"Doctor?"

Still no answer.

"Who is it?" Harry snapped. Behind him he heard a gasp from Meg. She had not been as blinded as he by the brightness of the lights and therefore could probably see better.

"It's me," a man's voice said.

"Who's me?"

"I think Meg recognizes me," the man said. "Apparently I've come at what is commonly known as an unpropitious moment."

He was close enough now for Harry to see that he was young, well-dressed, and very handsome.

"Hello, Ken," Meg said in a queer, distant voice.

18

MUCH TO HIS DISAPPOINTMENT, Harry liked Ken Varden almost at once—even in those first few awkward minutes of embarrassment. Had it not been for Varden's poise, his open-mindedness, there might have been a nasty scene. As it was, he accepted Meg's flustered invitation to come in, even pausing to kiss her lightly on the cheek.

Harry studied him critically, aching to find in him certain flaws and mannerisms that would betray him as second-rate, as one not worthy of Meg's loyalty or devotion. Not as tall as Harry, Ken carried himself well. Deep in the chest, with the solid shoulders of a good middleweight prize fighter, he had the look of a man who would avoid a battle, but who could take care of himself if he had to.

His pale-brown hair was cut short and brushed close to his head. His open face, wide-jawed and pleasant, advertised a casual approach, but a watchful one. All in all he had the look of a man who knew what he wanted—and how to get it.

Once again they made for the kitchen, and it was an effort for Harry not to take the chair closest to Meg. She looked from one to the other with momentary indecision and then sat next to Varden. She gave him some hot coffee and offered to fix him something to eat.

During the course of the one-man meal that followed, Varden told them that he had flown his plane to the airport a hundred miles away. From there he had telephoned the camp in midafternoon. Since there was no answer—what with Meg and Harry on the lake and Doc incapacitated—he had merely rented a car and driven on.

"As usual," he added laconically, "my timing was lousy."

Harry was going through a brief but intense period of jealousy. For a week now, he had had Meg all to himself. He had kind of fallen in love with her. Now he was in the unenviable position of seeing himself being usurped by an outsider. It did not occur to him that he had been the usurper and was now being returned to his proper place. At first, Meg divided her attention equally between the two men, but before long it was ninety-ten, with Harry on the short end. As time passed he felt more and more like an interloper.

"I imagine you two have become good friends," Varden said.

"We've always been good friends," Meg explained hastily. "For years and years. No secrets between us and all that."

"No secrets?" Varden repeated with a cocked eyebrow. "Then I can presume that Harry is up to date on our little brain-buster."

"That's a safe presumption."

Varden smiled. "And tell me—has the jury reached a verdict yet?"

Harry shook his head. "The jury has been loaded down with cases."

Varden leaned forward. Under the glare of the light bulb that hung over the table Harry saw that his eyes were tired and a stubble of beard covered his chin and jaw. Weary though he was, Varden still remained patient.

"Surely you have a private opinion, Judge Williams."

"Hey, you two," Meg protested, "I resent being talked about to my face."

The men ignored her. "Well, I do have a vague impression of the scope of the issue," Harry said, looking directly at Varden. "If conditions were altered only slightly, I'd probably challenge you to a duel for this fair lady's hand."

"Really?" Varden said delightedly.

"Really."

Meg lowered her lashes as her cheeks turned crimson. "No, Harry."

"Why?" Varden prodded. "I assume we're being candid with one another?"

"In the first place," Harry said, "this third person, who shall remain nameless, is probably one of the most level-headed, practical, enchanting, absurd, and splendid humans I've ever met. Wait—" he turned to Meg, "in the second place, I was hoping that you, Varden, would turn out to be a frost. A real loser."

Varden smiled, "I'm a winner?"

Harry laughed. "Yes, blast you, you're a winner."

"I'm not so sure about that," Meg offered. "Maybe he's got you charmed—that's why he's in public relations and advertising—but I know him better."

Varden cupped an inquisitive hand to his ear. "Do you hear ringing noises?"

"Sounds more like clanking," Harry said. "As if a truck were stripping its gears."

"With the pieces falling all over the highway."

"Listen, you birds!" Meg jumped to her feet and fixed them both with defiant eyes. "You're very clever and witty—but if you think you're going to decide my future like a couple of hog traders, you've got another think coming."

"Harry," Varden said softly, "if you had a chance to live in a Philadelphia suburb with a handsome, brilliant, and modest young genius, would you object?"

"I don't see how a girl could."

"This girl will," Meg stated flatly. "Ken Varden, you've browbeat me long enough. You probably thought that my coming up here would be just the thing to make me appreciate life in the big city. Wrong. I've seen and done enough this past week to know that I can stand on my own two feet—and if you want me, that's the only way you're going to get me."

Suddenly Ken dropped his casual act and paid strict attention to what Meg was saying. He looked at Harry for confirmation.

"That's right, Ken," Harry told him. "There's no pushing her around."

Varden tugged on an earlobe. "Mmmm. This smells strongly like revolt."

Meg laughed her musical laugh. "Not quite correct, Kenneth. A revolt is usually suppressed. A revolution is successful. This is a revolution."

"I think you mean it."

"Do I? Try me and see."

"Okay? What about us? Where do we go from here? Have you plotted out the course?"

Meg nodded primly.

"What is it?"

"I'm not saying. I'm going to let you try to sleep tonight—not knowing. Tomorrow, if I'm in the mood, I'll tell you how it's going to be." She put a hand to her mouth to stifle a yawn. "As of now, I'm off to bed. Good night, you pair of gorillas." But she belied her words by kissing each of them on the cheek. "First, I'll look in on Doc."

They watched her go, and then the kitchen seemed an empty, hollow place.

"What is she going to do?" Varden asked. "Surely she must have dropped some hints to you."

"Nothing!" Harry exclaimed. "Not a word."

"Why, she may wind up in Paris or Rome! I can't let her do that."

"You can't stop her. I doubt if anyone can really prevent Meg from doing what she wants to do—what she *has* to do." Harry grinned with diabolical pleasure. "She's a first-rate painter, you know."

"I know," Varden moaned. "That's just the point. I can't allow my wife to wear the pants."

"I doubt if that would be the case, but just be sure you

have *two* pairs of pants around the house." He poked his forefinger into Ken's chest. "Would you deliberately stop her from painting?"

"I don't know. I always thought of her art as a rival—even more of a rival than, say, you. I guess I'm the old-fashioned type. Stuffy and plebeian at heart. Want my wife in a frilly apron, busy baking pies and spanking the kids—you know."

"Some wives, perhaps. Not Meg. Never Meg."

"No," Varden agreed gently, "never Meg." He got up, blinking his eyes uncertainly. "How about leading me to a sack? If I expect to make any headway with her tomorrow, I'll have to be on my toes." He ran his hand over his hair. "Would she really ditch me?"

"She's capable of anything."

Varden laughed and punched him on the upper arm. "You know, I think it's a good thing that I came as soon as I did. A few more days of exposure to you, and she might wind up as a swimming coach."

"She could do worse," Harry protested with mock affront. "She could go in for copy-writing."

They left the kitchen and walked through the lower floor to the bedroom that adjoined Harry's. Varden eyed the bed and began to undress.

"Then you don't mind about the porch thing?" Harry said.

"I'd be a liar if I said I didn't mind," Varden admitted. "But it couldn't happen with a better guy. I think I can trust you."

Harry grunted. "That's the worst of it—you *can* trust

me. I'm afraid my ties back at school are too strong to chop off just like that."

"A girl?"

"Plenty girl—I know now that what I see in Meg is a reflection of what Dotty has."

"If she's that good," Varden said, "grab her—and grab her quick."

"Well, we'll have to see about that. Anyway," he stuck out his hand, "glad to have you aboard, Ken. Sleep easy. I don't think Meg'll be too hard on you tomorrow."

"Right, Harry. Good night."

Later, as Harry lay in his bed, staring up into the dark, the full knowledge sank into him of what had actually taken place this night. He'd had no idea how attached he was to Meg until he'd seen how naturally she'd stayed close to Ken. Did that mean that there had not been love between them? No, they had known love, a rare kind of love. They had glimpsed into a deep and unique type of relationship between a man and a woman—and regardless of what happened, nothing could ever really destroy what they had built between them.

From Meg he had gained something that he could have found nowhere else. She had given him a renewed faith in himself. To carry it beyond that immeasurable gift was tempting fate. The best way for him to repay her was to fulfil her wishes—and Doc's.

But there was one regret, and it came upon him as sharp and sudden as a toothache. All at once he realized that what he had cherished most with Meg was the *sharing*. Little of this would have had any value to him had he been by himself. It was like swimming a race without anyone to see it. The same thinking applied to the election in the village. What good would it do a man to be elected mayor of an uninhabited town? It was no different from a boy being the star of a one-man swimming team.

Lying there in the darkness, it seemed that he could see more clearly than ever before in his life. Just as Doc had needed him in the woods, just as the candidates needed voters, so did he, Harry Williams, need not only an audience—whether it was four hundred spectators or only Meg Crane—but he needed also a *team* to swim *with*. Had there been no team at State—no Rusty Barnes for that matter—conceivably there would have been no famous swimmer named Williams. The entire complex organization of the university was so set up that an unknown boy *could* gain fame and a certain amount of glory.

Professor Bryson had said nobody could go it alone. How true that was! What immense conceit for any one person to believe that he was *bigger* than all the others put together! That's what made dictators and demigods. Harry hated to let the thought form in his mind, but he knew he had become a self-crowned emperor of swimming, and when society, in the form of the school and the coach, had refused to recognize his exalted role, he had turned his back on them. In retrospect, he knew he had half-hoped that the whole athletic program of the university would collapse and that the student body, the board of trustees, and the general public would beg him to come back on any terms he wished. But from State there had been nothing except silence. Harry didn't need a crystal ball to tell him that his mutiny hadn't caused more than a temporary, momentary flicker on the university's academic waters. State had existed long before he had come along; it would be there long after he had been forgotten. And so would the swimming team. Just as Meg had lived without him for so long and would continue to thrive in the future. The reason was clear: *she didn't need him.*

With a shock that startled him to wakefulness, Harry also knew: *the State swimming team didn't need him either!*

He knew the answer to the philosopher's conundrum. No, there was no sound of the tree falling in the forest if there was no one to hear it fall.

And now it was too late for anyone to hear the sound made by Harry Williams in the swimming world.

19

As was his custom, Harry awoke with the first light of dawn. It would be some time before the sun edged above the horizon, so until then he could lie in bed with no compulsion to be up and doing. His state of mind resembled that of a man coming out of an anesthetic after an operation, and he was enjoying it.

He must have heard the voices for a few moments before they actually registered on his consciousness. A girl's voice was saying, "Are you sure this is the place?" Then a man's voice replied, "It has to be—if the map can be believed. Besides, there's Harry's car next to that old heap behind the shed."

"We *are* here terribly early," said the girl dubiously.

"Made better time than I thought possible," answered the man. "I think I'll give Harry the business about spending all his time in bed."

"All his time! Why, it isn't even five-thirty yet!"

The voices came closer until they were directly under

Harry's window, and he marveled at the realistic dream he was having. Gradually, he became aware that the voices must be real, and wakefulness crept up on him. Daylight was in the room.

Such voices! Almost as if Bud Hill had suddenly appeared with Dotty.

Bud Hill!

Harry threw back the covers and sprang from the bed, reaching for his trousers in the same movement. The voices began to fade. He yanked on a T-shirt and burst from the room, running barefoot over the wooden floor. When he got to the porch, he made out two figures down at the dock.

"Hey, you two!" he yelled. "What's going on here?"

"Quiet, you," Bud Hill replied. "You'll scare all the fish. Don't you know that now is the best time to catch the poor critters—while they're still dopey with sleep?"

With that he flicked the pole. The line arched cleanly into the air and fell with scarcely a ripple on the glassy water. But Dotty Bryson was somewhat less calm. At the sight of Harry tearing down the lawn, barefooted, uncombed, unshaven, she cried out and ran up to meet him.

They met halfway down the slope, and Harry swept her into his arms, whirled her around, and planted a resounding kiss on her upturned face.

"You big lug," she murmured and sealed off any countercharge with yet another kiss.

The delight that washed over Harry in this moment astonished him. Until the very instant he had laid eyes on Dotty, he'd had not the slightest inkling that he had missed her so achingly. His hours had been so crammed full of Meg that he thought there was no room for anyone or anything else. Now he knew that Meg had merely been substituting for Dotty. Well, not *merely*—actually she'd been a terrific stand-in. Still, here was Dotty in his arms, and here he was feeling as excited and pleased and happy as a kid on Christmas morning.

"One might spare a second for us peasants," Bud Hill muttered morosely from the dock. "Like, could I be directed in the general direction of the pantry, which I could pillage while you two smooch up a storm?"

"Bud," Harry said, "you look good enough to be considered human." He and Dotty strolled down to the dock, arm in arm.

"High praise. This wild pioneer country must have done things to your mind."

"Plenty!" He drew Dotty closer. She looked up at him with eyes shining. "And you, Dotty, look as fresh as a daisy."

"She should!" Bud snorted. "I was the one who drove all night while she slept in the back seat so's she could be bright and beautiful for you."

"A noble chore," Harry said, looking at her. "You've succeeded admirably, Bud. I think you've found your life's work."

"Don't I know it! Always a best man, never a groom."

"Hey, break it up," yelled a voice from the Main House. Harry spun around to see Meg regarding the scene with pretended severity. For once the sight of her did not make his heart turn over. It was all worn-out from spinning for Dotty Bryson.

"Come on," he said, "I want you folks to meet your hostess."

They let Ken Varden continue sleeping, and Meg and Dotty joined forces to rustle up breakfast. It was not until after they'd finished eating, and Harry was ready to settle down for a long chat with Bud that he remembered the patient.

"What about Doc?" he asked Meg. "Have you looked in on him this morning?"

As if in answer to his question, there came a prolonged angry wail from the region of the house where Doc's bedroom was located. Harry led the mass rush up the stairs and through the hall. Opening Doc's door, he saw the old man sitting upright in bed, clapping his hands and shouting his head off.

"When does a hungry man get fed around this house? I've been yelling for service for an hour."

Doc presented such an incongruous picture—lost in the voluminous folds of a nightshirt, his gray hair gone wild on his head, the bedclothes a complete shambles—that Harry had to grin. Seeing it, Meg, too, smiled, and then the smile broke into a giggle.

"This is a patient?" Bud Hill asked. "What do the healthy ones look like?"

Harry felt a lump in his throat when he saw the tears in Meg's eyes. He quietly handed her his handkerchief. Meg blew her nose and wiped at her eyes.

"What's to eat?" Doc bellowed.

Bud Hill put on his most pontifical manner and went to the foot of the bed and placed the tips of his fingers together. "I advise a bowl of lukewarm gruel, the bread crusts that Dotty didn't eat, and a glass of hot water."

Doc Howell, who had been studying Dotty Bryson with critical but friendly eyes, slowly turned his head until Bud was transfixed by the bright-blue orbs.

"Who," he said, "is this pipsqueak?"

"I'm the new male nurse," Bud said quickly. "Hush up or we'll wrap you up in a strait jacket."

"Why, you—"

Doc hurled back the blankets, swung his legs over the edge of the bed, and started to come at Bud. He managed to take one step, but the second step was too much. His weakened legs started to crumple; Bud sprang forward and caught him under the armpits and eased him gently back onto the mattress.

"What's the matter with the floor?" Doc gasped dazedly. "Since when is it hilly?"

"Since last night," Meg told him. "Now, you just lie quietly, Doc. I'll bring up something to eat right away. Sure you feel all right? Anything I can do? Want the doctor?"

"I don't want any sawbones fiddling around with me," Doc said weakly. "I just want to get my hands on that whippersnapper who keeps weaving from side to side at the end of the bed. I'll fix him."

Bud was actually standing still, but at Doc's words he began, wordlessly, to sway from one side to the other.

At a sign from Meg, they left the bedroom and went downstairs.

"Doctor Lee is due here any minute," she said. "He'll give Doc a check-up. I kind of think Doc will pass with flying colors."

Dotty and Meg, who had gotten along extremely well from the start, sent Harry and Bud outside while they set about to clean house. The boys made only a token protest and then happily wandered down to the wood-chopping department where Harry handed an ax to his friend and took one himself.

"What's new?" he asked finally. "I doubt if you came all the way up here just to see my ugly kisser."

"Maybe I got scared sleeping alone at night in that big house at school."

"Never mind the jokes. Give."

Bud Hill raised the ax in both hands, steadied himself, and then whammed it solidly on a pine log. The log split neatly in half.

"No one ever accused me of being a Boy Sunbeam," he said as he set up another target. "There's been lots of jaw-wagging back at school. Some of it—" Bud whacked the log with the ax— "just noise . . ." He lifted the weapon again, held it poised, slammed it down again. "But some of it makes sense."

"What kind have you been talking?"

"Both kinds," Bud grinned. "Mostly sense."

Harry picked up the butt end of a log and threw it against a tree. "Will you kindly start talking some now!"

Bud leaned the ax against the trunk of a tree and wiped his brow with the sleeve of his shirt.

"I'll give you the bad part first—Barnes and Bryson have got it in for you, but good. They've made a statement, through the *Daily,* that they 'deplore Williams' hasty action.' They feel certain that you will be on hand to apologize publicly prior to the Nationals. Both expressed highest confidence in your attributes as a contrite gentleman who's seen the error of his ways and as a swimmer who can splash State's names into headlines all over the country."

Harry waited while Bud sought for words to express his thoughts.

"At the same time they indicated that there are many worthy youngsters who would be happy to take a State scholarship if you were forced to forfeit yours. They are also sure that no high school or college would ever hire a coach who had refused to give his all for his school. In case there were any schools that did not know about such a man, they would be sure to pass on the blackball."

" 'The evil that men do'," Harry quoted, " 'lives after them. The good is oft interred with their bones. . . .' "

"So be it with Williams," Bud finished. "Only that's not true, kid. I gave you just one side of the picture."

"That's one side too many. When two guys like Bryson and Barnes gang up, there's no use in even looking at the other side."

Bud was grinning from ear to ear. The sun flickered on his rust-colored hair and filled it with flames.

"Then maybe I'd better not tell you about the petition."

"What petition?"

"The one circulated by the team."

"The swiming team?"

"Is there any other team on campus? Of course. Anyhow, some sly fiend got the team members to make out this declaration and then he managed to slip it into the *Daily* right past the nose of the sports editor."

"What did it say?"

"Oh, something to the effect that one Harry Williams be permitted to swim in the Nationals on his own terms, without recourse to the coach or any professor or the janitor. He should swim whatever races he wanted to swim. The team would back him to the hilt."

"But how could they enforce that?"

"Easy. The petition explained that unless Williams came in under those conditions, the rest of the team would refuse to swim at all."

Harry took to wandering around among the wood chips and broken branches. "This is fantastic. Why should they do that?"

"They remember the Conference meet," Bud said simply.

"Well, it's too late. I'm not going to the Nationals."

"Uh-uh. Petition or no, eh? Okay. I thought I'd mention it just in case you had nothing else to do that day."

"When do you have to be there?"

"Friday."

Harry had to pause for a few seconds to figure out the calendar. "Today's Wednesday?"

"Good guess." Bud was not grinning now.

"Well, you'd better get on your horse. New Haven's a long way from here." Harry picked up his ax again. "What events are you entering?"

"I was scheduled for the butterfly, the relay, and the four-forty."

"Fine. You ought to do well in them."

"But I won't."

"How come?"

"I'm not going."

"Why not?"

"Because you're not going."

Harry belted at a log angrily. One end of it flew off and spun through the air to land in the underbrush fifty yards away. "Let's not be babyish about this, Bud. A guy doesn't get too many chances."

"I know. And I want to go badly. My folks want me to go. But I won't. You're preventing me from going, Harry."

"I see," Harry said slowly. "The old squeeze play."

"Call it whatever you like. My terms are that you have to go. In fact, I shouldn't be surprised if the entire team agrees with me."

"So in the end I give in to Barnes and Bryson? This whole thing was worthless. My protest. My flight. In the end I slink back with my tail between my legs."

"Baloney!" Bud exclaimed. "You're going back *despite* them, not because of them. You're going back for me and the team—and for you."

Harry stood up straight, flexing his fingers, peering out over the water, remembering how he'd felt during the swim the other day, recalling the exhilaration, the unrestrained joy he'd known at no other time in the water. The four-forty in four-forty—a good fifteen seconds that could be chopped off in a pool with plenty of push-offs.

"Time, Bud. Time is so short. I don't see how we can be sure of making it by Friday—suppose the car broke down. . . ."

"We'll find a way. There has to be a way. Even if we have to leave here in an hour."

"But I can't. I can't leave Doc in this condition. His whole life and livelihood are at stake. He needs me here. In another six weeks the campers start coming. The place has to be ready, and Doc can't do it. It'll break his heart if he has to give up the camp after all these years. That's all he lives for."

"It'll break his heart if you don't hit those Nationals and the Olympics."

Harry recalled Meg's words. "Maybe so, but the camp is more important than I am."

"Heck! The camp is no more important than the individual and you know it. Doc knows it. Listen. That's what the team is trying to show. They prefer to have one great star come out of their ranks, instead of winding up merely as another good college team that can't be distinguished from a hundred others.

"Lindbergh flew the Atlantic only because he had learned how by the failures of others before him—so he really didn't do it alone. Einstein came up with $E = mc^2$ only because he built on Pythagoras and Archimedes and Galileo—and you can bet that those old-timers cheered louder than anybody when Einstein made it. Maybe Henry Ford didn't invent the first car, but he found out how to mass-produce it, thanks to experiments by a dozen others who had misfired."

Harry squinted at the water again. "You're putting me into some pretty fast company."

"In your field," Bud reminded, "you *are* fast company."

Harry licked his lips and shaded his eyes from the reflected glare of the sun off the water. "You're crazy," he said thickly.

"Yeah." Bud cracked another chunk of pine.

"How has Dotty reacted to all this?"

"She's told me that it doesn't matter to her what you do—she's with you all the way."

"You two," Harry said with affection. "Well—"

Something in his tone of voice made Bud glance up sharply. "Well, what?"

"Well, it's a shame we can't make it to New Haven in time. It might have been a kick to see Rusty's face when I showed up. . . ."

"Listen. We'll get there if we have to fly," Bud snapped.

Hearing a commotion from the direction of the Main House, they both turned to see Meg and Dotty and Ken Varden dancing around in a circle.

"Mountain madness," Bud muttered. "It gets them all in the end. Come on. Maybe they'll let us play, too."

Dotty met them halfway.

"You didn't tell me about these two," she accused. "They're engaged to be married."

"Things have changed," Harry noted. "Yesterday they were just engaged. What's going on?"

"I can't seem to make head or tail of it, but it seems that Meg and Ken have just made some kind of agreement. They did everything but sign contracts and have them notarized."

"Then she made up her mind," Harry said, "and it looks as though Ken won."

"I wouldn't say that," Dotty murmured darkly.

Meg dragged Ken toward them down the slope of the lawn, looking like someone who'd just won a kewpie doll at a carnival.

"I did it!" she chortled.

"I did it!" Ken yelled.

"Who did what?" Bud asked.

Meg and Ken both started talking at the same time. Bud held up his hand. "One at a time. please. You, sir, this may be your last chance to get a word in edgewise—speak up."

"Well, Meg and I are finally seeing eye to eye. She's going to marry me, and we're going to live in Philadelphia."

Meg laughed. "But only after a year's honeymoon in Europe where I'll get to go to every art school in sight."

"And if she shows promise at all," Ken said, "I may give her a crack at handling the art department in the agency."

"If I don't show promise," Meg said, "I get to handle the Dishes and Diapers Department in the apartment."

"Congratulations," Harry said, taking Ken's hand and

pumping it heartily. "I never thought you'd swing it."

Dotty kissed Meg's cheek. "Nice going. Show him who's boss. Then tell me how you did it." This last she said with an eye on Harry.

Ken laughed unconvincingly. "Not to change the subject, but Dotty tells us you're going to swim in the Nationals this week-end."

Harry shook his head. "I was, but it's impossible."

"How so?"

"As Bud put it so aptly, we can't be certain of getting to New Haven in time unless we fly."

"Well," Ken said. "Let's fly."

20

WITH THOSE TWO WORDS, Ken Varden put the keystone into place, and the bridge from Camp Skylark to the Nationals was built. Harry Williams' last objection was overcome—he would swim.

However, all the problems were not solved. It turned out that Ken's airplane was a two-seater and as he was the only licensed pilot, only he and Harry could go. That left Bud Hill out.

"Forget me," Bud said lightly. "I'd much rather stay here with these two delicious morsels."

Harry and Ken frowned their disapproval. "Is he safe?" Ken asked.

"Don't ask a man," Meg said. "Ask a woman."

"Well, is he?"

Meg glanced at Bud whose eyes were wide with innocence and youth. "I'm not telling," she said.

Bud began to twirl an invisible mustache on his upper lip. "Heh, heh, my lovely. You answer well. Stick with me and you'll be wearing radishes as big as diamonds."

They would not have to leave until the next day, so Meg Crane immediately took charge of the hours remaining to them.

"Practice, Harry," she ordered. "Now you've got the competition, although it's hard for me to believe that this freckle-faced urchin can even do the dog-paddle, much less a legitimate stroke."

"Ken," Bud wailed, "do I have permission to spank this fickle wench when she acts up?"

"You have my permission," Ken laughed, "but do you have the nerve?"

An assignment schedule was set up for the afternoon. Meg was to paddle the canoe and hold the stopwatch while Bud and Harry swam the measured four-forty as often as they could. Meanwhile Dotty and Ken would be in charge of continuing to clean up and fix up the camp itself and to administer to Doc Howell when necessary.

And that's the way they spent Wednesday.

Harry was gratified to see how Bud had improved. The redhead offered some very stiff competition in the practice races, with Meg egging him on all the way. With Bud really pressing him from behind, Harry clipped another two seconds off his time.

Whenever Bud protested that the work was too hard, Meg told him to quiet down or else she wouldn't let him swim at all. Bud shut up and became the mechanical pacing fish that Harry needed.

Ashore, Dotty Bryson and Ken Varden got to know

each other very well. At the outset, Doc Howell was bewildered by the sudden change in his staff, and just to see how alert the new one was, he kept them hopping with orders and commands. This went on until it came time for Dotty to give him his sedative. Doc fell asleep protestingly, with an order to whitewash the dormitory dying on his lips.

Supper that night was a festive affair that took place buffet style in Doc's "sickroom." The girls broiled three enormous steaks laced with garlic and herbs, baked some immense Idaho potatoes and soaked them in butter, whipped up some crisp, brown biscuits, and, to top it all off, concocted heaping portions of strawberry short cake that were almost buried under small piles of whipped cream.

Doc was served the meager diet ordered by Doctor Lee and consumed it only because he was maddened with hunger from the smell of steak and the sight of shortcake. He vowed vengeance of a particularly ruthless nature once he was back on his feet.

Harry observed, "Ken and I are getting out just in time—another day or so and Doc would be routing us out of bed before dawn for a hike or two."

They were just finishing up supper when Dr. Lee returned. Only now he was not alone. With him were four or five men from Bencove, men Harry remembered seeing at that nearly riotous gathering in front of Parker's General Store. Neither the mayor, Norm Wells, nor his assistant, Plumpy, were with them.

"Consultants?" Bud queried.

"In a way," Dr. Lee said when introductions were made all around. "Nonmedical consultants."

"We'll leave," Meg suggested.

"Not at all," Dr. Lee said. "I'd like you to be here and listen to what we have to say. Doc may give us a hard time."

Doc scanned the newcomers. "Hello, John. Pete." He nodded to each in turn—suspiciously. His eyes were alert, crafty—for the first time in a couple of days Doc was his old self.

Dr. Lee turned to Harry. "So you're the Harry Williams who has struck terror into the hearts of the politicians of Bencove. I should have guessed. I was looking for a pug with a cauliflower ear and a flattened nose."

"Huh?"

"I heard all about that picnic in front of the store the other day." He held out his hand and took Harry's, squeezing it warmly. "You made quite an impression, young man."

From across the room, Meg's right eye closed in a solemn wink.

"However," Dr. Lee went on, "this conclave has been called not for you, Harry, but for Doc Howell."

"You going to banish him?" Bud Hill asked.

"Hardly," one of the other men said, smiling.

"Doc," the one called John said, "you must know the difficulties we're having with Wells and his snippy assistant."

"I've heard."

"You must also know that so far there's been no opposition for Wells—announced opposition anyway."

"Right," Pete chimed in. "Wells is so sure he's going to be renominated and re-elected that already he's strutting around like a Balkan prince. And once he gets in again, Bencove will be transformed into a three-ring circus."

"Fool!" Doc muttered. "Once I get back on my feet—"

"That's what this delegation is here for," Doctor Lee said. "Once you're back on your feet, you're going to run for mayor."

"What!"

"We know your thinking on this matter of Progress and Expansion. We think it's sound and practical. Bencove needs you, Doc."

Meg rushed to the bed and hugged her uncle. "Yes. Yes. Yes."

Doc started to protest violently, but Meg put her fingers to his mouth. "Doc will be happy to accept," she announced calmly.

"But I can't! I've got camp and campers and . . ."

"Nonsense," Dr. Lee chuckled. "Activity like this will be the best thing in the world for you."

"Won't the opposition make an issue of his heart attack?" Ken Varden asked.

"If they do," John said, "we'll make an issue of his remarkable and complete recovery."

"Lee!" Doc bellowed. "I'll get even with you for this!"

"I can't wait." Dr. Lee turned to the others in the room. "Now, if you don't mind, I want to examine the next mayor of Bencove."

Everybody left the room in a chattering, gay mob. There were questions of whether Doc's health could stand a campaign, if there was a chance to win, and if the offer of the nomination had the full support of the people. The four townsmen handled the questions adroitly, answering each fully and affirmatively.

"I admit I don't know Doc very well," Ken Varden said thoughtfully, "but from what I've seen and heard of him I think he'd make a good mayor for *any* city." He shook his head ruefully. "It'd sure be fun to work with him on a campaign."

"I'd love to give speeches for him," Bud said.

"I'd love to *write* them," Dotty Bryson suggested.

Meg let out a little cry that Harry had come to recognize as an indication that things were humming in her brain.

"Why don't we do all that? I can do posters. Ken can think up slogans."

"Why not?" somebody asked.

Only Harry seemed unenthusiastic. "We've got to think about Doc in all this. After all, he's just had an attack and he's not up to his full strength yet. The strain might be tough to take."

"I'm sure that's the least of Doc's objections," Meg said. "If he's certain that the town needs him, he'll go through with it. You heard him talk to us the other night—he has deep feelings about a citizen's obligation to society. True, he has lived a sort of lonely life—by choice—but he has never forgotten that in the final analysis, he owes everything to the people. Don't you agree, Harry?"

Bud slammed Harry on the back. "You bet your life he agrees. Because he's just agreed to go along with the majority on the swimming issue. Two weeks ago he was ready to set up shop in the middle of the Sahara Desert so he would never have to look at water again. Something came over him up in this neck of the woods—and he's going to back up the team, while still retaining that stubborn streak of individuality. I don't know who did it or how, but it's nothing less than a small miracle."

At this moment Dr. Lee joined them and announced that Doc Howell was in A-1 condition and visitors should be wary lest he pin them in a wrestling match. There were good-byes and wishes for luck and promises that the citizens' delegation would remain in constant touch.

Meg collapsed into a chair. "Doc as mayor! It's a natural!"

"Oh, you probably were secretly rooting for Plumpy," Harry said.

Meg threw a biscuit at him. Harry ducked, grabbed Dotty's hand and, dodging biscuits, raced for the safety of the outdoors. Laughing and out of breath, they walked out to the end of the dock. There they stood silently for a long time, hand in hand, shoulder to shoulder, listening to the sounds of the night.

"It's hard to believe," Dotty murmured. "I was so worried about us just a little while ago."

"So was I. But it hasn't all been my doing. There were Doc and Meg. I didn't have a chance."

"Then you don't feel you are compromising or reneging?"

"No. I feel that I am doing the right thing—in every life there has to be some give and take. Look at Meg and Ken. They were about as far apart as the North and South poles. I wouldn't have given a dime for their chances. Now . . ." He spread his hands.

"Now there's hope for us," Dotty smiled in the darkness.

"There's hope. But I sure wish you could be in the stands at the meet."

"I won't have to be there. I know you can do it."

Meg and Ken emerged from the Main House. They were swallowed up in the darkness, and only Bud Hill was visible, silhouetted against the porch light.

"Hey," he yelled. "Where is everybody?"

There was no answer.

"Hey, I'm all alone!"

Then from the upper floor came the clear voice of Doc Howell. "Get up here, you freckle-faced monkey. We've got to talk politics."

"Who, me?"

"You," came the reply.

Even on the dock Harry could hear the sigh that Bud loosed.

"Why wasn't I born a beautiful woman?" Bud said as he went into the house. "Always a best man and never a groom. Blimey, 'ow's a bloke ever goin' to git anywhere when 'e's a fifth wheel every time?"

Still muttering and grumbling, he obeyed Doc's summons and left the night to the people who would enjoy it most.

21

THE FIRST THING Harry and Ken Varden did on their arrival in New Haven was to place a phone call to Camp Skylark. After reassuring all and sundry that they had made the flight without mishap, Harry spoke privately with Dotty. During the time in the air he'd had plenty of time to think about her—about *them*—and he wanted to put the results of his thoughts into words. The gist of it was that her act of faith in coming to him was just what he had needed to rekindle the flame of pride and ambition in him.

"And Harry," Dotty said before they hung up, "do you intend to see Dad?"

"I guess so. I assume he'll be present with Coach Barnes."

"What are you going to say?"

"Gee, I don't know. I haven't thought about it."

"Will you do something for me?"

"Anything."

"Will you talk to him and tell him you were sorry you caused all the rumpus?"

"But it wasn't only me—" Harry started to protest.

"I know that," she said. "And very likely Dad knows it, too."

"If he knows, then why should I do that?"

"Look at it from his side," Dotty said. "You've managed to have everything work out your way. You bucked the coach and the school; you got me to do anything you say; and on top of that you're one of the best swimmers in the country."

"Yes," said Harry uncertainly, not knowing what she was getting at.

"Those are all the things that Dad wanted when he was in college. Only now we know that he didn't have the courage and the strength you have. He couldn't handle more than one or two things at a time. In the end, he surrendered a couple of things that meant a great deal to him. If he were to hear you say that you, too, had had your moments of doubt, that you knew you weren't right every minute—well, maybe you can imagine how good it would make him feel."

"You're asking me to do a difficult thing, baby," murmured Harry. Outside the phone booth Ken Varden was signaling him that the taxi had come and was waiting for them. Ken kept pointing to his wrist watch.

"I'll do what I can," promised Harry. "Honest, I will."

"I know you will," she replied. "I know you'll do what is right." In her voice was a faint hint of sadness. Harry hated to cut off the conversation on that note.

"If you think it'll help . . ."

"Of course. Also, it'll blow away any qualms he has about us."

"He has qualms about us?"

"You know Dad," she said mildly. "He takes stands on issues; he has deep-rooted convictions. He was bound to have strong opinions about us. This way, he'll feel a lot less defeated about losing me."

"I think I understand," said Harry.

"I knew you would," she said brightly. "For you it won't be very much—but for him—"

"Okay, sweetheart," he said. "Look. I've got to go. Ken is throwing a fit. See you."

"Good-bye, Harry, and good luck."

Harry left the telephone booth, lost in thought. Dotty had just asked him to do something that might have gone completely against his principles a month before. Even now, he was undecided about how he would handle it. To tell Professor Bryson he was wrong about the whole matter would be a lie—an outright lie.

He had still not decided when the taxi began to hum through the traffic of downtown New Haven.

"Here we are," chortled Ken. "By the time we leave, they'll be calling it New *Williams.*"

The appearance of Harry Williams in the State section of the vast locker room adjacent to the pool was nothing less than a sensation. Holland was there, so were Dixon and Reynolds and Shaw—the nucleus of the squad. Of course Bud Hill was missing, but his spirit hovered nearby, and now that Williams had shown up, the team members reacted like schoolkids at vacation time.

Even the most optimistic of the gang didn't give State a chance to swim away with the team honors at this meet. But they had great hopes that individuals would be able to shine and thereby prove that despite its lack of size, State did have quality. While State was considered best in its conference, this conference did not necessarily boast the best teams.

After the back-slapping, hand-shaking, and exchanges of information on past activities, and the introduction of Ken Varden, Harry asked Holland, "Is there a place for me on this collection of water-logged minnows?"

The freshman sprinter hugged Harry close. "There'd better be—or I'll start knocking a few skulls together."

A loudspeaker high on one of the walls blared with the announcement of one of the heats, telling all contestants to appear at the pool. Holland and Dixon and some of the others started to leave. Harry felt left out, wondering if he hadn't come too late after all.

"Where's the coach?" he inquired of Reynolds casually.

"Probably out front with all the judges and officials."

"Thanks."

Harry told Ken to find a seat near the State sector. They shook hands, and Ken found his own way out. Harry left by the other door and emerged into the great pool area. It was larger than State's pool—much larger. But the air was as warm and humid, smelling strongly of disinfectant and chlorine. The yells of the spectators bounced and rebounced off the tiled walls and ceiling.

At one end of the pool was a chaos of desks, chairs, wires, microphones, photographers, swimmers, coaches, officials, and messengers. High over the floor was a catwalk ramp where the timers stood to watch the races. When Harry entered, a heat was in progress, with each of eight lanes occupied by a churning swimmer determined to make the finals. The audience, while attentive, did not really get too excited over these preliminaries. Visible among the crowd were the banners and signs proclaiming the names of a score of colleges and universities.

Watching the scene, Harry forgot his own immediate concerns and was wrapped up in the atmosphere. Memories of a hundred similar scenes flooded in on him. He had come very close to giving all this up, to turning his back on this spectacle. And suddenly it burst upon him that it didn't matter if he was the Number One, if his was the name on everyone's lips, if he was the biggest star. What mattered was that he could participate and be a part of it all . . .

At the close of the heat, which State won with ease, Harry sought out Coach Rusty Barnes.

The big, graying man was off in a corner talking earnestly with the other State men. He had on his sweatsuit and his tennis shoes, and around his neck was the inevitable whistle hanging from the leather thong. A tug gripped Harry's heart as he realized he had actually missed his old nemesis during the past few weeks. He waited until the others had gone and Barnes was alone.

"Hello, Coach."

The big man turned. "Oh, Williams. It's you. How come you're not in your suit?"

"Well, I didn't know. I wanted to—"

"Nonsense. Into those trunks, boy. The four-forty heat is coming up in half an hour." He paused. "You do want to swim the four-forty?"

"Sure, I do, but what about—"

"What about nothing. You're all registered and signed in." Their eyes met briefly, but in that instant Harry saw the coach's flicker with amusement. A meaty paw clapped Harry's back. "Heck, kid, I knew you'd come. A guy with your spunk couldn't miss this. Now, get a move on, and check with me when you're ready."

Harry needed no urging. In less than five minutes he had undressed, showered, and climbed into his trunks. Coach Barnes was waiting near the diving board when he came out again. Holland was with him.

"Harry," the coach said, "maybe you and I haven't settled all our differences yet, but that's not important now. You're here to win a couple of races. My job is to help you the best I can. Now, Holland's been here a couple of days. He can give you a run-down on the guys to look out for."

Holland laughed. "That's easy. The Hawaiians. There are about ten sprinkled on all the teams, and each one is potentially a first-place man. You have to watch them—the one named Feliciano especially. He swims like he's tired, and then all at once it's like he ties on a motor and you're swallowing his wake."

Barnes consulted a mimeographed sheet on his clipboard. "But don't worry only about the Hawaiians.

There's an Ivy League kid named Hoover who's supposed to be just about the hottest thing in this part of the country."

"So all I have to do is beat Feliciano and Hoover and I'm in?" asked Harry innocently.

"That's right—and they're both in your heat today. How do you feel?"

"Pretty good," said Harry. That wasn't quite true. Inside he felt his stomach boiling with nervousness. "Except I haven't been in a pool in a while. Now if this were a lake—"

"Imagine it's an ocean, if it'll help," Barnes told him. "Unfortunately, there is almost no time for you to practice. You'll have a few minutes before the race starts, and maybe you can get the feel of the pool then."

Every swimmer knows that although water is the same substance the world over, it can feel differently in various pools. Some pools are considered fast, others slow, although their dimensions may be identical.

"How is the pool?" Harry asked Holland.

"If anything, I'd say it's a little slow."

"That's good, I think," Coach Barnes offered. "A lake is slower than a pool, and now that you've had some lake swimming you may have a slight advantage. A fast pool might be of greater assistance to the other lads."

Harry found himself enjoying this huddle. He had hardly ever joined them at other meets. It was surprising to find out how much Barnes knew about the details of the opposition. Holland, too, was alert and observant. In fact, without their advice Harry wouldn't have been particularly keen on going into the water with a couple of sharpshooters like Feliciano and Hoover. He was glad he had come as a member of a team.

"Coach."

"Yep?"

"Is Professor Bryson here today?"

"He is," said the coach. "He's got a seat just behind our boys' bench."

Harry followed Barnes' horny finger and easily picked out the familiar, stern features of Professor Bryson. With a start, he saw that Ken Varden was sitting right next to him. As yet they didn't appear to be acquainted, but if Harry knew Ken, it wouldn't be long.

"How long have I got before I go on?"

Barnes glanced at the wall clock. "Ten minutes. Why?"

"I've got to see Professor Bryson. Could you ask him to step down here a moment, Rusty?"

"What for?" the coach asked suspiciously.

"I've something to tell him and I can't do it with two thousand people watching."

"Is it good or bad?"

"That depends on which side you're on."

Coach Barnes lumbered over to the grandstand, tapped Professor Bryson, bent to whisper in his ear, and then pointed at Harry. Bryson frowned darkly, nodded, and rose.

"Harry," he said noncommittally, offering his hand. "Nice to see you. Rusty," he added to the coach, "I owe you a new hat."

"You bet I wouldn't come?" Harry asked.

"I've never been known as an astute gambler," said Dotty's father. "How is my little girl?"

"Wonderful. I mean, she's the loveliest—that is . . ." stammered Harry.

"Forget it, I know what you mean. I agree." The professor hesitated, obviously waiting for Harry to talk.

Harry took a deep breath. This was turning out to be as rough as any race he'd ever swum. And still, it wasn't impossible. The core of resistance in him had melted, and he found it was easier to view matters objectively.

"Professor Bryson," he began, "I just wanted you to know that I've been thinking a lot since I left State last month. It hasn't been an easy time for me. I've had to rearrange a lot of my thoughts. But I did realize that I owed you an apology. Or at least an explanation."

"Not at all—"

"It's true. You tried to tell me I was heading for trouble, and I more or less laughed in your face. I should have listened to you, sir."

"Now, Harry—"

"No, Professor. Don't object. Look, I've got to get going now, but I'll see you later."

Their hands met firmly. "Good luck, Harry. I mean it."

Professor Bryson watched Harry respond to the call for the entrants for the four-forty. His glasses seemed misted from the humidity, so he took them off and polished them absently as he made his way back to his seat.

"Remarkable," he said half-aloud. "Remarkable."

"What is that, sir?" said the boy next to him.

"Huh? Oh, was I speaking? Couldn't help myself, I guess."

"Anything wrong?"

"No. No, nothing's wrong. Everything's right. You see, I know one of the swimmers in this race."

"So do I."

"Well, I just saw him win the toughest race of his life."

"But they haven't even been in the water yet."

"I know," smiled Professor Bryson, "I know . . ."

The starter held his pistol in the air and asked for silence. He ran his eye along the line of eight poised swimmers. A hush fell over the auditorium.

"Swimmers take your marks . . ."

The crack of the pistol split the air, and Harry Williams split the water before the echo had died away. He was in the sixth lane, with Hoover in the fifth and Feliciano in the seventh, and all eight men hit the water within a fraction of a second of one another. Harry was back in the element he loved, and this time he was pitted against boys who represented the stiffest competition in the country.

The water parted under his rhythmic, thumping strokes as he started the first length of the fifty-yard pool. Four hundred and forty yards to go. Nearly nine full lengths. Accustomed as he was to swimming sixteen lengths in a short-course pool, Harry was nearly tempted to try to gulp up the nine lengths in nothing flat. But he knew he'd have to conserve his energy. Hawaiians were the closest things to human amphibians in the world, and this Feliciano was famous for his finishing kick.

Harry was swimming in such a manner that on the odd-numbered lengths he would be able to see Feliciano over his left arm; on the even-numbered lengths he would see Hoover. So he kept his eye on the Hawaiian for the first lap, noting that the boy had a peculiar slapping kind of stroke that looked awkward and wasteful. Holland must be wrong about this kid.

Then his fingertips touched the end of the pool, and he contracted his body in a single motion and shoved off with his feet. Now he could see the windmill style of Hoover—an eighteen-year-old who looked as tireless as a pneumatic drill. The boy had little grace, but he was keeping abreast of Harry and that was what counted.

As he hit the starting end, Holland bent close over the water and yelled, "Two!" into Harry's ear. It was unnecessary. For years Harry Williams had kept track of his laps and had never missed. Nevertheless it was a nice thing for Holland to do.

Springing off, Harry's head was, for a split second, clear of the water and he could hear the rising roar of the crowd. He had a glimpse of three other swimmers still coming toward this end, which meant that he had a lead on at least half of the competitors. But on either side of him, as tenacious as leeches, were Hoover and Feliciano.

By the end of the fifth lap, a pattern began to set in. The youngster, Hoover, with the windmill strokes, had taken the lead by a full two yards, and the crowd was urging him on. Second and third, never more than a head apart, were Williams and the Hawaiian.

For the first time in many seasons, Harry Williams felt the chilling breath of fear skitter through him. Neither of these boys looked the type to fold under pressure. Like himself, they seemed to thrive under it. There would be no breaking of spirits; no demoralizing by superior style; no winning by default. Whoever won this race would have to *win* it; would have definitely to defeat the others. Since none had swum against the others before, there was no precedent.

Now Harry's entire being was concentrated in his arms and legs; he recalled everything he had ever learned from Doc Howell and even Coach Barnes. There was not an instant when he felt he could relax and coast. In this three-man race a missed stroke, a bad kick-off, a choked breath would mean defeat.

Holland yelled, "Six!" Harry knew that when he yelled "Eight" there would be only forty yards to go.

Feliciano was still matching him tirelessly, stroke for pounding stroke. Harry decided to test him. He stepped up his arm beat by a fraction. Instinctively, the Hawaiian did the same. Then they were both kicking off to start the eighth lap and Harry could see Hoover. The gap between them had narrowed to a yard, but it had been a hard-won yard. Hoover wouldn't be easy.

Time and distance were running out simultaneously. Harry had to make his move. First of all he had to beat the one immediately in front of him. Into his mind flashed the memory of Meg Crane drawing him on from the canoe.

At that time he had summoned up an incredible reserve of energy, and there must be some left. Harry began to increase his arm and leg beat and slowly crept up on Hoover. Fortunately, at this moment Hoover could not see him, which gave Harry his opportunity to close the gap between them. It was only a guess, but he felt sure that the people in the stands must be going crazy as the three swimmers, separated by no more than an eyelash, thundered down the pool for the last full length before starting the final forty yards.

Seeing that he had closed swiftly on Hoover gave Harry a spurt of confidence that he knew Hoover couldn't overcome. He had beaten Hoover. Next was Feliciano. There were only a few seconds remaining before the last kick-and-turn, and Harry tried to figure some strategy. It seemed logical that Feliciano would think that he, Harry, would wait for the last forty yards before turning on the steam. Therefore, Feliciano would probably depend on his stamina to match him and outreach him then.

So thinking, Harry changed his strategy. The judges' end of the pool was but five yards away.

Harry delved to the very bottom of his reservoir of power and *sprinted* those five yards!

The move caught Feliciano completely off guard and he fell back by a stroke. The kneeling Holland screamed, "Eight!" as Harry touched the tile, went under in a modified somesault, and twisted on himself. Until now, he'd heard Feliciano's teammate yelling the lap number at the same time. This time Holland's voice was a solo. Harry Williams had the slight advantage he needed.

Heading back up his lane for the last forty yards, Harry could look directly to his left. He did see Feliciano's fingertips as they clawed frantically at the water, but he could *not* see his head.

The liquid slipped past Harry's glazed eyes, and he was breathing, stroking, kicking as though a metronome were guiding his actions. His feet were like twin outboard motors behind him. Ahead was the catwalk with the timers leaning over each lane anxiously. There was no tile to slap this time—he had only to pass under the catwalk at the forty-yard mark.

Every sinew, every fiber, every tissue in his body hummed with unharnessed energy and strength. With his head in the water he didn't know when he passed the finish line—or if he had passed it first.

But he heard the ear-shattering roar that had been growing from the spectators as he slapped the end of the pool and lifted his head from the water. It seemed to him that Feliciano hit at the same time—and Hoover, too. Maybe, after all, he hadn't made it.

Barnes was up on the apron with Holland and some others, all yelling at him. Officials were running in every direction. Nearly all eyes were fixed on the silent timers high over the pool as they consulted their watches.

Harry found his footing, reached over to Feliciano, and wrapped an arm around the boy's neck. The Hawaiian responded with equal affection. Few things draw men closer together than a stiff, fair competition. Arm in arm they staggered to Hoover's lane.

A voice from the loudspeaker asked for silence and then

said: "Results of the Four-Forty. The winner, in a new world's record for the long course—Harry Williams!"

The voice must have said what the time was, but Harry didn't hear it. He only heard the renewed cheers of the crowd and the sincere congratulations of the two men he'd beaten.

Somehow, he made it onto the apron of the pool where he was pummeled by a delirious Rusty Barnes. Tears were streaming down the coach's cheeks. A lump rose in Harry's throat, and he turned away. It was necessary to walk past the stands to get back to the locker room, and his steps were punctuated by the applause and whistles of two thousand spectators. It was like a dream. All the races he had ever won in the past faded into insignificance against this one.

Passing the State bench, he looked up into the stands. It was a volcano of activity, but one person was far and away the wildest.

His hair was mussed, his usually impeccable tie and shirt were askew, his glasses were dangling from one ear. He did not look very much like a dignified professor at all . . .

And then Professor Bryson, pushed by Coach Barnes, was beside Harry, unable to speak, able only to hug him close. Together they walked along the edge of the pool toward the locker room.

THE END

COALITION BARGAINING

A STUDY OF UNION TACTICS AND PUBLIC POLICY

INDUSTRIAL RESEARCH UNIT
DEPARTMENT OF INDUSTRY
WHARTON SCHOOL OF FINANCE AND COMMERCE
UNIVERSITY OF PENNSYLVANIA

The Industrial Research Unit is the business and labor research arm of the Department of Industry, Wharton School of Finance and Commerce. Founded in 1921 after World War I as a separate Wharton School Department, the Industrial Research Unit has a long record of publication and research in the labor market, productivity, union relations, and business report fields. Major Industrial Research Unit studies are published as research projects are completed. Advanced research reports are issued as appropriate in a general or special series.

RECENT INDUSTRIAL RESEARCH UNIT STUDIES

No. 40 Gladys L. Palmer, *et al.*, *The Reluctant Job Changer* (1962)

No. 41 George M. Parks, *The Economics of Carpeting and Resilient Flooring: An Evaluation and Comparison* (1966)

No. 42 Michael H. Moskow, *Teachers and Unions: The Applicability of Collective Bargaining to Public Education* (1966)

No. 43 F. Marion Fletcher, *Market Restraints in the Retail Drug Industry* (1967)

No. 44 Herbert R. Northrup and Gordon R. Storholm, *Restrictive Labor Practices in the Supermarket Industry* (1967)

No. 45 William N. Chernish, *Coalition Bargaining: A Study of Union Tactics and Public Policy* (1969)

Coalition Bargaining

A STUDY OF UNION TACTICS
AND PUBLIC POLICY

BY WILLIAM N. CHERNISH

University of Pennsylvania Press *Philadelphia*

Library of Congress Catalog Card Number: 69-16538

Manufactured in the United States of America

8122-7589-6

TO MY MOTHER AND FATHER

FOREWORD

Dr. William N. Chernish's study of coalition bargaining is the first major work on this subject since the Industrial Union Department, AFL-CIO, established a program to re-orient collective bargaining relationships in major companies and industries. The completeness of the case studies and the enormous amount of factual material which is so well organized and digested will make this study a prime reference source for all future research on the subject. In addition, the public policy discussion in Chapter XI, particularly with reference to the National Labor Relations (Taft-Hartley) Act, would seem to raise serious questions concerning the evenhandedness of the administration of that law.

Dr. Chernish who, in addition to the Ph.D. degree, holds a Bachelor of Science degree in mechanical engineering from Duke University and a Master of Business Administration in industrial relations from the Wharton Graduate Division of the University of Pennsylvania, first became interested in coalition bargaining as part of an industrial relations seminar project. He had already chosen the subject as a dissertation project when, in the early summer of 1967, a number of companies proposed that the Industrial Research Unit sponsor a thorough analysis of the scope, extent, success and impact of coalition bargaining. For this purpose, a number of small grants were made to the Unit by these companies.

These grants were accepted with the explicit understanding that the author and the Industrial Research Unit would have complete control over all phases of the project—the procedures and methods to be used, the areas to be studied, the analytical techniques, the conclusions, and that the study would be published regardless of results. With ready agreement on procedures, the resultant unrestrictive grants permitted the study to be expanded and to be made much more extensive than was originally envisioned. Complete cooperation by both companies studied and by the Industrial Union Department contributed immensely to the extent and depth of the work.

Dr. Chernish's study was first done as a dissertation at the University of Pennsylvania in Business and Applied Economics. His dissertation committee unanimously encouraged publication. The members were Professor Reavis Cox, Department of Marketing; John Perry Horlacher, Department of Political Science; and Edward B. Shils and the undersigned, Department of Industry. In accordance with the rules of the University of Pennsylvania Press, two outside readers were asked to comment on the book by the Director of the Press: Professors George H. Hildebrand, Cornell University, and Herbert H. Heneman, Jr., University of Minnesota, both recommended the work highly for publication. It was then revised in accordance with suggestions from these readers and others, and accepted for publication.

Herbert R. Northrup, Chairman
Department of Industry
Wharton School of Finance and Commerce
University of Pennsylvania

September 1, 1968
Philadelphia

PREFACE

Although recent journals and periodicals have begun to treat with some aspects of coalition bargaining, it became evident to this writer about one year ago that there was no major work which attempted to analyze all of the various facets of the concept. In fact, the Industrial Union Department of the AFL-CIO was, and is, still experimenting with various approaches to the problem of dealing with large diversified employers, in attempting to gain better bargains for the employees and unions. It was, therefore, during an attempt to do research on the topic of coalitionism that the lack of material became evident. And, thus the decision was made to prepare a major study on coalition bargaining and its impact upon the various sectors with which it deals.

The study itself involved more than a year of full-time work on the part of the author. During this year, it was decided to make use of a case study approach to the problem of coalition bargaining, and to examine the concept as it actually works in practice. Because of the dearth of literature on the topic at this point in time, it was necessary to examine the concept from its most elemental sources—the actual situations which came about as a result of the IUD-sponsored programs. In addition to demonstrating how the bargaining actually works, the cases also serve to point out the variety of approaches, the flexibility with which the programs may be implemented, and the impact of law and its administration.

The book is organized in the following manner: Part One deals with the background material deemed appropriate to coalition bargaining, and develops the nature and operation of the coalition concept. It contains an overview of the reasons that coalitions come about, and gives a general picture of how the coalitions are organized and how they operate.

Part Two deals with the significant cases in coalition bargaining. Contained here are examinations of the coalitions which faced American-Standard, Johns-Manville, American Home Products, General Electric and Westinghouse, Union Carbide, 3M, the nonferrous industry, and several others. From these cases it is possible to gain a more detailed picture of the operation and impact of coalitions, and to begin to become aware of the variety of approaches possible by the unions.

Part Three examines first the public policy implications of the coalition concept, and treats with the problems brought about for both companies and the public as a result of coalition situations. Then the final chapter attempts to examine the overall course of coalitions, and to speculate somewhat as to the future of such bargaining.

The methodology of the study is essentially one of examining the various coalitions, and then attempting to draw generalizations where appropriate. The cases described are the ones which were deemed to be the most important, although others of less importance are also noted for comparative purposes. Data gathering involved more than 50 interviews with officials of various companies that had either faced coalition bargaining situations, or who were thought to be potential targets of such programs. In general, the person interviewed at each company was the vice-president of industrial relations, or his immediate subordinate where that individual had specific responsibility for labor relations matters. Likewise, the Industrial Union Department of the AFL-CIO proved to be a most valuable source of information. Numerous interviews were conducted with officials of the IUD, including the executive director, and many of the coordinators who had been charged with responsibility for guiding the coalition bargaining committees. Both companies and unions provided the author with valuable insights, and were extremely generous in making available numerous memoranda, documents, and other pertinent material. The study would not have been at all possible without the total cooperation of both union and industry groups. It is only because all parties were so generous with time and data that it was possible to examine the entire concept of coalition bargaining in such depth.

It would be virtually impossible to thank all of the union and company representatives who contributed to the study, but several gentlemen deserve special thanks. Jack Conway, former Executive Director of the IUD, made possible the communication with his group by opening his files to me, and by encouraging the IUD people to explain fully the whole idea of coalition bargaining. Among the many helpful individuals at the IUD were Mrs. Gheretein Wilson, Messrs. Don Doherty, and Steve Harris. Among the company representatives interviewed, all of whom were most helpful, several deserve special mention: Messrs. Gerald F. Gamber, retired from American-Standard; Ralph M. King of Johns-Manville, Virgil B. Day of General Electric, Clark C. Frame of Westinghouse, Earl L. Engle of Union Carbide, Charles F. Tourek of 3M, Douglas Soutar of ASARCO, William Kirkpatrick of Anaconda, Edmund Flynn of Kennecott, Robert C. Landon of Rohm and Haas, Francis A. O'Connell of Olin-Mathieson, W. E. Koger of Ingersoll-Rand, William F. Harwick of Campbell Soup, and Fred Edwards of Armstrong Cork.

During the year in which the author spent in preparing this study, funding was kindly made available through a research fellowship from the Industrial Research Unit of the Department of Industry, Wharton School of Finance and Commerce, University of Pennsylvania. It was during this time that I was supported, and was able to prepare a doctoral dissertation, from which this volume evolved.

A special word of appreciation is due to Dr. Herbert R. Northrup, Chairman and Professor of Industry at the Wharton School of Finance and Commerce who served as dissertation supervisor, and advisor on the many problems, large and small, which cropped up. It was only through Dr. Northrup's patience, his encouragement, knowledge, and guidance that the completion of this study was made possible.

The author wishes to thank also Mrs. Margaret E. Doyle for assistance in many administrative matters, Mrs. Marjorie Denison and Miss Elsa Klemp for editorial assistance, and Mrs. Helen White, Miss Phyllis Hess and my sister, Carol, three tireless typists, who toiled under trying circumstances.

Although all possible care was taken to insure accuracy at all stages, any errors of commission or omission are solely the responsibility of the author.

September 1, 1968 William N. Chernish

CONTENTS

LIST OF TABLES

Part One

BACKGROUND AND NATURE OF COALITION BARGAINING

CHAPTER I

INTRODUCTION

Coalition bargaining is an attempt by a group of local and international unions, usually in an industrial setting, to bargain with a multiplant, multiunion employer on a joint basis for all of the employees represented by those unions. Because of the fact that the effort is usually a unilateral response to a bargaining weakness on the part of the unions, and because of the nature of the union tactics inherent in such a program, the term "coalition bargaining" is preferred to "coordinated bargaining" for the purposes of this study. Additionally, the actual bargaining programs employed by the union groupings often go much beyond the stage of simple coordination of activity, and actually involve the formation of coalitions for bargaining purposes.

THE IUD ROLE

Although union groupings and coalitions have occurred in the past, the current coalition bargaining programs that are studied here have generally been under the sponsorship of the Collective Bargaining Services Section of the Industrial Union Department, AFL-CIO, commonly referred to as the IUD. Prior to April 1964, the Industrial Union Department had been primarily concerned with the general problems of the industrial unions, and had been actively engaged in a broad-based organizational effort to bolster the sagging ranks of the industrial union affiliates. In 1964, however, a special division was created by the IUD whose primary task was to be the development of coalition bargaining.

The general *modus operandi* of the IUD with respect to any one company or industry coalition has been to work with a committee of union representatives of the particular target companies. In most cases, the company committee is the basic unit from which an industry committee may also be composed. As of late 1968, with few notable exceptions, the IUD had all but abandoned the industry-wide approach.

From the time that the Collective Bargaining Services Section was formally established in April 1964 until the November 1965 Sixth Constitutional Convention of the IUD, the number of bargaining committees "coordinated" by the IUD had grown to 60 company and industry committees. By July 1966, this number had risen to 77, and the late 1968 roster lists more than 90 company and industry committees in various stages of "coordination." The mere existence of a committee, however, does not mean that the unions are actively engaged in forming or pressing a coalition effort upon a company, but merely that future interest and perhaps potential exist for a coalition. In fact, some committees have been all but forsaken as active bargaining groups, but are nevertheless carried on the rolls as potential groups for future efforts.

In light of the fact that in less than four years, the IUD had created sufficient interest to generate the sheer number of committees of unions at various companies, the appeal to union leaders must be substantial. And, in view of the bargaining results in some of the situations where the coalition efforts have been pursued with determination, the economic results in terms of benefits and strikes have been significant. Most serious coalitions have produced some benefits for the unions participating, but several have also resulted in extended multiplant strikes that proved extremely costly to both sides.

One further consideration presents itself as of the date of this writing. That consideration is one brought about by the recently announced alliance of the United Automobile Workers and the Teamsters union. What Walter Reuther, the father of coalition bargaining, may attempt to do with this alliance is difficult to predict at this time.

The purpose of this study, then, is to examine the various facets of coalition bargaining programs, beginning with the reasons for the formation of coalitions to the actual implementation of the union programs, and then to the results of the various coalition bargaining attempts.

Some Pertinent Questions

Before proceeding, it is pertinent to pose several questions regarding the entire concept of coalition bargaining. All of these questions are analysed in the succeeding chapters, but a very brief examination is appropriate at this time.

1. *What is coalition bargaining?* As has already been noted briefly, coalition bargaining is the joining together of a number of local unions, having different international affiliations, for the purpose of bargaining with a company or an industry as a single unit. It is a form of joint bargaining which seeks to increase union bargaining power in dealing with a firm that has several locations which are represented by different unions, and which usually has plants that are able to substitute production, or which deal in different markets, so that a single plant strike by a single union has minimum effect on the overall ability of the company to produce and to generate profits.

2. *How is coalition bargaining different from other forms of joint bargaining?* The recent coalition attempts which have been guided by the IUD differ in several respects from the joint efforts that have become common in certain other sectors of American industry. In general, the coalition programs have involved locals of different international unions, whereas other joint industrial efforts have been guided by the international to which the locals have been affiliated—automobile and steel are two examples. Multiunion efforts at joint bargaining for various craft unions have been common in some segments of the railroad and construction industries, but the coalition programs have primarily involved the industrial unions, and have had craft unions join only when they have represented employees in an industrial setting. Furthermore, and most important, coalition bargaining programs are usually aimed at companies which operate in more than one market, and which do not usually wish to bargain jointly for its various operations. Other

types of joint bargaining arrangements may have come about on a voluntary basis, but the purpose of a coalition program is to engage a company in joint bargaining regardless of whether it is willing to do so on a voluntary basis.

3. *Why does coalition bargaining occur?* Essentially, coalition bargaining occurs as a union attempts to gain greater bargaining leverage in order to deal with a company whose structure makes it able to successfully stand against a single plant strike. The conglomerate corporation has been cited as one example of the sort of company which unions seek to engage in coalition bargaining because they are not able to extract sizable gains through existing bargaining relationships. In fact, the concept of coalition bargaining is one that seeks to enhance union economic strength in dealing with any firm which operates more than a single plant, and where employees are represented by more than one international union.

4. *What is the impact of coalition bargaining?* The practice of coalitionism has a definite effect upon the structure of the participating unions themselves, by moving the locus of power away from local and international unions, and therefore further from the membership. Such a joint effort has had an impact on the union leadership, and has also been a factor in attempting to further induce the merging of various international unions. Coalition bargaining has had an effect, too, on the overall industrial relations picture of the various companies and industries which have experienced coalition attempts, as well as those who have been faced with the possibility of such attempts by the IUD and its affiliated unions. Day-to-day union-management relationships have also been affected, and the dealings with the employees and the employee representatives have been changed as a further result of coalition bargaining. Furthermore, one must conclude from an analysis of various situations described here that coalitionism would tend to increase the likelihood of more frequent, larger, and longer strikes, and therefore have an impact upon the public which cannot long be overlooked. In addition, the situations described below in the General Electric, Union Carbide, and especially the nonferrous cases all point to the need for a thorough analysis of our labor legislation and its administration. This is the subject of Chapter XI. The following chapter examines the nature and development of coalitionism, and then the cases in coalition bargaining are studied.

CHAPTER II

THE NATURE AND DEVELOPMENT OF COALITION BARGAINING

Coalition bargaining is a new industrial relations development, which differs in form and substance from previous bargaining structures. In this chapter, the distinctions between coalition bargaining and other forms of bargaining structure are examined; note is taken of earlier coalition bargaining attempts; the purpose of coalition bargaining is explored; and finally, explanation is given of how the Industrial Union Department of the AFL-CIO (IUD) has developed and operated a bargaining committee.

Background and Purpose

Grouping of local unions or international unions for bargaining purposes is neither new nor unique. This is particularly true where unions are organized on a craft basis. In the building trades, for example, various construction crafts frequently bargain jointly with a local association of building contractors. Likewise, various craft unions in the printing trades often bargain jointly with one or more newspaper or printing concerns. Such bargaining also traditionally covers one local labor market or just one company in that labor market.

In some industries, notably the shipyards and the railroads, various crafts have joined together for regional or industry-wide bargaining. The West Coast shipbuilding industry bargains with a group of craft unions joined together in local bodies of the AFL-CIO Metal Trades Department. The railroad shop crafts, through the AFL-CIO Railway Employees Department, bargain with the nation's railroads on a national basis. Sometimes they are joined by other railroad crafts in their bargaining; from time to time other railroad craft unions join in the same bargaining front, or break away to bargain on an individual, or different group basis.

Multicraft bargaining differs from coalition bargaining in several important respects. It is, first, usually confined either to one labor market or to one industry, whereas coalition bargaining extends corporate-wide to a number of labor markets and to diverse industries if the corporation's activities are found in more than one area. Second, multicraft bargaining involves a common front on the part of various craft unions, each having a contract, or series of contracts, in the same plants. Although more than one union in one plant may be involved in coalition bargaining, the essence of coalition bargaining is the grouping together of various industrially organized locals of two or more international unions into a common bargaining structure, usually with each plant having one, or one principal local rather than a multitude of craft unions.

Coalition bargaining also differs from the traditional multiplant or companywide bargaining in that such bargaining usually involves either the already noted multicraft structure, or the local affiliates of a single international union negotiating as a group with one company. Coalition bargaining likewise differs from multicompany or even industry-wide bargaining, as we have known it in the past, again because traditionally the bargaining involves a group of companies and either one industrial union with local affiliates in each plant, or a confederation of craft unions, each with a local in the plants. And, most important is the fact that other types of joint bargaining efforts have come about on a voluntary basis; whereas the various coalition efforts have been designed to engage the companies in multiunit bargaining against their will.

Coalition bargaining thus arises out of a coordinated effort on the part of two or more international unions to institute joint bargaining on a corporate-wide or multiunit plant basis. The purpose is to extend the bargaining structure to a corporate-wide, and probably eventually industry-wide basis, in order to exert maximum bargaining pressure on the company or industry.

Some Pros and Cons of Joint Bargaining

If one observes the industrial relations patterns of various industries, it quickly becomes obvious that some firms and some industries engage in various forms of joint bargaining, and prefer to deal with their union, or unions, in such a manner. It is, therefore, useful to examine some of the reasons for such a decision, and to weigh the general disadvantages of joint bargaining.

An employer may join with other employers in a similar market in order to prevent a strong union, or unions, from "whipsawing"—that is forcing one employer to yield to a union demand and then applying that demand (or more) to a second, then to a third, and so on. Without such employer joint bargaining, unions can force a small employer to sign an unpalatable agreement or face economic disaster. Then the agreement becomes, by union pressure, the agreement for the industry in that market area.

Multiemployer bargaining also tends to equalize wage and fringe rates and work rules. This may be of some advantage to an employer who operates in a small competitive market, and in a market in which competitive constraints are such that the cost of a wage increase negotiated jointly may be passed on without substantial effect upon the employer. Moreover, should a strike ensue from such bargaining, the costs of the work stoppage will be of greater concern to the union involved because of the fact that greater dues will be lost, and greater strike benefits must be paid, where applicable. Perhaps more important from the employer standpoint is the fact that a work stoppage will shut down the operations of the competitors as well as his own, thereby providing greater insurance that a permanent loss of business will not ensue.

In some cases, joint bargaining is deemed beneficial to an employer because negotiating costs may be reduced since the bargaining need be conducted only once, and that greater expertise may be called into play in order to overcome a lack of sophistication in labor relations matters which may come about where bargaining is strictly local.

For some companies, joint employer bargaining may lead to a greater degree of communication and awareness of the operations of the others, and is sometimes beneficial in pursuing grievance and arbitration matters. Some firms are therefore able to prevent losing through contract interpretation or arbitration what has been won in negotiations.

Such joint bargaining is commonly found among small concerns, and particularly those selling a non-storable service. Individual restaurants, supermarkets, newspapers, and transportation concerns are at a distinct bargaining advantage when facing strong unions. Such industries frequently attempt to present a united front in dealing with unions, and often all shut down if one is struck. The objective is not only to increase the leverage on the union, but also to encourage each employer to stand fast with the knowledge that no company is profiting by a strike against one.

Of course, even for small service concerns, multicompany bargaining has disadvantages as well. In many situations, it is the weakest link which may be the determinant of the outcome of the bargaining. A weak union can hold back gains for union members in other companies. Likewise, a weak firm can reduce the effective bargaining posture of all of the companies in the joint effort.

One of the major problems with joint bargaining is that it frequently requires that considerable time and effort be spent by all participants in an effort to settle a problem of one, or a small group. The net result can be a work rule limiting every company instead of solving the problem for one. In a similar manner, differing approaches to problems by different companies tend to make successful joint bargaining difficult.

Another real problem with joint bargaining lies in the fact that when a work stoppage comes about, the scope of the strike is much broader than is the case with individual, local bargains. This may mean that the pressure brought about by the public, and by other outside forces is likely to be greater, and thus the likelihood of intervention becomes a more real possibility. With such intervention, a settlement based on political rather than economic constraints becomes more likely. The results are most frequently a higher economic settlement.

A different type of joint bargaining exists in automobiles or steel where locals of one union deal with a company or group of companies. Although these companies are diversified, they are largely one basic product concerns. They are quite different from the highly diversified conglomerates which operate in several industries and face different competitive pressures for different products. The conglomerate faced with coalition bargaining finds that his competitors may be dealing with different unions under different assumptions and settle with very different wage and benefit costs. Moreover, the products involved may have many ready substitutes and competitors in other industries.

In such situations, employers believe that they must maintain differential wage rates at various locations, and must be able to maintain flexibility of operation—something which becomes increasingly difficult as bargaining becomes centralized, and as master agreements begin to emerge which place greater emphasis on uniformity across the firm.

Furthermore, industry in general has been reluctant to accept the concept of joint bargaining, and more specifically, coalition bargaining because of the very real fact that a mature and successful coalition would have increased bargaining strength by virtue of the fact that such a coalition is able to threaten, or actually to engage in, a strike which could cripple the operations of the entire firm. In effect, such a coalition would prevent the company from "whipsawing" the unions—preventing the unions from succeeding in gaining settlements through coalitions which the individual locals would be unable to gain on their own. One of the stated goals of the IUD is to make such gains.

It is fair to state that a large portion of American industry in general is totally opposed to coalition bargaining, and to other forms of joint bargaining. Such opposition comes about for the very pragmatic reason that it seeks to prevent the unions from increasing what it considers to be an already excessive power, both at the bargaining table, and, through political support by government intervention in labor disputes, which is more likely to result if coalition bargaining expands the scope of negotiations.

Unions, also, are not unanimous concerning coalition bargaining. Essentially, such bargaining involves a loss of autonomy which strong unions need not surrender, and even weaker ones are reluctant to cede. We shall note, however, that coalition bargaining has been pressed by strong unions with imperialist ambitions and by weaker ones anxious to increase their bargaining power.

ANTECEDENTS OF THE COALITION MOVEMENT

Coalition bargaining without being termed such, has in fact been attempted before, but never on such a massive scale. The United Papermakers and Paperworkers (UPP) and the International Brotherhood of Pulp, Sulphite and Paper Mill Workers of the United States and Canada (IBPSPMW) have historically bargained on a coalition basis which usually extends region-wide for one company, but which historically included nearly all West Coast pulp and paper mills in one unit. Converting plants are not generally found in the same bargaining group as basic mills. In some areas, the coalition includes craft locals of the International Brotherhood of Electrical Workers (IBEW), the International Association of Machinists and Aerospace Workers (IAM), and sometimes other unions. In other cases, either one paper union or the other represents all plant workers in a mill.

Coalition bargaining in this industry is the result of the craft approach of the Papermakers. If the Papermakers Union had originally opened its doors to all mill workers, the union split probably would not have occurred. The divided union jurisdiction within a single industry resulted in coalition bargaining that is, in effect, analogous to bargaining by a metal trades council or other craft groups.

In the meatpacking industry, throughout the 1950's, a former AFL and former CIO union either bargained jointly with one or more of the major companies in the industry or cooperated closely in their strategy and goals. At Armour, for example, the two major unions and the company worked jointly on problems arising out of automation and plant shutdowns.[1] Since the merger of the two unions in the summer of 1968, the merged organization has continued to press coalition bargaining, for example striking the Campbell Soup Company as will be examined in Chapter X.

[1]See George P. Shultz and Arnold R. Weber, *Strategies for the Displaced Worker* (New York: Harper and Row), 1966.

The cooperation of the meatpacking unions began before the American Federation of Labor and the Congress of Industrial Organizations merged. After the AFL-CIO merger in 1955, the prospects for union cooperation increased. The actual techniques of coalitionism then had their earliest developments in the electrical manufacturing and aerospace industries. The situation in the former industry is discussed in detail in Chapter IV of this study. In the latter industry two unions have been involved, the International Association of Machinists and Aerospace Workers (IAM), and the United Automobile, Aerospace and Agricultural Implement Workers (UAW).

United Aircraft

The coalition movement in the aerospace industry, involving the IAM and the UAW, had a strike test as early as 1960 when the two unions joined together in a strike against the United Aircraft Corporation which affected some 40,000 people in New England and Florida. More than a year before the first of a series of six contracts expired, the unions issued a joint statement which indicated that they would band together for the purpose of multiplying their bargaining leverage.

This early effort had many of the same hallmarks as do the present IUD programs. The unions engaged in various forms of negotiating delays in order to have a series of contracts become open at the same time; engaged in strike actions after local memberships had voted to accept a settlement; and seemed to be unwilling to negotiate meaningfully in order to seek a quick end to the work stoppage which took place at six separate locations.

In this strike, the unions not only made no significant gains whatsoever as a result of the coalition effort, but in addition, the UAW lost bargaining rights at United Aircraft's Sikorsky plant to an independent union that later affiliated with the Teamsters. In fact, United Aircraft elected to keep all of the plants in operation during the strike period. This brought about the collapse of the work stoppage because most of the employees returned to work by the end of the fourteenth day of the strike. It is also interesting to note that in no plant was the union membership (based on a dues checkoff) more than 50 percent of the work force, and that the strike votes had been conducted among a much smaller minority of the workers.

Other Aerospace

In 1962, the IAM and the UAW maneuvered most of the major aerospace companies into common expiration dates and pushed for higher wages and the union shop. One company, Douglas, yielded to an agency shop demand. The others declined, an extralegal fact finding board was appointed, and a recommendation made that a union shop be granted if two-thirds of the employees voted in favor of it. Most of the companies accepted this proposal, but the employees stunned the unions by voting against compulsion. Lockheed refused to agree to a vote, and later settled with the Machinists also without a union shop after a Taft-Hartley injunction had ended a short strike.[2]

In 1968, the aerospace industry faced another IAM-UAW joint effort which again generated demands for large wage increases and the union shop. McDonnell-Douglas and Lockheed were the first to settle, with large wage increases, but the union shop demand was dropped. Later in that year, the UAW, already having left the AFL-CIO, denounced its no-raiding part with the IAM, and sought bargaining rights at the huge IAM-represented McDonnell plant in St. Louis. It would appear unlikely that IAM-UAW relations in aerospace would soon recover from this bitter fight.

UNION RATIONALE FOR COALITION BARGAINING

The Industrial Union Department (IUD), established when the AFL and CIO merged, and until 1968 headed and largely staffed by Walter Reuther, is the sponsor and coordinating agency for coalition bargaining. The former Executive Director of IUD, Jack T. Conway, a long-time Reuther aide, has repeatedly stressed the aims and purpose of coalition bargaining. In two sentences, for example, he summed up his rationale that corporate growth is the reason and coalitionism is the logical result:

> The best possible situation is one union per industry by mergers. But, with separate unions, we must come up with methods of dealing with the industrial giants in a coordinate effort.[3]

[2]For a history of this dispute, see Harold M. Levinson, *Determining Forces in Collective Wage Bargaining* (New York: John Wiley and Sons, Inc.), 1966, Chapter 2.

[3]Statement made by Jack T. Conway, former Executive Director of the AFL-CIO's Industrial Union Department (IUD) at an International Chemical Workers Union Collective Bargaining Conference, as reported in the *Daily Labor Report,* November 30, 1965, p. A-9. Conway resigned in June 1968, shortly after the UAW was suspended by the AFL-CIO.

Mr. Conway has also declared that the IUD is merely reacting to developments in American society which necessitate changes within the labor movement to maintain the best interest of the worker. He stated:

> . . . We created a new—and needed—instrument to meet these new conditions.
>
> These new conditions have not been of our making, and it is not necessary for me here to speculate with you about the reason they have arisen. But we are all aware of the drastic change that has taken place in industry with the growth of industrial conglomerations. There may be some rationale for the Columbia Broadcasting System to own the New York Yankees. There might be some slight basis for International Telephone and Telegraph to own the American Broadcasting Company; even less for it to own Avis. But I am unable to find any valid reason why the meat packing firm of Armour should own the Baldwin Locomotive Company or why the soap maker, Procter and Gamble should make coffee.
>
> The reasons, as we all know, are financial rather than the outgrowth of a rationalizing of the industrial process. Technology is developing new products and firms in declining industries like textiles are reaching out into other industries in search of survival. Also, extended prosperity has provided more cash for corporations and their natural reaction is to look for profitable places to invest. Emphasis on research and development has led to a natural alliance of firms with new products and new ideas. Growth and bigness have become ends in themselves in the industrial world and the broader the range of corporate interests the more impressive are its financial statements.
>
> This merger and acquisition characteristic of industry is not new but the pace is accelerating. Between 1954 and 1958 there was an increase of 59 percent in the number of companies operating in more than one industry. In 1964 alone there were nearly 1,800 acquisitions —or business mergers—a gain of 21 percent in the span of a single year. This upward trend continued in 1965 and 1966.
>
> Obviously, this presents the labor movement with problems because the power to make decisions on the basic issues has been placed even further from the point at which the issue is generated. And no one union organization, as presently constituted, has the resources to join the issues at that level.[4]

[4]See Jack T. Conway and Woodrow L. Ginsburg, "The Extension of Collective Bargaining to New Fields," in the *Proceedings of the Nineteenth Annual Meeting*, Industrial Relations Research Association, San Francisco, California, December 1966, p. 304.

The reasoning of the architects of coalition bargaining then states that the growth of corporations in size and into different industries dictates a need for larger and more far-reaching unions to counter their moves. The labor movement has been in the past an association of unions held together in a federation by some general goals and ambitions. But, in many cases, dealings with employers have been conducted on a local basis with varying influence from the international union, and even less from the AFL-CIO. The IUD leadership has felt that the emergence of the multiplant, multi-industry corporation is forcing an amalgamation of the various competing unions within the labor movement to counter the extended powers of the corporation. In its official publication, the IUD states:

> Much of the labor movement is trying to "make do" from day to day with a structure fashioned decades ago and now fastened upon it by tradition and an inability to devise the means of meeting contemporary needs. The necessary evolution is not taking place fast enough so that the labor movement can carry out its mission effectively in a new and changing environment.
>
> There is no tax incentive to force unions into change, but change they must. They must take the time for deep self-analysis leading to self-improvement. There are many courses open to them, of which coordinated [coalition] bargaining is only one.
>
> The paramount consideration at this moment is for all of the labor movement to face reality and to move quickly and in so doing be able to perform its historic bargaining role in a world of change.[5]

Thus, the IUD has maintained that coalition bargaining is not the only answer to dealing with larger and more powerful employers possessing greater economic strength, but in the absence of union mergers, it is certainly the method which has been given the greatest amount of attention.

Why Strength is Needed

The IUD officials have repeatedly stated that the rise of conglomerate corporations, and of corporations that deal in more than industry has been the most important factor in bringing about a restructuring of

[5]See the article by Jack T. Conway in the January-February 1968 *Agenda* entitled "Coordinated Bargaining . . . 'Historical Necessity'." The IUD *Agenda* is the official monthly publication of the Industrial Union Department, AFL-CIO.

the collective bargaining programs on the part of the AFL-CIO unions. But why has this become "necessary"? The reason for this restructuring —the use of coalition bargaining—is simply an expedient method of increasing union bargaining strength.

The IUD leadership has stated that there are at least four distinct advantages to be gained by banding together in a coalition for purposes of collective bargaining:

> Coordinated collective bargaining is going to lead, I think, to a great growth in organizing because it provides, better than any index we have yet devised, a measure of where we need to shore up our strength for an effective confrontation with those in the private sector who make economic decisions that affect the lives of so many.
>
> The development of coordinated collective bargaining has made even more clear the need for the creative use of modern computers for handling contract and company data. I think that it was Professor [John T.] Dunlop who pointed out that while in the early days unions were more proficient than their opponents across the bargaining table in preparing their case, today they are lagging behind. That is a deficiency that I hope we can overcome, partly through the aid of the tool of electronic data processing.
>
> The growth of coordinated collective bargaining will do much to eliminate, or at any rate soften, some of the jurisdictional disputes which have sapped much of the strength of the labor movement and which have led to so much adverse publicity. It has directed the attention of our organizations from a struggle over the right to represent a limited number of workers to a struggle to increase the total number of union members. I know you will not misunderstand me if I liken our fight in the economic field to dividing up a pie of economic abundance instead of fighting over a pie of scarcity.
>
> And, finally, through coordinated [coalition] bargaining we are making it evident, once again, that the struggle at the bargaining table is a struggle on behalf of the entire labor movement, not just one particular segment of it. Where there is a basic issue at stake, both the labor movement and industry know that the entire resources and commitment of the labor movement will be involved.[6]

Although these four benefits may be gained by the labor movement as a whole, and by the unions participating in a coalition effort, it

[6]Conway, "The Extension of Collective Bargaining . . .", *op. cit.*, p. 303.

is patently clear that there is one central reason for coalition bargaining: to increase the union strength at the negotiating table. This is accomplished by using the threat of, and if necessary, the bringing about of a multiple plant strike if the employer faced with the coalition is unwilling to meet the demands promulgated by the united union front.

The Counsel of the IUD, in addressing the New York University Conference on Labor, stated one such justification for the use of coalition bargaining:

> In many situations, collective bargaining cannot operate effectively unless it is conducted on a multi-unit basis. For example, many national corporations have uniform pension or insurance plans covering employees in most or all of their plants. A union which represents only one small unit out of many covered by such a plan cannot expect to have an effective voice in determining what benefits the plan will provide. Only if all or a substantial number of units covered by the plan negotiate jointly on pensions and insurance can the employees, through their unions, play a meaningful role in determining what the plans will provide. . . .[7]

The IUD proponents stress, when discussing the topic of coalitionism with international and local union leaders, that something is to be gained by banding together that would be unattainable by the various unions acting independently. The IUD spokesmen cite various areas of "frustration" that may be causing problems within a local as well as other issues that have been sought but not received in negotiations. They intimate that these "frustrations" may be removed if local autonomy in bargaining is exchanged for a place in the more powerful coalition effort. Coalition bargaining is thus designed to increase the bargaining strength of the unions by proceeding under a united front and presenting identical demands of all locations.

THE DEVELOPMENT AND OPERATION OF AN IUD BARGAINING COMMITTEE

In order better to understand the manner in which the Industrial Union Department has conducted its program of coalition bargaining,

[7]Attorney Jerry D. Anker, together with David Feller, has been the chief architect of the IUD legal program to have coalition bargaining sanctioned by the NLRB and the Courts. See, for example, Jerry D. Anker, "Pattern Bargaining, Antitrust Laws and the National Labor Relations Act," in *Proceedings of New York University Nineteenth Annual Conference on Labor,* April 18, 1966, p. 101.

the organization, development and operation of a typical committee in dealing with a firm or an industry are examined in this section.[8]

IUD Committees

The key group for the purposes of coordinated bargaining is the committee, through which all activity transpires. Generally, the committee is made up of participating representatives of the local and national unions dealing with a multiplant, multiunion employer, but also the formation of industry committees is sometimes attempting to seek to tie together all of the firms within a broadly defined industry for the purpose of collective bargaining on a national-industry basis.

The 1965 "Agenda for Tomorrow," the official report of the Industrial Union Department, reported the existence of some 60 committees, an increase of 36 for the year; by July of 1966, the number had risen to 77, and in 1968 there were some 91 coordinating committees listed by the IUD, including six industry committees.[9] For purposes of classification and identification, the IUD lists the various committees according to the stage of information and bargaining in which they fall, beginning with "information service," then to "coordination of bargaining," and finally "national" or "pattern-making negotiations," which is the ultimate goal for all committees. So far, only one company, American Home Products, has publicly agreed to conduct company-wide negotiations on certain items through the coalition efforts of the IUD.

There are several other committees, however, that the IUD places in "national" category. Included among them are: American-Standard, Johns-Manville, 3M, Olin Mathieson, Union Carbide, Rohm and Haas, and the refractories industry. The reason given for the inclusion of these committees in such a grouping is that "significant progress has been noted toward the goal of national bargaining in each case."[10] Since the 1965 report was issued, however, several companies and one industry have been added to the "national" list. Wilson Sporting Goods, Armour, and the nonferrous metals industry have all been targets of coalition bargaining, with the result in the nonferrous industry being a strike that affected more than 90 percent of the industry for more than seven months.[11]

---

[8]Much of the material contained in this section was gathered in numerous personal interviews with IUD officials during the Summer and Fall of 1967.

[9]See Appendix A, which lists the various IUD-company committees.

[10]Interviews with IUD staff members, Summer 1967.

[11]See Chapter IX for discussion of the nonferrous situation.

Among the company committees listed as being in the stage of coordinated bargaining are: Robertshaw Controls, General Aniline & Film, and Harris Intertype. Although the distinction for purposes of listing may be subtle, or be even more subject to the aspiration level of the IUD coordinator, the main differentiating feature of the committees in the coordinating state is that information is being exchanged among the various negotiating units, and the meetings may be conducted in the presence of the Coordinator and/or members of the negotiating committees from other company locations. Generally, it would seem that committees are placed in this classification until the IUD senses some real degree of progress in dealing with the employer on a national basis.

The third type of committee is the most elementary one, and is simply a committee for information exchange among the various unions dealing with a company or an industry, with all information being channeled through the Industrial Union Department. Committees are held in this classification until the timing is proper for a move toward negotiations, until an adequate sales job has been completed, or until enough strength is amassed to make some other move. All committees begin at this stage, and some never progress beyond.

In all cases, the IUD has assigned various staff personnel to guide each committee carefully, and fully to document any significant event which occurs as a result of company or union activity. It maintains extensive files which are periodically updated, and the committee member unions are notified by letter of any activity in their area. Meetings are also a part of the regular communications system that the Department has established in order to aid the various local and national or international unions.

Establishment and Operations of the Committee

Although there does not seem to be a single pattern or model for the establishment and operation of a company or industry committee, all are handled in approximately the same manner, as diagrammed in Table 2–1. The general plan devised by the IUD is one that permits a great deal of flexibility for response to the unions and company or industry in question, and is one that gives the committee coordinator latitude in handling the situation as he sees fit, subject to review by the executives of the IUD and by the officials of the responsible international unions.

TABLE 2–1

ESTABLISHMENT AND OPERATION OF AN IUD COMMITTEE

Step	*Resulting Action*
1. Request for Assistance	Contract Analysis Financial and Corporate Analysis International and Local Notification
2. Informational Meeting	Presentation of Analysis Request Cooperation
3. Organize Sub-Committee	Further Analysis Prepare Preliminary Coalition Plans
4. Decision to Engage in Coalition Bargaining	Request Agreement on Unity Request Local Authorization Compile Uniform Bargaining Demands Establish Steering Committee Establish President's Committee
5. Begin Coalition Bargaining	
6. Begin National Bargaining	
7. Industry-wide Bargaining	

Source: Personal Interviews with IUD officials, Summer 1967.

Theoretically, all requests for services of the IUD must be initiated by one or more of the affiliated unions, either locally or at the international level. Furthermore, all official communication must be channeled through the internationals involved, and the locals must clear all matters with their respective parents before requesting or joining in IUD efforts at bargaining. When a local feels that it could benefit from some form of coordinated bargaining, a request is made to the IUD through the international (Step 2, Table 2–1). At that point, the IUD begins its preparatory work.

The research group begins to collect all available information regarding the company involved. This would include such items as annual reports, financial news letters, documents filed with the Department of Labor, and almost any publicly available documents relating to company activities, products, officers, finances, etc. Specifically, the IUD seeks information to provide a comprehensive bargaining guide for the participating affiliates. The document prepared contains a brief history of the company and its operations, growth, products, subsidiaries, foreign operations, markets, and size and ranking of the operation, both as a national manufacturer and as a measure of its market share in its own sphere of operations.[12]

Financial information compiled includes such items as total sales, with breakdowns where appropriate, growth figures, profits, and dividends, rates of return, cash flow, sales per employee, executive compensation, profit sharing, and any other measure that might be of benefit as a bargaining tool in seeking to extract extra gains for union members. The figures are calculated to emphasize the profits and other items which would tend to indicate that the worker is not receiving his "fair share" from a healthy corporation. For many union locals, this IUD report is the first compilation of such figures that has been made available to them.

Contract Analysis

As a critical part of the information assembly stage of committee development, and as long as a committee is in existence, the Collective Bargaining Section conducts a thorough program of contract analysis. The IUD considers a contract analysis and comparison the most vital bit of bargaining information that could be supplied to a committee for negotiating purposes. To facilitate this program, the IUD has amassed a large collection of current labor contracts. It considers it especially critical to obtain and to analyze each labor contract of a firm with which a committee is dealing, or plans to deal, in a coordinated effort.

To strengthen the contract analysis, the IUD experimented with a computer system for contract analysis and information storage. Essentially, the IUD was using an in-house program on rented machines to provide a highly efficient information retrieval system for bargaining

[12]The "Company Report" is the key document prepared by the IUD in the early stages of a coalition effort, and may vary in length from about five to more than 130 pages, as was the case in the nonferrous industry coalition.

preparation. As each contract was received, it was analyzed according to a form which, through some 200 entries, provides an extreme degree of flexibility in reporting; it made provision for analysis of nearly every conceivable type of standard contract clause, as well as for the inclusion of goals of the unions in the near future.

Once a contract was analyzed and classified, the information was coded and stored on magnetic tape along with similar data from contracts of more than 200 other employers. When retrieval was desired, it could be gained in any number of different ways. Some examples of printouts might be: the reconstruction of a single contract, a clause-by-clause comparison of all the contracts of a company or industry, comparison of wages or benefits in an industry or in a region, summaries, and tallies of almost any sort. If the IUD had fully developed its files, it could have had a flexible source of almost any type of information that might be gained through contract or wage and benefit comparisons. This would have been a very important bargaining tool for the unions.[13] This activity was suspended in 1968 because of the lack of funds caused by the defection of the United Automobile Workers.

Developing Participation

When sufficient information has been received and compiled at IUD headquarters, all interested locals are invited to an "informal get-together" in Washington, or some other convenient meeting place. The purpose of the first meeting is "merely to get acquainted." In attendance are representatives from as many locals as possible, the respective international representatives, and members of the IUD, including a committee coordinator, whose job is to guide the group to a successful end—national or pattern bargaining. Presentations are made by the members of the IUD staff regarding the various parts of the company report and contract analysis, laying special emphasis on profitability of the company and inequities between the various locals regarding wages, benefits or conditions. It is at this meeting that the critical issue of contract termination dates is examined, for therein lies a key to successful coalition bargaining. Additionally, the representatives to this meeting are encouraged to submit to the assembled committee special prob-

[13]See *Daily Labor Report,* June 23, 1967, p. 1.

lems, aims and goals of their particular local. From this, a certain group consensus can be precipitated to be used in future meetings. Apparently, no commitments are made nor are any definite plans formulated at the first committee meeting—unless it is the decision to band together as a committee for future action.

At a time when the IUD coordinator senses that a particular group is ready to work together in some concerted manner, he will invite them to enter into a coordinated bargaining agreement and form a steering committee. The formation decision is not one lightly made. The coordinator must take cognizance of the group's feelings, the degree of apparent cooperation and harmony, the willingness to maintain the necessary pressures upon the employer, and the timing of the move. Here too, timing is essential to the success of the coordinated bargaining effort. The coordinator seeks to congeal the committee at a time such that all procedures may be completed just prior to a date when a series of contracts expire within a short span of time, generally less than three months, and preferably with one or more of contracts to cover large plants or plants critical to the company's operation or profit.

By doing this, the IUD may be able to put added pressure to settle on the company in one or both of two ways. If the plant with the first expiration date is the more critical of those involved, the union can use the threat of a strike as bargaining leverage. The leverage can, however, be increased by letting the workers at the first plants continue production, without a contract, until the subsequent contracts expire.[14] At such a time as when the unions have enough plants working without a contract to call a particularly costly and crippling strike, enough bargaining strength may have been generated to form a pattern settlement. It may be possible, too, that the mere threat of a multiplant shutdown will be sufficient to gain a pattern settlement acceptable to all participating bargaining units. One of the key demands remains the insistence on coincidental contract expiration dates of coordinating units; for by doing so, the union bargaining power is enhanced considerably.

The benefits to the union derived from coalition bargaining at any point in time can be expected to be significantly greater on successive rounds of negotiations. Although the "foot-dragging" can bring about

---

[14]A vital part of the bargaining strategy calls for the union committee to continue meeting with the company in order to avoid any charge of refusal to bargain. Although "foot-dragging" occupies a major role in bargaining, no union official will admit that the delay is intentional or that a local is not prepared to settle.

pressure to settle, and can bring about a pattern settlement, it also allows for formal inclusion of common contractual termination dates. When several plants have been drawn into a common bargaining situation by action of the date mechanism, it becomes increasingly easy for the unions to include new bargaining units and thereby increase their power. At such time as it is possible to threaten a major multiplant strike, the bargaining strength is at its apex. From there, coalition is assured, probably irrevocably, for such a concession once given is not easily retrieved.

Authorizing and Staffing the Coalition

To continue discussion of the actual committee operation, it is necessary to return to the point where the coordinator feels that coalition formation is imminent. At such time, the coordinator announces his intention, seeks a consensus and binds such groups as are amenable to the idea. The next step is to gain formal authorization to engage in coalition bargaining by an affirmative vote of the local membership. Apparently this may be done on a formal or informal, democratic or dictatorial basis, according to the composition and tradition of the local unions, or the need to accomplish the results. The committee member unions then submit to an agreement that each will accept no contract, nor contract clause unless it is acceptable to *all* members of the committee. Occasionally, however, a local group may bolt from the group and sign an "inferior" contract without approval of the other members.

Upon receiving the authority to proceed with coalition bargaining by the locals and internationals which are in a position to engage in concerted action, the coordinator calls and prepares for a meeting whose purpose is dual: 1) to select a steering committee, and 2) to formulate specific bargaining goals. A third step is taken informally at this point as well: to have the president of each international union involved appoint himself or another officer of that international to a group known as the "President's Committee".[15] The steering committee is charged with the responsibility of sitting in on all negotiations of

[15]"When the time for bargaining coordination draws near, a president's committee is convened so that each president or his representative may be aware of, and in agreement with the overall approach. This last step was adopted by the IUD's Executive Board on Dec. 15, 1966, in an effort to avoid mistakes that have sometimes allowed promising situations to wither away. It has been shown that if coordinated bargaining is to achieve its greatest gains, the international unions' top leadership must make key policy, planning and strategy decisions." Source: AFL-CIO Executive Council Report to AFL-CIO Convention, *Daily Labor Report,* December 16, 1967, p. D-1.

the coalition group and of determining the pattern of bargaining to be pursued at each location. It is the president's committee, however, that decides whether or not a particular company offer will be accepted, what counteroffer is to be made, and in general sets policy for, and oversees the coalition's bargaining with the company.

The IUD coordinator is not officially a member of either the steering committee or the president's committee, and has no vote; nevertheless, in order to prevent any single local or international from gaining substantial or even total control of the group, it is the IUD coordinator who serves as chairman of the coalition committee. Thus, although the IUD directly represents no worker, is not elected nor certified by the rank and file, and holds no vote in a coalition bargaining committee, it does occupy a most critical and powerful place in the coalition structure.

The Key Demands

The IUD committees have centered their uniform demands around the following issues: pension plans, vacations, insurance of various types, and holidays. Several other demands are usually included—but they all have a common factor: ease of applicability on a companywide basis. Such matters as wages, work rules and conditions and related local items have not been included as uniform demands up to this point. It can be expected, however, that a situation such as now exists in either steel or automobiles is the goal: a comprehensive master contract that makes allowance for local issues to be negotiated in the form of supplemental local agreements.

The most elementary form of coordination employed by the IUD is that of merely maintaining information exchange among the participants during negotiations at a plant location. Additionally, the company may be faced with the IUD coordinator at negotiating sessions. His function is to present the IUD program to the company, then to report back to the members of the steering committee all significant developments. The power to accept or to reject company proposals in this sort of bargaining situation is somewhat clouded. In most cases the local committee claims full power and authority to negotiate to a settlement, contrary to the agreement entered into by the participating locals and international unions.

An outgrowth or expansion of this type of bargaining comes about when the IUD encourages and schedules "visitors" to sit in on negotiating sessions. These visitors are actually members of negotiating committees from other plant locations. In most cases to date, they have claimed to serve as "observers" to gain knowledge of the company strength, attitude, position and offers, in an effort to seek equal or better concessions, and to prevent company representatives from presenting different positions at various locations, a practice which the IUD claims to be quite common. The logical following step is to have the members of the steering committee become actual participants in the negotiations and official spokesmen for the local unions. To date, the IUD has had substantial industry opposition to this method of bargaining, but has had considerable support from the National Labor Relations Board, as will be noted in Chapter XI.

Techniques

In all cases of coalition bargaining, the principle is the same: to exercise the threat of companywide collective strength to obtain the best settlement possible. And in all cases the principal tool to pry out the settlement is the same: a common termination date for all company labor contracts. When the IUD amalgamates the strength of the entire work force of a company, or a substantial portion of it, by threatening to strike all or most of the company's operations, it has a powerful bargaining tool.

The matter of timing has been noted previously, but cannot be overemphasized, for it is the key to success of the union program. It is essential to initiate action when a number of contracts expire within a short space of time, preferably within a few months. If contracts permit, the union will refrain from reopening the contracts that expire first, until such a time as when several can be opened for renegotiation concurrently. If it is necessary to reopen on a given date, or if the company forces an opening, negotiations do begin, with some form of coordination apparent, either by having the steering committee and coordinator in attendance, or by coordination-communication with the IUD and the committee. The script then dictates that the negotiating committee continue to negotiate on all issues, with special emphasis on the IUD-committee demands, but fail to reach agreement on any issue without steering committee approval. And, approval is forthcoming only if the company offer can be used as a pattern in the future negotiations. More common is the practice of "foot-dragging", or just continuing to meet with company representatives, exchanging proposals and counter-proposals, discussing and rediscussing. The union committee attempts to stall by every means possible, stopping just short of anything that might bring "refusal to bargain" charges against it.

Although many unions have long held to a tradition of "no contract, no work," the IUD strategy directly contradicts the old and once-sacred practice. By working without a contract, while continuing negotiations, the locals who first became involved in bargaining are able to stall until they force the company into a situation where it is threatened by a multiplant walkout.

At such a time, the union coalition may be able to force the entire situation to a head. The preferred alternative from the labor standpoint would be to have the company agree to national bargaining—to sign a master contract covering demands of all participating locals. From there it could include other locals in the coalition and have the common terms extended. The IUD would also insist on a common contract expiration date in order to preserve and perpetuate the strong bargaining position it had achieved. Failing in a move to force national bargaining, however, would not mean failure of the effort. Through continued coordination and communication of whatever sort, the locals are in a position to know what has been offered at the various locations, and can then attempt to amalgamate offers and demands to gain pattern bargains. If possible, the unions hold out until identical offers are made at each location.

Again, a critical union demand lies in common contract termination date. For it is common termination that permits the union more easily to force coalition bargaining for the next round of negotiations.

Problems and Questions

In light of the "successes" of coalition bargaining as expressed in numerous press releases and union publications, and in view of the problems caused for employers faced with the coalition effort, it might seem that the IUD has managed to create an unassailable program. There are, however, chinks in the armor.

Although the number of committees of some sort has risen to a new high of over 90, there have been an undisclosed number of attempts to form company committees that proved unsuccessful. In some of these, the desire for local autonomy, especially in a situation dominated by a strong local in a field of weaker ones, has not permitted coordination. In other cases, it seemed to be impossible to reach any consensus as to demands, timing, leadership, and other phases of coordination. In still other cases, it was found that the local leadership was simply not interested in having the IUD do its bargaining for it, feeling that the company-union relationship was satisfactory to those involved, or that coalition bargaining would reduce the political power and prestige of the local leadership.

A second unexpected problem has also arisen for the IUD; that being the manner of holding a committee together for a second round of coordinated bargaining after a "successful" first round. It is claimed that in one situation, for example, that the IUD coordination was so successful in gaining concessions on major points, that there are no longer any issues significant enough to pull all of the locals together again for another coalition effort. Such a case, however, seems to be the exception rather than the rule.

Shifts in the Union Power Structure

The activity of the IUD in the areas of coalition bargaining would appear to effectuate certain fundamental changes in previously existing power balances in the union movement. When a local union agrees to bind itself to the IUD program, it necessarily cedes its own authority to reach agreement on any issue covered by the program to the steering committee or the president's committee. It cannot, in most cases, agree to settle without approval by those bodies, and has thereby given up a certain amount of local autonomy that it previously possessed.

The international union faces a similar dilemma. In some cases, it is forced to abandon goals and policies that it had previously held desirable, and is required to heed the wishes of the coalition as expressed by the president's committee. Thus, there is a second shift in the decision making center in all negotiations: from local to international, and from international to the coalition's president's committee.

Some international unions have responded to the challenge of the

IUD program by making changes in their constitutions or operating procedures to embrace better the concept of coalition bargaining. The International Chemical Workers Union, for example, has recently amended its constitution to make international ratification of each local contract a prerequisite for recognition by the parent body. It has altered its normal bargaining scheme to adapt to the IUD coalition efforts, and has voted a 25 cent per month increase in its strike fund to provide greater support to locals who strike in support of its programs.

When the general shift in the union power centers brought about by coalition bargaining is examined in conjunction with the established goals of the IUD, certain conclusions come to the fore. One is that when coalition bargaining is extended to its logical end—that of national bargaining—all local issues will be suppressed in deference to joint bargaining on common economic issues, and that treatment of local matters would be neglected, or contained in separate local negotiating sessions. The IUD counsel has referred to this problem by stating:

> Under the rule which has been suggested, [to force an employer to deal with the coalition] it may well be that multi-unit bargaining would be required on some issues, such as pensions and insurance, and unit-by-unit negotiation on other issues, such as seniority, work rules, or even wages. There is nothing unusual in this kind of dual bargaining approach. It is found today in a number of industries, most notably in basic steel, where some issues are negotiated on an industry basis, some on a company basis, and still others on a plant-by-plant basis.[16]

With such an approach, however, it is doubtful whether many other industries would be pleased with the prospect of letting the union take two separate "bites at the apple" while threatening an extended shutdown (as does the Steelworkers) at each negotiation. Even a plan of national and local contracts such as exist in the automobile industry has obvious limitations for industrial peace. Here, too, the unions get at least two chances to force concessions from the company and two chances to shut the company down. Failure to settle at either level in a coalition arrangement simply results in a multiple strike situation.

---

[16]Anker, *op. cit.*, p. 104.

Summary

The IUD summarizes its approach as follows:

> The answer [to dealing with multiplant corporations] lies in coordinated [coalition] bargaining. Recognizing that economic sanctions by a single unit or union are often no threat to the well-being of a conglomerate, affiliates and non-affiliates [of the IUD] alike have, in self-defense, been forced to band together to deal with these new giants. Abandoning whatever historic rivalries that may have existed, the unions join together through the Collective Bargaining Services Section's basic mechanism, the company committee to further their goals.[17]

It is through this mechanism that the IUD has been able to formulate a potent new weapon to use in dealing with, and extracting extra gains from employers of all sizes, whether conglomerates or simply multiplant, multiunion operations. The IUD bluntly states that one of its efforts "reduced one company's profits by tens of millions of dollars," and resulted in settlements that "ran substantially greater than had the coordinated effort not been made."[18]

The cost of coalitions have been great to some of the companies that have been faced directly as well as those which have been threatened. Although the immediate wage and benefit gains of the coalition unions have not been significantly higher than may have been expected under the traditional bargaining patterns, other short- and long-term costs have been assumed by the companies, such as costs of strikes, and the cost of dealing with a coalition at future negotiations when the unions are able to bargain for a number of units whose contracts expire within a short period of time, and are therefore able to exert greater bargaining leverage. But, the cost to the unions and the employees has also been substantial in terms of lost local autonomy and protracted strikes called solely because of the existence of a coalition and its demands.

How coalition bargaining works out in practice is best understood by a detailed examination of a number of bargaining situations where it has been attempted. This is done in the following eight chapters of this study.

[17]AFL-CIO Executive Council Report . . . , *Daily Labor Report,* December 6, 1967, p. D-1.
[18]*Ibid.*

Part Two

CASES IN COALITION BARGAINING

CHAPTER III

COALITION BARGAINING AT AMERICAN-STANDARD: AN EARLY TEST

The 1964–1965 case involving the American Radiator & Standard Sanitary Corporation (American-Standard) and several of the unions representing its employees provides an illustration of the manner in which the Industrial Union Department of the AFL-CIO (IUD) conducted early coalition programs. The case also serves to point up the results of one of the first legal tests of coalition bargaining *per se,* and one which provided a testing ground for the unions in applying the concept of coalitionism against a company that sought to maintain the established structure of collective bargaining.

THE COMPANY

The American Radiator & Standard Sanitary Corporation has long been a leading manufacturer of plumbing fixtures and of heating and air conditioning equipment, but in the recent past, the Company has broadened its operations to include the manufacture of plastics, air handling and heat transfer equipment, instrumentation and controls, and through the acquisition of the Mosler Safe Company, it entered still another field.[1] And, in 1968, the Company acquired the Westinghouse Air Brake Company.

In 1966, American-Standard employed an average of 15,200 people in the United States in addition to 21,900 in its foreign operations. That year, total sales were $569 million. Operations were carried on in 91 domestic plants and branches plus more than 35 foreign locations. What began as the merger of two firms producing plumbing and heating equipment in 1929 has thus grown into a corporation that now operates in many different areas. (See, for example, Table 3–1.)

TABLE 3–1

PRODUCTS OF AMERICAN RADIATOR & STANDARD SANITARY CORPORATION

Use	*Product Examples*
For homes	Plumbing, air conditioning, heating, water softeners, disposers.
For education, commercial, and institutional buildings	Air conditioning, heating and ventilating, plumbing, molded seat and desk components, nuclear reactors for teaching and research.
For public utility power plants	Fluid drives, mechanical draft blowers, heat exchangers and condensers, electrostatic and mechanical dust collectors.
For processing industries	Fluid drives centrifugal compressors, fans and blowers, dust collectors, controls, refrigeration units, heat exchangers, gauges, boilers, steam generators.

[1]Much of the information contained in this section may be found in Standard and Poor's, *Standard Corporation Descriptions,* pp. 6539–6541, June 12, 1967.

For other manufacturers	Controls, switches and instruments for aircraft, home appliances, the automotive industry, refrigeration and air conditioning components and controls, molded plastics, heat exchangers, merchant pig iron, contract research and development.
For government, defense and space agencies	Contract research, development and production in the fields of spacecraft attitude control, high temperature technology and related instrumentation, military and aerospace instruments, advanced metallurgy.

Source: Standard and Poor's, Inc., *Standard Corporation Descriptions,* June 12, 1967, pp. 6539–6541.
Note: This data does not include Westinghouse Air Brake.

The American-Standard corporate structure has for many years been established along divisional lines with each of the operating groups having a great deal of autonomy and freedom of operation. Each of these operating entities had been held responsible for its own policies and practices, including those dealing with employee and labor relations. It was not until after 1955 that a corporate labor relations group was established, and its responsibility was, and has continued to be, largely of an advisory nature.[2]

Bargaining History

With one significant exception, collective bargaining at American-Standard has been conducted on a local basis, with negotiations handled by local plant personnel acting with the advice of divisional staff representatives. The only exception to this principle is a group of six small locals of the International Brotherhood of Operative Potters (Potters) who bargain with the company for a single contract on a voluntary basis.[3] The Company also deals with the Standard Allied Trades Council at the Louisville plant on a joint basis, but the individual contracts arrived at concern only the employees of the various craft unions at this plant. (See Table 3–2.)

[2]Personal interview with Gerald F. Gamber, former Vice President, American Radiator & Standard Sanitary Corporation, New York, July 19, 1967. Mr. Gamber was active in the case before his retirement in December 1967.

[3]The exception to the local bargaining rule with the group of Potters Union locals which have been included in a multiple unit contract, reportedly to protect the locals from a possible raiding by the Teamsters Union.

In past bargaining, the United Steelworkers of America (USW) and the International Union of Automobile, Aerospace and Agricultural Implement Workers of America (UAW) which together represent more than 5,000 American-Standard employees took the lead in negotiating new plans and benefits. In fact, the strength of the Steelworkers was such that it was able to gain much of the USW pension plan—including the 13-week vacation—for its bargaining units. Many other pension plan features first gained by the Steelworkers in local bargaining were later extended by the Company to include all production employees on a plant-by-plant basis. Thus, gains made by one bargaining unit were made available in varying degrees to other groups while maintaining separate contracts. As a result, American-Standard in effect had one pension and insurance plan negotiated on a local follow-the-leader basis.

TABLE 3–2

AMERICAN-STANDARD
UNION REPRESENTATION

Plant Location	*Size of Bargaining Unit*	*Union*
Baltimore, Maryland	540	UAW
	80	IAM
Buffalo, New York	1,125	USW
Cincinnati, Ohio	700	USW
Columbus, Ohio	610	UAW
Dearborn, Michigan	1,430	UAW
Detroit, Michigan	670	UAW
Kewanee, Illinois	300	IBB
	115	MAW
Louisville, Kentucky	1,680	SATC (a)
Monson, Massachusetts	400	IAM
Potters, USA	1,600	BOP (b)
Richmond, California	115	IAM
Toronto, Ontario	170	BOP
	520	USW
Windsor, Ontario	84	UAW

(Employees: United States 9,365; Canada 774; Total 10,139)

Union abbreviation code:

BOP International Brotherhood of Operative Potters of the United States and Canada
IAM International Association of Machinists and Aerospace Workers
IBB International Brotherhood of Boilermakers, Iron Ship Builders, Blacksmiths, Forgers and Helpers
MAW International Molders and Allied Workers Union
SATC Standard Allied Trade Council
UAW International Union of United Automobile, Aerospace, Agricultural Implement Workers of America
USW United Steelworkers of America

(a) The Standard Allied Trades Council represents employees at the Louisville plant of the Plumbing and Heating Division through a council formed by the following 13 craft unions:

1. Bricklayers, Masons, and Plasterers' International Union of America, AFL-CIO.
2. The Enamelers' Union, Local No. 8, affiliated with the International Molders' and Allied Workers' Union, AFL-CIO.
3. Office Employees International Union, AFL-CIO.
4. Metal Polishers, Buffers, Platers, and Helpers' International Union, AFL-CIO.
5. International Brotherhood of Teamsters, Chauffeurs, Warehousemen and Helpers of America.
6. International Molders' and Allied Workers' Union, AFL-CIO.
7. International Brotherhood of Firemen and Oilers, AFL-CIO.
8. International Brotherhood of Electrical Workers, AFL-CIO.
9. United Association of Journeymen and Apprentices of the Plumbing and Pipe Fitting Industry of the United States and Canada, AFL-CIO.
10. International Association of Machinists, Local Lodge No. 681, AFL-CIO.
11. International Association of Machinists, Local Lodge No. 1344, AFL-CIO.
12. International Association of Machinists, Local Lodge No. 1390, AFL-CIO.
13. United Brotherhood of Carpenters and Joiners of America, AFL-CIO.

(b) The Potters contract in this case represents the employees at five separate locations that were combined by mutual consent.

Source: Labor-management agreements, the Industrial Union Department and Company documents.

It was apparently in 1960 that some of the locals commenced what was later to become an intensive effort at coalition bargaining. At that time, the Company had attempted to contain the unions in their demands, and twice tried to break away from the patterns established by the steel industry which had been traditionally carried over by the USW to the American-Standard plants. Thus the Company was attempting to localize bargaining even more, while the unions were pushing for a wider bargaining structure.

THE ATTEMPT AT COALITION, 1964–1965

When the Collective Bargaining Services Section was established by the IUD in 1964 to develop the concept of "coordinated bargaining," the USW and the UAW, dominant at American-Standard, turned to the IUD for assistance in dealing with the Company. The IUD called a meeting of interested parties in Washington in June 1964. This gathering was actually the second called for the express purpose of discussing "coordinating action" against American-Standard. The first meeting was held in Detroit early in December 1963 at the request of the UAW local there.[4] It was decided by those attending that help should be sought from the IUD in order to strengthen the unions' position *vis-à-vis* the Company. The purpose of the IUD-sponsored meeting in June 1964 was:

> . . . to coordinate their efforts to get the feeling of the rest of them to see if they had the same feeling of frustration, if they could get together, coordinate our information and make one aware of what was happening in the other plant.[5]

The first IUD-sponsored meeting in Washington was attended by some 31 delegates from the IUD, Machinists, Boilermakers, Auto Workers, Steelworkers, Teamsters, and the SATC. Although the original purpose of the meeting was to "coordinate efforts," it soon became evident that other goals were formulated for pursuit by the unions.

In a letter mailed to those attending the meeting, the Coordinator assigned to the "IUD-American Radiator and Standard Sanitary Corpo-

---

[4]See for example "Respondent's Brief for Board," August 27, 1965, *American Radiator & Standard Allied Trades Council,* 155 NLRB No. 69, p. 6.

[5]*Ibid.,* p. 7.

ration Committee Unions," Don Doherty, summarized in report form, the actions taken by those attending the meeting.[6] The bargaining strategy that was adopted soon became evident to the Company. It also was apparent to both sides that the controversy could develop into one of the first legal tests of coalition bargaining before the Board and before the Courts.

The Bargaining Strategy

The first procedural bargaining step agreed to by the Washington group meeting was to make formal request, through the international union presidents, for the Company to meet with representatives of the group for the purpose of joint negotiation of a company-wide pension plan.

A second step to be followed if the Company refused to meet on a national basis was to be the presentation of union demands at all locations which had pension reopeners in 1964. In order to strengthen the position of uniform pension demands, the Committee also decided that negotiations would be "coordinated" through the IUD and a "steering committee"[7] whose job would be to sit in on negotiations to ensure that common goals would be reached[8] with regard to the specific list of fourteen pension plan improvements.[9]

As a final binding and strengthening step, the committee agreed that:

> It was the unanimous decision of the delegates that no local union should agree to any changes in the Pension Plan until they are agreed to by the Steering Committee.[10]

Thus it is apparent that the committee members in fact agreed to cede negotiating responsibility in the area of pensions to the Steering Committee which was composed of representatives of the various unions

---

[6]See "Trial Examiner's Decision," August 6, 1965, in *American Radiator & Standard Sanitary Corporation and Standard Allied Trades Council,* Case 155 NLRB No. 69. Also "Charging Party's Brief Before the Board," in *ibid.,* September 15, 1967.

[7]See "Report of Meeting of the IUD Committee" of *The American Radiator & Standard Sanitary Corporation,* prepared by Don Doherty, Coordinator, IUD. Undated but following the meeting of June 11–12, 1964.

[8]"Brief for Petitioner," *American Radiator & Standard Sanitary Corporation* v. *National Labor Relations Board,* Circuit Court of Appeals, Sixth Circuit, August 8, 1967.

[9]See "Report of the Meeting . . . ," *op. cit.,* pp. 1–2.

[10]"Report of the Meeting . . . ," p. 3. Also "Brief for the National Labor Relations Board," *American Radiator & Standard Sanitary Corporation* v. *National Labor Relations Board,* February 1966, p. 4.

represented in the coalition,[11] and which was supposed to attend all negotiating sessions with the Company.

The Coalition in Action

During July and August 1964, the members of the American-Standard coalition group attempted to complete the first step toward achieving a single pension agreement when the presidents of the international unions of the group sent substantially identical letters to the Company President, J. A. Grazier stating that:

> . . . we notify you that our American Radiator and Standard Sanitary Corporation local unions desire to negotiate changes in their pension plans through a newly created national coordinating committee made up of representatives of the International Association of Machinists, the International Brotherhood of Boilermakers and Blacksmiths, the United Automobile Workers of America, the United Steelworkers of America, the International Brotherhood of Teamsters, and the Standard Allied Trades Council.
>
> * * *
>
> We hereby request the American Radiator and Standard Sanitary Corporation to meet and confer with the American Radiator and Standard Sanitary Corporation, National Coordinating Committee representing local unions at your plants which are affiliated with the aforementioned International Unions at a time and place mutually agreeable for the purpose of negotiating changes in the Company's pension plan.[12]

American-Standard declined all of the requests made by the internationals for such joint bargaining. The answer sent by the Company Vice-President to the IAM is typical and stated:

> We cannot comply with your request to meet and confer with a group not legally certified as collective bargaining representatives for employees. It is our intention to abide by the terms of agreements made with certified representatives, and we will meet with IAM representatives to negotiate changes in the American-Standard Non-Contributory

---

[11]The Steering Committee, as appointed by the various groups consisted of: A Machinist local committeeman, a Boilermaker's local president, a UAW international representative and a sub-regional director, a Teamsters economist, and the president of the Louisville SATC.

[12]Letter to J. A. Grazier, President, American-Standard, New York, July 6, 1964 from James R. Hoffa, President, International Brotherhood of Teamsters.

Pension Plan in accordance with terms of pension agreements now in effect.[13]

Because of the rejection of the first coalition move by the Company, the IUD and the American-Standard Committee began to implement the alternative plan: preparing for coalition bargaining. The first of the union pension agreements to terminate was that with the SATC at the Louisville Plumbing and Heating Division plant which had an expiration date of November 30, 1964.[14] The representative of the SATC at a meeting received a report from the IUD meeting and adopted a motion "to invite the National Steering Committee to participate in the Louisville negotiations."[15] Although the Steering Committee was "invited to participate," its members were not designated to serve as part of the Louisville bargaining committee, and were not specifically authorized to sit in on negotiations. Also, there is no evidence that any of the local unions that comprise the SATC ever passed a resolution or had a vote designating members of the IUD Steering Committee as bargaining representative for the employees; nor apparently was any vote conducted among any of the rank and file to see whether it desired to have the IUD bargain for it, nor to see if the employees were willing to support the program evolved by the committee.[16]

When the first negotiating meeting was opened at Louisville on September 22, 1964, the plant representatives of the Company found that there were a number of "persons other than delegates and members of the SATC present."[17] When several of these people were asked to introduce themselves, and later sign a roster, several indicated that they were from other plants and that they were representing these plants. (Table 3–3) When the Company objected to the presence of the "outsiders" and suggested a separate caucus room for them, the local president indicated that the others "were on the Negotiating Committee," and asked if the Company was refusing to bargain.[18]

---

[13]"Brief for Petitioner," *op. cit.*, p. 7.
[14]"Trial Examiner's Decision," *op. cit.*, p. 3.
[15]"Brief for the National Labor Relations Board," *op. cit.*, p. 5.
[16]"Respondent's Brief for Board," *op. cit.*, p. 12.
[17]"Brief for Standard Allied Trades Council," Intervenor, Sixth Circuit Court of Appeals, *American Radiator & Standard Sanitary Corporation* v. *National Labor Relations Board*, p. 5.
[18]"Respondent's Brief for Board," *op. cit.*, p. 14.

TABLE 3–3

UNION NEGOTIATING COMMITTEE IDENTIFICATION

When a roster was passed around the table for signature by those in attendance at the request of the Company negotiator, some 26 signatures were appended by the representatives on the Union's side, including the following entries:

Name	*Title*	*Representing*
Don Doherty	Coordinator, IUD	SATC
Chester Nichel	Kewanee Plant	IBB
Frank W. Braver	Det.	UAW 254
Henry Sommerfeld	Det.	UAW-254 President

Source: "Trial Examiners Decision," *American Radiator and Standard Sanitary Corporation*, 155 NLRB 69.

It was further stated by the union that IUD Coordinator Don Doherty would be the spokesman for the SATC on pensions at Louisville and the other plants where negotiations would be held. The unions also stated that "they were there to negotiate a national package."[19] When it became obvious to the Company negotiators that the "outsiders" would not leave the room, the meeting was adjourned.[20]

When negotiating sessions were opened at each of the other American-Standard plants in the coalition group,[21] the Company faced essentially identical situations: the local union bargaining committee was augmented by the IUD Coordinator and one or more other union representatives from other local and international unions that held bargaining rights at other American-Standard plants. In each case, the union committee presented the same set of pension demands that had been drafted by the IUD committee in its meetings; the local unions apparently had no voice in this matter at all.

In each instance, the Company refused to meet with the expanded committees, objecting to the fact that bargaining was to be done by representatives of unions not legally certified to represent the employees of the plant involved. Bargaining was suspended while the Company

[19]"Respondent's Brief to Board," *op. cit.*, p. 14. See also "Trial Examiner's Decision," p. 4.
[20]"Brief for Standard Allied Trades Council," *op. cit.*, p. 6.
[21]*Viz:* Dearborn, November 23; Detroit, December 14; and Columbus, December 29, 1964.

was considering its legal position. Eventually, however, meetings were reconvened when the parties agreed to sign a letter of "protest" which stated that the Company would meet with outsiders present, but that such bargaining would not prejudice the Company's position in unfair labor practice charges filed by the unions with the National Labor Relations Board (NLRB) in regard to the Louisville negotiations.

Following the adjournment of the September 22nd meeting at Louisville, the Union made no further requests for negotiating meetings until October 27th, more than one month later, when it sent a telegram to the Company president asking for the resumption of negotiations at Louisville, and implying that discussions had been, and would be confined to that location.[22] In an attempt to ascertain the full meaning of the Union telegram, and to reaffirm the Company willingness to bargain for Louisville at Louisville, a telegram asking if "your [SATC] telegram means that you are requesting a meeting with only such representatives [Louisville] in attendance."[23]

The union again stated its willingness to negotiate a pension plan exclusively for the Louisville unit, but still held the position that it had the right to choose its own negotiating committee.[24] The Company countered, in a letter, that it did not challenge the union's right to select its bargaining committee, but noted that negotiations had always been private, and closed to outsiders. The letter further suggested that bar-

[22]The telegram from Robert Aubrey, SATC to American-Standard President Grazier, October 27, 1964 stated:

> This will also reaffirm what was stated by myself in our meeting of September 22nd, 1964 and that is the Standard Allied Trades Council is only negotiating pensions for the employees at the Louisville plant of American Radiator and Standard Sanitary Corporation.

[23]The telegram from American-Standard Vice President G. F. Gamber, October 28, 1964 to SATC read:

> In reference to your telegram of October 27, 1964 to Mr. J. A. Grazier, Louisville plant management representatives are more than ready now as they have always been to meet with the appropriate certified bargaining representatives of the Louisville plant employees on pension negotiations exclusively with respect to the Louisville Plant. Please advise if your telegram means that you are requesting a meeting with only such representatives in attendance. It had been my understanding that your position in the meeting of September 22, 1964 was somewhat different than is stated in your telegram.

[24]Aubrey's letter to Gamber, November 6, 1964 reads as follows:

> The Standard Allied Trades Council which is the Certified Bargaining Representative for the Louisville Plant employees, is willing now and as we stated on November [sic] 22, 1964 to negotiate on pensions exclusively with respect to the Louisville Plant. If you have any other understanding of our position, other than this, then you are misinformed.
>
> As far as who will be in attendance at these negotiations, it is still our position that we retain the right to select our negotiating committee for such negotiations.
>
> We are ready to meet for these negotiations with enough advance notice to notify our full committee.
>
> Please answer this letter as soon as possible, for time is a matter of consequence.

gaining be resumed on the same basis as it had been in the past.[25] (This is the letter which the General Counsel of the NLRB later held to be a refusal to bargain in good faith.)

After the parties agreed to extend the pension agreement for an indefinite period, bargaining was not resumed until January 22, 1965, when a "consent" letter was signed at the Union suggestion which permitted negotiations to proceed "under protest," and without prejudice to the case before the Board.

The meetings continued at Louisville and at the other locations until and after the Board hearings when agreement was finally reached that did bring improvements in the company-wide pension plan and other economic benefits,[26] in addition to giving the unions contract termination dates at the various plants which will facilitate a repetition

---

[25]Emphasis supplied by Sixth Circuit:

What was the basis of the complaint was a letter dated November 10, 1964, by American Radiator to the president of SATC which attempted to move forward with negotiations without waiting for Board resolution of the charges made by SATC relating to the September 22 meeting. The letter follows:

"Dear Mr. Aubrey:

"Mr. Gamber has asked me to answer your letter to him dated November 6, 1964.

"*We have never contested your right to select the members of your negotiating committee for negotiations or any other collective bargaining purpose.* Our negotiations, however, involve only the Louisville Bargaining Unit. They are private negotiations and have never been open to the public or to outsiders from other bargaining units outside Louisville.

"As you know, an unfair labor practice proceeding is now pending before the NLRB filed by your Union against our Company testing the rights of these outsiders to attend Louisville negotiations meetings. (Case No. 9-CA-3332) *May we suggest that while this matter is being decided, we continue negotiations on the same basis as in the past years, without the outsiders being present.* If it is finally determined in the NLRB proceedings that these outsiders have a right to be present, we must, of course, follow the law and so determine that they can resume attendance at the meetings under such conditions as may be set in the ruling.

"*This proposal will enable negotiations to resume immediately and we hope will result in an early and peaceful settlement of outstanding issues relating to the Pension Program.*

"*Please let us hear from you after you have given this matter consideration.*

"Very sincerely,
/s/ "H. J. Brown
H. J. Brown, Manager
Industrial Relations."

[26]See letter from Don Doherty, Coordinator, Collective Bargaining Section, IUD to American Radiator & Standard Sanitary Committee, April 7, 1965. This letter also states in part:

(1) The primary purpose of this round of coordinated bargaining was to improve the company-wide pension plan—this has been done and a pattern established which can be followed by the remaining unions throughout the company.

(2) The local unions which joined together in coordinated bargaining should stand together so that no individual local would be left on a limb. This too has been done and every local union was afforded the opportunity to have a signed agreement prior to the other locals relinquishing the coordinated bargaining.

(3) Efforts should be made so that further improvements in "company-wide policy items" could be made through coordinated bargaining in the future—this too has been done because the improvements in the pension plan serve as a concrete example of what can be achieved through coordinated bargaining.

of such coalition activity when the pension plan next opens for negotiation.

LEGAL ACTIVITIES

When the Company refused to meet with the union committee at Louisville because of the presence both of union representatives from other plants and of the IUD, the SATC filed refusal to bargain charges under Section 8 (a) of the National Labor Relations Act. While in the process of investigating the complaint, the General Counsel of the Board found no merit in the charge that the Company had refused to bargain in good faith at the September 22 meeting, but did charge that the Company letter of November tenth which stated the American-Standard position with regard to negotiating in the presence of outsiders was a failure to bargain. The General Counsel cited no other specific instance in which the Company was to be charged with an unfair labor practice.[27]

It was further the position of the unions and of the General Counsel that, other evidence notwithstanding, the two occasions on which the unions indicated a willingness to negotiate exclusively for a settlement at Louisville, meant that the IUD Committee had unequivocally dropped its demand for a national package. Testimony was presented by American-Standard to refute such claims: in no case did the unions specifically disavow the coalition demand for national bargaining; and in several instances, negotiators at various locations repeated that the demands had not been changed.[28]

The Trial Examiner held that the wording and the intent of the letter was such as to indicate that the Company had failed to bargain in good faith with the SATC and whomever it chose to sit at the negotiating table. In his decision, Examiner Downing states:

> There is no issue concerning the appropriateness of the single [Louisville] plant unit . . . , nor concerning the SATC's representative status therein. The central issue is whether Respondent [American-Standard] could properly refuse to meet and negotiate with the Union because of the presence of advisors and experts selected by the Union from its affiliated and international bodies, including persons from the Indus-

[27]See "Brief for the National Labor Relations Board," *op. cit.*, pp. 2, 12.
[28]"Respondent's Brief for Board," *op. cit.*, pp. 29–39.

trial Union Department of AFL-CIO and representatives of unions at Respondent's plants other than at Louisville. Further issues concern Respondent's defense of conspiracy and its contention that the Union itself was not bargaining in good faith.[29]

The various briefs and defenses filed by the Company pointed specifically to the "further" issues noted briefly by the Trial Examiner, namely, that the SATC was not free and able to agree to changes in the Pension Plan because of the existence of the coalition and its requirement that any offer be approved by the Steering Committee. The Company presented evidence to demonstrate that the unions were not free to settle and were, in fact, still attempting to force joint bargaining on the pension issue.[30]

The Trial Examiner dismissed the American-Standard contentions by noting:

> . . . the evidence did not establish that the Union was a party to any "plot" or "conspiracy" to force Respondent against its will in company-wide bargaining. It is true (as the Union concedes) that the unions represented on the Steering Committee adopted a common set of proposals on pensions and that their ultimate objective was to arrive at uniform agreements at each plant. But once Respondent rejected the unions' request to negotiate on a multiplant basis, SATC sought to achieve its objective through negotiations confined exclusively to the Louisville plant.
>
> * * *
>
> It is to be noted, of course, that the merits of company-wide bargaining or of a uniform pension plan are not before us and that it is immaterial whether they may be good or bad, desirable or undesirable. For whatever Respondent's reasons, it was free to bargain or not, as it chose, on matters which were without the scope of mandatory subjects of bargaining. . . . And though the Union could lawfully seek to persuade Respondent to the type of bargaining which it requested, it could not (as the General Council concedes) engage in restraining or coercive conduct or threat of such conduct to enforce its request.[31]

The Examiner concluded that American-Standard refused to bargain by its letter of November 10, and that it should then be ordered to

[29] "Trial Examiner's Decision," *op. cit.*, p. 2.
[30] See, for example, "Brief for Petitioner," *op. cit.*, pp. 3–67.
[31] "Trial Examiner's Decision," *op. cit.*, p. 11.

bargain with the Union and whatever committee it chose. The Board upheld the Trial Examiner.[32]

When the matter was carried to the Sixth Circuit Court of Appeals, the Court concluded simply that the Board had had no evidence to support the charge. Judge O'Sullivan stated in his opinion:

> The allegedly guilty conduct of the company consisted merely of writing a letter suggesting to the union a mechanism which would allow negotiations to continue; it asked for the union's consideration of the suggestion. In our view this does not add up to a refusal to bargain, violative of Sections 8(a) (1) and (5).[33]

Thus a case that gave early promise for a test of the theory and practice of coalition bargaining was decided with little or no statement relevant to any issues of coalitionism.

Analysis

This early test of the unions' strength in bringing about coalition bargaining may be regarded by the IUD as a victory of sorts. It was not able to gain legal support for its "outsiders" in a negotiating session, nor was it denied that support. The question of whether the unions may band together and be bound not to settle without approval by a Steering Committee was also not answered.

The IUD effort did result in twelve specific improvements in the pension plan on a national basis, although a single contract was not gained, and the stage was set for repeated coalition efforts in future negotiations. The IUD was successful in reaching full agreement at any location, working on an extended contract until the threat of a multi-plant work stoppage was able to bring sufficient pressure on the Company to settle.

When American-Standard began bargaining with the coalition unions for the second time, a decision had not yet been rendered by the Sixth Circuit, and the legal status of "outsiders" was thus unclear. The Company, however, sought to minimize the effect of the unions, and agreed only to meet with the group "under protest." Although Ameri-

---

[32]*American Radiator & Standard Sanitary Corporation* and *Standard Allied Trades Council,* 155 NLRB No. 69.

[33]*American Radiator & Standard Sanitary Corporation* v. *NLRB,* 65 LRRM 3071, August 8, 1967.

can-Standard endeavored to persuade each union to complete negotiations with respect to pensions, as the pension agreements expired at that particular location, but apparently was not willing to lock out the employees or pressure a union into a strike situation in order to force the issue.

The practical effect, then, of the foregoing is that at five locations at least, the Company has a uniform pension plan, although there are five separate pension agreements, all of which have the same termination date.

CHAPTER IV

COALITION BARGAINING AT JOHNS-MANVILLE: THE IMPACT OF REPEATED ATTEMPTS

The experience of Johns-Manville (J-M) with coalition bargaining is of special interest in several respects: (1) the roots of early attempts at joint bargaining with the Company go back as far as 1945 when two locals banded together to seek some common contractual terms; (2) the Company has been through several "successful" rounds of coordinated or coalition bargaining as evaluated by the unions; (3) the Industrial Union Department, AFL-CIO (IUD) is attempting to expand the scope of activity in the bargaining arena by including the job evaluation and incentive programs of the Company in its area of expertise. It has already sponsored a school for J-M local union officials to acquaint them with the principles of Industrial Engineering and with the J-M system in particular.

These factors as well as others pertinent to the development of coalition bargaining at Johns-Manville are discussed below.

THE COMPANY

The Johns-Manville Corporation was incorporated in New York in 1925 to take over the assets of the H. W. Johns Manufacturing Company of New York and the Manville Covering Company of Milwaukee which were founded in 1858 and 1886, respectively.[1] The Company has continued to grow through expansion and acquisition to the point where it is now "the largest American manufacturer of products made from asbestos, magnesia, and diatomaceous earth."[2] The output of the Company covers more than 100 product lines that include: roofing materials, insulation products, building materials, brake linings, clutch facings, acoustical materials, asbestos-cement pipe, bridge construction materials, asbestos fiber, materials for the electrical industry, diatomaceous earth for inert filters, glass fiber yarns and mats, insulation, flooring materials, and a host of others.[3]

The Company currently employs 21,500 persons and operates nearly 50 plants and mines in the United States and Canada (see Table 4–1). J-M recorded net sales of more than $512 million in 1966 with a net income of more than $38 million.[4] In 1966 J-M dealt with some 19 different international unions which represent most of its production employees.

TABLE 4–1

JOHNS-MANVILLE CORPORATION
PLANT LOCATIONS AND ORGANIZATIONAL STATUS

Alexandria, Ind.	UPP	Rock wool and allied products
Antonito, Colo.	IBT	Perlite
Chicago, Ill.	OCAW	Electrical tapes, adhesives, rubber tapes and cements
Chillicothe, Ohio	URW	Asphalt and vinyl floor tile
Cleburne, Texas	GBBA	Fiber glass insulation
Cleveland, Ohio	OCAW	Asphalt roofing and shingles
Coalinga, Calif.	IUOE	Crude asbestos
Corona, Calif.	GBBA	Fiber glass insulation, acoustical panels

[1]Standard and Poor's, *Standard Corporation Descriptions,* July 31, 1967, p. 7253.
[2]Standard and Poor's, *op. cit.*, p. 7252.
[3]*Ibid.*
[4]*Ibid.*, p. 7254.

Defiance, Ohio	GBBA	Fiber glass insulation, acoustical panels
Denison, Texas	IAM	Asbestos-cement pipe
Florence, Colo.	IBT	Gypsum products
Fort Worth, Texas	UPP IBT	Rag felt, asphalt roofing
Franklin, Pa.	-	Extruded thermoplastic pipe
Green Cove Springs, Fla.	ICWU	Asbestos cement pipe
Hayward, Calif.	ILWU	Flooring
Houston, Texas	UMW	Reinforced fiberglass plastic panels
Jarratt, Va.	PSPMW IBFO IAM IBEW	Insulating board products
Joliet, Ill.	IAM	Nonmetallic minerals
Las Vegas, Nev.	IUOE	Gypsum products
Laurinburg, N.C.	-	Friction materials
Lawrence, Mass.	UMW	Melamite plastic laminates
Lompoc, Calif.	ICWU	Diatomaceous earth products
Long Beach, Calif.	ICWU	Industrial insulations, asbestos-cement pipe
Los Angeles, Calif.	UPP	Asphalt roofing, pipe line felts, coatings
Madison, Ill.	USW	Asphalt roofing and shingles
Manville, N.J.	UPP	Asbestos products, roofing and flooring materials, rockwool, pipe, etc.
Marrero, La.	OCAW	Asbestos-cement pipe, floor tile, shingles, roof cements, etc.
Marshville, N.C.	-	Packings and friction materials
Nashua, N.H.	UMW	Asbestos-cement products
Natchez, Miss.	IWA IAM	Insulating board, acoustical materials
New Orleans, La.	OCAW	Paper mill
North Brunswick, N.J.	FLU	Metallic gaskets
No Agua, N.M.	IBT	Perlite
North Billerica, Mass.	UMW	Lightweight fire-resistant asbestos board

TABLE 4–1

JOHNS-MANVILLE CORPORATION
PLANT LOCATIONS AND ORGANIZATIONAL STATUS
(Continued)

Parkersburg, W. Va.	UGCW IBEW	Fiber glass insulation, acoustical panels
Penbryn, N.J.	UE	Fiber glass insulation
Pittsburg, Calif.	IAM UPP	Asbestos products, roofing, shingles, paper mill
Richmond, Ind.	UAW	Fiber glass insulation, acoustical panels
Rockdale, Ill.	IAM	Perlite roof insulation
Savannah, Ga.	IAM	Asphalt roofing and shingles
South Gate, Calif.	PSPMW IBT	Gypsum products
Stockton, Calif.	IAM	Asbestos-cement pipe
Tilton, N.H.	UPP	Asbestos insulation
Waterville, Ohio	IBT	Glass fiber, fiber glass rovings
Waukegan, Ill.	ICWU	Asbestos products, roofing, friction materials insulations
Zelienople, Pa.	UBCW	Insulating brick, refractories, acoustical tile
Canada		
Advocate, Baie Verte	AWU	Asbestos mining
Asbestos, Que.	Syndicat	Mining and milling, asbestos products, insulation materials
North Bay, Ont.	PSPMW	Insulating board products
Port Credit, Ont.	ICWU	Warehouse
Reeves, Ont.	USW	Asbestos mining
Toronto, Ont.	ICWU IUOE	Mineral wool insulations, asbestos-cement pipe

Union Abbreviation Key

AWU —The Asbestos Workers Union
FLU —The American Federation of Labor—Congress of Industrial Organizations—Federal Labor Union
GBBA —Glass Bottle Blowers Association of the U.S. & Canada

IAM	—International Association of Machinists & Aerospace Workers
IBEW	—International Brotherhood of Electrical Workers
IBFO	—International Brotherhood of Firemen and Oilers
IBT	—International Brotherhood of Teamsters, Chauffeurs, Warehousemen and Helpers of America
ICWU	—International Chemical Workers Union
ILWU	—Warehouse, Processing & Allied Workers Union, International Longshoremen's & Warehousemen's Union
IUOE	—International Union of Operating Engineers
IWA	—International Woodworkers of America
OCAW	—Oil, Chemical & Atomic Workers International Union
PSPMW	—International Brotherhood of Pulp, Sulphite & Paper Mill Workers
Syndicat	—Syndicat National de l'Amiante d'Asbestos, Inc. & the Federation Nationale Des Employes De L'Industrie Miniere, Inc.
UMW	—International Union District 50, United Mine Workers of America
UPP	—United Papermakers and Paperworkers
URW	—United Rubber, Cork, Linoleum & Plastic Workers of America
USW	—United Steelworkers of America

Source: Johns-Manville Corporation, Labor Relations Department.

It is because of the diversity of the nature of the Company and its products, plus the existence of a union council—as will be seen below—that Johns-Manville became a prime target for the IUD in its drive to obtain coalition bargaining on a large scale.

The Move to Coalition

Johns-Manville has historically bargained on a local basis. Contracts with local unions have expired at various intervals, and cooperation among the various local unions, even those affiliated with the same international, has been relatively rare. Nevertheless, there have been local attempts for coalition bargaining prior to the recent IUD program.

Early Coalition Attempts

The earliest attempt at what was eventually to become coalition bargaining at Johns-Manville came to light in 1945 and 1946 when the

Manville, New Jersey, plant local of the United Papermakers and Paperworkers (UPP) and the Federal Labor Union local[5] at Waukegan, Illinois jointly announced that neither local would agree to any settlement which did not give each a general wage increase of at least 11.5 cents per hour, and further agreed, but did not announce that no settlement would be reached unless a union shop provision was included in the agreement.

The demand for the union shop was the real goal of this coalition which resulted in strikes at both locations at the same time. The goals of the unions were not satisfied at that time, and both strikes were eventually settled on terms approximating those offered earlier by the company.[6]

Following the union's failure at Waukegan and Manville in 1945–1946, there is little evidence of any sort of concerted union activity until the early fifties when an informal agreement was reached by four locals of the International Chemical Workers Union (ICWU or Chemical Workers) which called for each plant local to settle for "a uniform wage offer, a union shop, and other contractual language, particularly in the area as it related to the words 'best qualified.' "[7] Apparently, this agreement was never put into practice.

In 1955, a coalition relationship was established between two UPP locals and the Marrero, Louisiana, Oil Chemical and Atomic Workers (OCAW) local, but was quickly dissolved when the UPP locals signed contracts on time or ahead of schedule, without waiting for the Marrero local to act.[8]

Further attempts were made by the OCAW to bring about a coalition through a special call to J-M locals of all international unions for committee meetings at its International Convention in St. Louis during August 1956. No locals of other internationals responded.[9]

Despite these failures, the International Chemical Workers Union

---

[5]Memorandum from R. M. King, General Headquarters, Johns-Manville, January 18, 1965. See also *"Case Study* Johns-Manville." Industrial Union Department, AFL-CIO. Distributed June 28–29, 1967 at Collective Bargaining Conference, Statler-Hilton Hotel, Washington, D.C. The Federal Labor Local later became Local Number 60 of the International Chemical Workers Union.

[6]Personal interview with Johns-Manville Company officials, August 1967. New York, New York.

[7]King Memorandum, *op. cit.*, p. 1. It will be seen that many of the current goals of coalition bargaining are not at all different from those espoused in 1952. The locals included in that effort were: Lompoc, California; Watson (since closed), Waukegan, Illinois; and Toronto, Ontario, Canada.

[8]*Ibid.* The UPP locals were Manville and Ft. Worth.

[9]*Ibid.*

sent invitations one month later to numerous J-M local unions to attend special meetings in Buffalo in connection with its International Convention.[10] In this case, success was more apparent: several locals sent representatives and formed what became the J-M Inter-Union Council, a body that continued to exist, exchange information, and meet informally with the company until October 7, 1965 when the Council formally became the IUD-Johns-Manville Committee under the direction of the Industrial Union Department.[11]

The Johns-Manville Inter-Union Council

At the September 1956 Convention of the ICWU, the J-M delegates not only met with the purpose of exchanging information that would be of benefit in bargaining with the Company but also adopted a set of procedures and bylaws to govern the Council. In addition, several separate committees were established to deal with specific bargaining objectives.[12]

A second meeting of the J-M Council was held in January 1957 in St. Louis where additional action was taken. Here, a company-wide bargaining program was adopted that included uniform improvements in sick leave, vacations, company paid insurance, retirement, and a union shop provision. The group attempted to implement its goals through use of tactics which have become common tools of coalition bargaining: delay and failure to agree on terms so that several local agreements could be terminated at one time; stressing of different demands at different locations; frequent and detailed communication among locals during negotiations; and complete information exchange when agreements were finally consummated. It was at this time that the Company first received formal demands from local union officers for Company-wide negotiations regarding changes in the Johns-Manville retirement plan.[13]

---

[10]*Ibid.*, p. 2. Responding plants were: Lompoc, Dutch Brand, Long Beach, Waukegan, Toronto, Nachez, Marrero and Manville.

[11]Letter from Don Doherty, Coordinator, Collective Bargaining Section, Industrial Union Department, AFL-CIO to IUD-Johns-Manville Committee, February 3, 1966. This letter summarizes the results of the October 7 meeting of the J-M Council at the Disneyland Hotel in Anaheim, California.

[12]See note 5, above.

[13]*Ibid.* In each case, the demand for company-wide bargaining came from the local president to Mr. A. R. Fisher, President of Johns-Manville. To each of the five (Alexandria, Indiana; Marrero; Ft. Worth; Asbestos, Quebec, and Long Beach) the Company responded similarly: "that individual plant locations have the responsibility and the authority to bargain on all matters relating to the Labor Agreement as well as to fringe benefits." From King memorandum, p. 3.

The Council continued to meet at intervals—at least once each year—for the purpose of information exchange and to discuss mutual problems. It would appear that the unions made little in the way of gains from the company and that the meetings served largely as information exchanges and social outlets. When the J-M Council held a meeting in San Francisco on December 1 and 2, 1962, however, there was a noticeable change in tempo and in the mood of the delegates. Delegates of the eight plants represented agreed that added emphasis should be placed on certain bargaining goals, and that the IUD should be called on for expertise in the areas of job evaluation, incentives, and retirement.[14] It was at this time that Don Doherty, then on loan to the IUD from the Chemical Workers, began appearing at J-M negotiations for the purpose of assisting locals in the benefits area.

The IUD Provides Leadership

The Industrial Union Department reacted quickly to the call for assistance from the Council. When a meeting was held in Washington in April 1964, thirty-five people were in attendance, including eleven from the staffs of various internationals, and five from the IUD staff.[15] The IUD was well prepared for this meeting, and was able to make an impressive presentation to those attending, both local and international. Information was presented regarding plant location, size, product, and organizational status, Company financial information, and a survey of the various collective bargaining agreements.[16]

The interest shown by the IUD in the activities of the J-M Council created a new spirit of enthusiasm among the members. Among the items which were of particular interest to the locals were demands for improvements in the retirement plan, for Company payment of 100 percent of all insurance plans, for a ninth holiday, improved vacation plans, and a union shop at all locations. In those states where "right-to-work" laws are in existence, the locals were urged to bargain for a clause that would become operative should these laws be repealed or superseded.[17]

---

[14]King memorandum, p. 5.

[15]IUD memorandum entitled "Attendance at the IUD-Johns-Manville Committee Meeting at Washington, D.C., April 16 and 17, 1964."

[16]See materials distributed to delegates, mimeographed; and memoranda to locals following the meeting. It should be noted that such a presentation has become routine when the IUD is attempting to organize a new committee, but the J-M case was one of the first of its kind.

[17]King memorandum, p. 5.

Another outgrowth of that meeting was that the IUD made Mr. Doherty available to any local that requested his assistance. Thus, by sponsoring and designing the meeting of the J-M Council, the IUD began to assume leadership of the group, and by making a coordinator available, it began to assure itself of continuing leadership.

The IUD Agreement

In order to bind the locals of the Council more securely, and to strengthen the collective bargaining program as drawn up by the IUD for the meeting, the IUD sponsored and received approval of a policy for strike assistance for any local which became involved in a work stoppage in support of the Council program. Among the outstanding provisions of the program were:

a. Each local should vote to send strike assistance as designated by the Committee in the amount of at least one dollar per month for each member in their local *to any local which strikes in support of the Council program.*
b. Such strike assistance to be sent directly to the local on strike.
c. The strike assistance to be sent as designated by the following committee:
    1. The Council secretary[18]
    2. The International Union Coordinator of the striking local
    3. The IUD Coordinator
d. All locals to adopt this program at once and certify this adoption to the Council secretary.[19]

In September 1964 at a meeting in Montreal attended by representatives of ten locals of the twenty-nine in the Council, and by representatives of five of the thirteen internationals a resolution was passed that would bind the unions to the programs developed by the Council. Although the minutes of the meeting are silent as to the intent, form, or program adopted, a letter to "All Johns-Manville Locals" from Don Doherty, Coordinator, dated September 29, 1964, clearly sets forth the spirit of the resolution. The letter states, in part:

> Your urgent consideration is also requested for the attached collective bargaining program. Having adopted the collective bargaining reso-

[18]It is interesting to note that the minutes of the Council meeting of September 24, 1965 state that Don Doherty was elected Secretary, in addition to his position as IUD Coordinator.

[19]IUD memoranda dictated by Don Doherty, undated, "Strike Assistance Program of the *Johns-Manville Inter-Union Council.*"

> lution, please consider and adopt the collective bargaining program as attached. This program, however, should only be adopted with the full recognition of the binding moral commitment which your local has assumed in adopting the collective bargaining resolution—specifically —once you adopt the collective bargaining program, you may not settle your negotiations for less than stated in the program without clearance from the Johns-Manville Inter-Union Council.[20]

Enclosed was a copy of the program for bargaining as adopted by the Council. The five points cited as specific goals were (1) Union shop, or the highest level allowed by the applicable law; (2) Pension and insurance improvements (24 items); (3) Lessening the time gap between contract termination dates; (4) Improvement in the vacation plan; (5) Additional holiday and extra holiday premium.[21]

In order to strengthen the program adopted by the Council vote, each local was asked to ratify a "Collective Bargaining Resolution," which stated in part:

> . . . It is clearly understood by the membership of our union that we are bound only to those Council programs that our union membership sees fit to adopt. It is further understood that once we have adopted any Council program, we will be bound to take any action, including strike action, if necessary, in order to implement the program.
>
> The only way in which our union can be released from the binding effect of such action is to be released from the Johns-Manville Inter-Union Council in session, or in the event the council is not in session, by the steering committee of the Council.[22]

This document also provided spaces for proper identification of the local union and places to indicate date of meeting, number of members in attendance, number in the plant, and total membership. Space was also provided for a union seal and official signatures. Locals were asked to complete a "Certification" form which provided for a breakdown of the vote on the resolution.[23]

---

[20]Letter from Don Doherty, Coordinator, Collective Bargaining Section, Industrial Union Department, AFL-CIO to "All Johns-Manville Locals," September 29, 1964.

[21]*Collective Bargaining Program,* dictated by Don Doherty, Industrial Union Department, undated.

[22]"Collective Bargaining Resolution"—no other identification.

[23]*Certification* to be returned to Don Doherty, Coordinator, Johns-Manville Inter-Union Council, at IUD Headquarters, Washington, D.C.

There is no record available of the number of locals that adopted or rejected the resolution, but later developments would indicate that at least eight locals embraced the Council's collective bargaining program.[24]

Thus, the Johns-Manville Inter-Union Council continued to meet, formulate strategy and to prepare to exert its pressure upon the company in seeking uniform settlements in its various negotiations. And, what came to be regarded by the unions as its first "success" came about in negotiations concluded in 1965.

The 1965 Negotiations

Although the Industrial Union Department claims that a Coalition effort in 1963 linking two locals resulted in the winning of a union shop provision, it was the "second round of coalition bargaining" that proved to be most significant for both parties.[25]

In the spring of 1965, the contracts between the Company and five local members of the J-M Council at four locations were due to expire.[26] When negotiations opened at each separate location, the Company was appraised of the common goals of the coalition and was advised that failure to satisfy the aspirations of the Council would result in a strike at each of the plants.

As negotiating sessions continued, it became evident to the Company that the unions whose contracts were first to expire had no desire to engage in meaningful bargaining, but were merely interested in narrowing the time span between the expiration of the first and last contract termination dates. In fact, negotiations continued without success until May sixth when the plants at Waukegan, Long Beach, and

[24]An IUD memorandum of February 24, 1965 calls for a "special meeting of the locals involved in the collective bargaining program. . . ." There are eight cited specifically. It has been further noted that a very effective sales approach was used in presenting the proposition to the various local meetings, and that there was little difficulty in having the Resolution adopted. It is difficult to determine whether or not the membership had a clear understanding of the implications of such an affirmative vote, or whether the program was viewed simply as an easy method to make greater gains in negotiations.

[25]See for example: *"Case Study* Johns-Manville." The locals were Manville, UPP, and Marrero, La., OCAW.

[26]The locations, dates, and unions were as follows:

Location	Date	Union
Waukegan, Illinois	March 31	ICWU
Long Beach, California	April 4	ICWU
Natchez, Mississippi	April 22	IWA IAM
Toronto, Ontario	April 8	ICWU

Natchez[27] were struck. It was not possible for the Toronto plant to strike at that time because the legal requirements of the Ontario Labor Relations Act had not been satisfied.[28]

Although the coalition originally set forth a list of demands which encompassed most of the collective bargaining goals of the J-M Council, the issues had been narrowed to three by the strike date: the Company percentage of payments for hospital, medical, and surgical insurance, the nature of the medical insurance program, and the wage increase offered by the Company.[29]

While the United States plants banded together by the coalition were striking, the mechanics of Ontario law were being utilized to permit the Toronto plant to strike. The Company continued to negotiate with this local and made a final offer which was rejected by the membership who "refused to buy the settlement without the coordinated effort,"[30] and struck on June 20, 1965. Thus, Johns-Manville suffered its first serious multiple-plant strike as a result of the IUD-guided coalition effort. Yet, by that time, the sole issue of consequence on the bargaining table involved what portion of the insurance would be paid by the Company. The union had already withdrawn their attempts to obtain common contractual expiration dates.[31]

The settlement of the strikes did not come about until June twentieth when the Vice-President and Director of Labor Relations for Johns-Manville was invited by a mediator of the Federal Mediation and Conciliation Service to go to Cleveland and meet with Walter L. Mitchell, President of the Chemical Workers Union. The following day, a stipulation of agreement was executed which provided that the amount of the increased percentage of insurance that was to be borne by the company would be subtracted from the amount of the wage increase on the table at the time.

---

[27]A special meeting of the J-M Council was held in New Orleans on April 23, 1965 (see Doherty memorandum dated April 13, 1965 to Johns-Manville Local Union) and the IUD coordinator appraised the union Council on May 4 that strike notices had been sent to the Company calling for a strike two days later. (See Doherty memorandum dated May 4, 1965 to Johns-Manville Inter-Union Council Unions.)

[28]Doherty memorandum, May 4, 1965.

[29]The Asbestos, Quebec local of the Canadian National Trade Union (CNTU) was also involved in this coalition effort, but failed to follow the proper legal procedural steps to permit a strike, and fell out from the Council program. It was later expelled by the IUD-Johns-Manville Committee, October 7, 1965.

[30]Interview with IUD Coordinator. Washington, D.C., August 28, 1967.

[31]See for example, letter from Don Doherty to Johns-Manville Inter-Union Council, May 6, 1965.

Later Efforts

In spite of the fact that the IUD and the unions claimed "unqualified success"[32] in gaining two-year contracts at each of the struck plants, there was no evidence of coalition bargaining during any of the 1967 negotiations at any of the five locals. The 1967 negotiations at these plants were again negotiated locally.[33]

Such silence does not mean that the union effort against Johns-Manville has been abandoned. Quite to the contrary, the IUD has undertaken a project with the J-M committee that may provide an entirely new area of operation for coalition bargaining—job evaluation and wage incentives.

The local unions have apparently complained that the Company has a uniform manual for establishing the various job standards and wage-incentives throughout all of the J-M operations, but that there has not been uniform application of these procedures. In response, the IUD arranged to sponsor a two-week school at the University of Wisconsin's School for Workers for representatives of the J-M unions. The purpose: to discuss thoroughly "the full range of industrial engineering as practiced in the Johns-Manville Corporation."[34] According to an IUD official:

> While no one really expects that all of the problems associated with industrial engineering will disappear simply because each local will have qualified people trained in the subject, such training is necessary. The local unions through the IUD-Johns-Manville Committee will then be in a position to draft appropriate collective bargaining programs so as to solve some of the existing problems and to establish realistic positions relative to the whole area of industrial engineering. This training program, therefore, is really the first step in establishing the type of programs which will help all of the unions in this regard.[35]

[32]Memorandum from Don Doherty, IUD to all Johns-Manville Unions, July 20, 1965.

[33]See footnote 28 above. One significant development in 1966 negotiations came about as a result of an IUD-sponsored program to replace the existing contributory pension plan with one that was wholly non-contributory—with a provision that previous employee contributions be returned upon request, a provision that was included in the IUD program at the insistence of one local, and apparently based on very poor information, or on misinformation.

It was expected by the unions that very few employees would exercise a refund option, but the IUD now estimates that more than 90 percent of the qualifying employees withdraw amounts ranging from seven hundred to fifteen thousand dollars of retirement funds that will probably not be used for old-age security.

[34]Memorandum from Don Doherty, IUD to IUD-Johns-Manville Committee, July 5, 1967.

[35]*Ibid.*

The impact upon the Company of this program was not significant as of mid-1968. Although the coalition-formulated demands have been presented to the company where contracts are open, no concessions have been made by Johns-Manville.

Summary

The relationship between Johns-Manville and the coalition of its local unions is one that presents several important points and shows how a committee can be brought together—and held—for the purpose of applying constant pressure to a large industrial firm.

In a sense, the coalition effort at J-M has been a model one for the IUD: certain gains were made in pensions and insurance, and the union shop was extended to some of the locals participating in the effort. At the same time, the IUD achieved one of its major goals: that of providing leadership for the group and achieving substantial impact on policy determination for collective bargaining with the Company. By so doing, it has effectuated a transfer of authority from the local level beyond the internationals unto itself. It has created a position for itself that the locals will find difficult to ignore in future bargaining efforts.

The Company, however, continues to resist successfully the union effort to move toward company-wide bargaining. It has taken multiple-plant strikes in order to minimize the economic impact of the expanded bargaining unit, and seems to have been reasonably successful in thwarting the spread of the coalition group. It has continued to resist yielding on a common contract termination date, which means that the unions will have to go through the same process in the future to gain added bargaining leverage for the coalition.

The IUD's continuing efforts to service the J-M local unions by such measures as an educational program relating to job evaluation and incentive plans indicate a strong desire to establish a strategic leadership position among the J-M locals. On the other hand, although IUD resources were called upon by the locals in the 1966 and 1967 bargaining, no concerted movement was attempted perhaps because of J-M's willingness to take a strike in 1965. Future bargaining structure, therefore, may vary according to the IUD's estimate of J-M's capacity to resist and the local unions' willingness to risk strikes.

CHAPTER V

THE COALITION AT AMERICAN HOME PRODUCTS: WHERE THE CONCEPT WAS ACCEPTED

In the fall of 1962, the Vice-President of American Home Products Corporation agreed with a "top level committee" of union officials to negotiate changes in pension and insurance plans through national bargaining.[1] The result of this effort, initiated by the Industrial Union Department of the AFL-CIO (IUD) marked the first occasion in the development of coalition bargaining in which a company voluntarily agreed to participate in such a coalition effort. It also marks the *only* publicly announced such agreement to date. Because of the uniqueness of the American Home situation, it is of interest to examine the development and the effects of the coalition effort with this company.

[1]See, for example, "Excerpts from Report to Industrial Union Department, AFL-CIO, Seventh Constitutional Convention," March 12, 1968, as reported in the *Daily Labor Report*, March 12, 1968, p. E-3.

THE COMPANY

American Home Products Corporation employs more than 35,000 people and in 1966 had annual sales in excess of $909 million, and net income of nearly $94 million.[2] Yet, although it is heavily involved in the manufacture and sales of consumer products, only a small segment of the American population knows of the Company by its corporate name. American Home, with its subsidiaries, makes pharmaceuticals, biologicals, nutritionals, animal health products, packaged drugs, toiletries, foods, candies, chemical specialties including waxes, polishes, insecticides, cleaners, and an extensive line of utensils, hardware, cookware, and commercial equipment—all marketed under such brand names as Ekco, Brach, Whitehall, Wyeth, and a host of familiar product names. (See Table 5–1)

TABLE 5–1

AMERICAN HOME PRODUCTS CORPORATION DIVISIONAL PRODUCTS

Division	Products
Ethical Drug Division	Medicinal, pharmaceutical, biological, vitamin, and nutritional preparations sold primarily through professional channels and not advertised to the general public. The principal names are Wyeth, Ayerst, Ives and Ft. Dodge, and Sabin oral polio vaccine.
Packaged Drug Division	Publicly advertised medicinal, pharmaceutical, vitamin and dentifrice preparations, and cosmetics, grouped under the overall name of Whitehall Laboratories. Major brand names include Anacin, Kolynos (dental paste and powder), BiSoDol (powder and mints), Freezone, Preparation H (for relief of hemorrhoidal conditions), Infra Rub analgesic cream, Dristan (decongestant), Sleep-Eze, Heet (liniment),

[2]Standard and Poor's, *Standard Corporation Descriptions,* June 12, 1967, pp. 6551–53.

	Neet (depilatory), Jo-Cur (hair set), and Sudden Beauty (hair spray); also the O. M. Franklin Serum Company line of veterinary biologicals, pharmaceuticals, and instruments.
Housewares Division	Small nonelectrical houseware items, such as kitchen and barbecue tools, flatware, cutlery, home baking utensils, egg beaters, can openers, stainless steel pots and pans, bathroom and bedroom accessories sold under various trade names, including Ekco, Flint, Geneva Forge, and Berkeley; sliding door hardware, drawers, knobs, hinges, and cabinet hardware; trays, carts, racks, and other food handling equipment; steel lockers and shelving for schools and other institutions, baking pans and material handling equipment for commercial bakeries; disposable rigid aluminum foil containers for bakeries, frozen food processors, restaurants, and vending machine companies, and the machinery for the filling, capping, sealing, and closing of the containers. Also, reconditions and coats commercial baking pans with silicones, and spray-coats Teflon, silicones, and other chemical coatings on metal products for industrial customers.
Household Product Division	Includes more than 350 items: floor waxes, polishes, insecticides, germicides, disinfectants, deodorants, lighter fluid, cleaning preparations, lubricants, cements, dyes, and other products. Principal brand names include Black Flag, Antrol, 3-in-One Oil, Wizard, Plastic Wood, Griffin, Sani-Flush, Easy-Off, Easy-On, Woolite, Aerowax, Aero Shave, Radiant, Diaper Pure, Dri-Brite, and Sani-Drain.

TABLE 5–1

AMERICAN HOME PRODUCTS CORPORATION DIVISIONAL PRODUCTS
(Continued)

Food Division	Italian-style foods under the name Chef Boy-Ar-Dee, including packaged spaghetti dinners and sauces, Beefaroni, ravioli, spaghetti and meat balls, cheese and sausage pizzas, and meat-ball stew. Other product lines include Dennison's Mexican-style foods, Franklin dry toasted nuts, Jiffy-Pop popcorn, and Gulden's mustard.
Candy Division	Largest producer in the nation of general line candy under the name of E. J. Brach & Sons, including chocolate and chocolate-coated candies, hard candies, and miscellaneous items, the greater part of which are prepackaged or individually wrapped.
Foreign Division	This division manages all foreign subsidiaries and branches which make and sell Company products throughout the free world. It is responsible for 21 percent of total sales.

Source: Standard and Poor's, *Standard Corporation Descriptions,* June 12, 1967, p. 6551.

The Company, which functions both as an operating and an overall management enterprise, was founded in February 1926 as a consolidation of several manufacturers of proprietary drugs. It has continued to expand, primarily through acquisition. It now operates seven divisions which include 47 plants in the United States and Canada. American Home's headquarters is its own office building in New York City. In addition to domestic operations, American Home also maintains offices and laboratories in 27 countries.

LABOR RELATIONS BACKGROUND

During the early sixties, at the time when the Industrial Union Department began to express an interest in "coordinated" bargaining,

American Home Products had about 40 plants at which the employees had chosen union representation, and approximately 15 more nonunion manufacturing locations.[3] The Company had long maintained a strict policy of conducting all negotiations at the local level: the local management officials, with assistance from staff representatives, bargain directly with the committees elected by the membership of the certified local bargaining unit, with possible assistance from international union representatives.

Also, part of the Company labor relations policy since 1940 was the establishment of a single pension plan which originally was extended to *every* American Home employee, from janitor or helper to the chairman of the board of directors. A similar single plan provided for insurance benefits for all employees. In effect, these plans were installed and adjusted on a unilateral basis by action of Company officials: when, after study, it was deemed desirable to make changes or improvements in one of the plans, the changes would be granted to the salaried and nonunion employees, then offered to the unions at the next contract opening, or if the unions requested early reopening of pension or insurance agreements. Thus, it is claimed that there was never any real bargaining on either of these issues, and no local ever chose to strike in support of demands in these areas.[4] If a union did begin to press its demands, however, the Company would allegedly agree to higher wage increases than normally would have been granted, in order to assuage local union demands for benefit changes.[5] Undoubtedly, the diversity of Company operations, both as to geographical distribution of plant locations, and, more important, the wide range of products manufactured, lent a great deal of support to union claims that a single plant strike at American Home Products would do very little to damage the sales or profit posture of the Company.

American Home had in fact previously responded to pressure by a group of local unions acting in concert. The 15 Teamsters locals joined together and successfully negotiated the substitution of the Teamster pension plan in lieu of the Company plan. Thus, when the IUD effort

---

[3]Personal interviews with various staff members, Collective Bargaining Services Section, Industrial Union Department, AFL-CIO (IUD), Washington, D.C., summer 1966. Fifteen of the locals were represented by the Teamsters who had gained the IBT pension plan.

[4]*Ibid.*

[5]See "Case Study—American Home Products," a document presented by the IUD staff to the IUD Collective Bargaining Conference held in Washington, D.C., June 28–29, 1967.

began, American Home was no longer in the position of having pursued the policy of strictly local bargaining and a uniform pension and insurance setup. The Teamsters, however, did not participate in the early IUD coalition effort.

TABLE 5–2

UNIONS PARTICIPATING IN AMERICAN HOME PRODUCTS COALITION

Unions	*Locals*
Oil, Chemical and Atomic Workers	5
United Packinghouse, Food and Allied Workers	2
Retail, Wholesale and Department Store Union	2
Amalgamated Meat Cutters and Butcher Workmen*	1
International Chemical Workers Union	1

*A second Meat Cutter local included in the coalition lost bargaining rights to District 50.
Source: "Case Study—American Home Products," presented to the IUD Collective Bargaining Conference, Washington, D.C., June 28, 1967.

THE DEVELOPMENT OF THE COALITION

Early in 1962, the IUD, which was just beginning to develop the machinery to engage in coalition bargaining, met with 11 American Home locals for the purpose of launching a concerted effort to engage the Company in national bargaining on pensions and insurance. Apparently this was done upon the instigation of the Oil, Chemical Atomic Workers International Union which had five locals in the group.[6] The existing pension and insurance agreements were scheduled to expire in 1964, and the Company was studying changes to be made and then offered to the union-represented groups. When a "top level committee from the unions" approached Company officials with the proposition that bargaining on these fringe issues be conducted on a national level for the 11 locals, the American Home representatives were apparently

[6]The OCAW has been a leading supporter of various coalition efforts, and has participated in more such groups than perhaps any international. The other unions were: United Packinghouse Food and Allied Workers (2), Retail, Wholesale and Department Store Union (2), Amalgamated Meat Cutters and Butcher Workmen of North America (1), and International Chemical Workers Union (1).

The current roster of active participants now also includes: the United Steelworkers of America, International Association of Machinists, International Brotherhood of Teamsters, Chauffeurs and Warehousemen, and the United Furniture Workers of America.

not adverse to the concept of coalition bargaining. For a period of about a year and a half following, as the labor agreements of the 11 unions expired, each negotiated an exception to the no-strike clause that permitted a walkout over the terms of a pension and insurance agreement during the life of the labor contract.

The IUD and the unions, meanwhile, were in the process of studying the technical aspects of the American Home pension and insurance agreements, and of formulating a complete set of demands to satisfy the various coalition members. When the Company and union representatives met in Chicago, the result was agreement to improve the pension plan and provide for a minimum benefit for all company services, and also to extend the insurance plan to include basic 365-day hospitalization and institute a comprehensive major medical program.[7] The first effort at coalition bargaining covered only the pension and insurance areas, and resulted in local agreements which were to run for five years, bearing common termination dates.

Following the initial round of coalition bargaining, the Company extended the improvements to all other locations in a manner similar to that utilized in the past: first to salaried and nonunion employees, and then to other union locations if they chose to accept the improved arrangement. American Home apparently felt that it had operated under a single plan in the past, and wished to continue to do so, the difference being that eleven locals under IUD leadership now had a voice in the formulation of the plan—backed by the contractual freedom to bring about a multiplant work stoppage on the pension and insurance issues.

Recent Coalition Efforts

The IUD has noted its desire to extend coalition bargaining at American Home Products into other benefit areas for the 11-union group. It has requested multiplant bargaining to improve provisions with respect to holidays, vacations, and other fringes as well as to seek a cost-of-living escalator clause. The Company has refused to agree to such an extension of the scope of bargaining.

Furthermore, the unions have attempted to extend the range of the

[7]See "Section of AFL-CIO Executive Council Report to AFL-CIO Convention Summarizing Activities of Industrial Union Department," as reported in the *Daily Labor Report,* December 6, 1967, p. D-1.

coalition by including four more international unions, and their respective locals, in the IUD group.[8] American Home has likewise refused to permit the expansion of the group, and has indicated that it will deal only with the same 11 unions when pension and insurance agreements are again open for negotiations.

The situation has been further complicated for both unions and Company since the initial agreement was reached as a result of recent acquisitions by American Home. In 1965, the Company acquired Ekco Products Company which had about 20 unionized plants, and which had its own pension plan. A second acquisition was the E. J. Brach & Sons candy company, thereby adding an entirely new group of employees with a different labor relations background. A third problem is the already noted fact that about 15 company locations are represented by the International Brotherhood of Teamsters, which bargained for, and obtained the Teamsters pension plan in lieu of the American Home Plan. It would seem, then, that there is a group of at least 35 locals which the Company does not wish to include in the basic plan, and which would not be welcome in future coalition efforts. American Home Products therefore finds itself in a position where it is no longer administering and defending a single pension and insurance scheme, but is instead operating three separate and distinct plans.

In bargaining at the local level, the IUD has taken credit for improved labor and wage agreements for those locals which have participated in coalition meetings, including a package at Wheeling, Illinois in September 1967 which "amounts to 6.9% the first year and 4.9% the second year. . . ."[9] The IUD also claims that the right to strike over pension and insurance issues is being extended to other locations.[10]

ANALYSIS

American Home Products is the only company which to date has publicly agreed to embrace the concept of coalition bargaining, "and the experience has not been unpleasant."[11] It would appear that the

[8]See *Attendance List,* American Home Products Presidents' and Delegates' Meeting, July 6, 1967, LaSalle Hotel, Chicago, Illinois.

[9]See letter to "American Home Products Presidents' Committee and Delegates," from Stephen J. Harris, Assistant Director, Collective Bargaining Section, IUD, September 11, 1967.

[10]*Ibid.*, August 25, 1967.

[11]Statement attributed to Lowell E. Johnson, Vice President of American Home Products Corporation at American Management Association Annual Personnel Conference in Chicago, Illinois at a Panel Discussion. Reported at 61 LRR 102, February 14, 1966.

decision made in 1962, however, has been subject to review, and that such a decision may not have been repeated. Certainly, American Home Products has opposed an extension both of the scope and breadth of coalition bargaining.

The IUD was able to generate a great amount of publicity favorable to its cause, and favorable to the spread of coalitionism to the various unions and rank and file when American Home agreed to cooperate. It still cites American Home in nearly every major discussion of its programs and holds it forth as an example to be emulated. In practice, however, little was gained in the form of tangible benefits for participating unions. Certain improvements were made in pension and insurance issues when representatives of 11 unions—of a total of 40—met with Company officials. But, it is somewhat doubtful that sufficient interest could be generated to bring about a multiunit strike on these issues, and therefore doubtful that the coalition made gains significantly in excess of what the Company was prepared to offer to all employees in any event.

There is additional objective evidence that coalition bargaining on pensions and insurance at American Home Products did not overly enthuse the membership. In May 1967, District 50 wrested bargaining rights for the La Porte, Indiana plant, from the Meat Cutters. Prior to the election, a letter was sent to each employee by Steven J. Harris, assistant Director of the IUD Collective Bargaining Section. Harris spelled out the gains for which he claimed IUD was responsible, and promised that if the workers rejected the District 50 bid, their local would win great gains in the future as "a participant with 25 other local unions in the IUD American Home Products national negotiation. . . ."[12] The next month Harris wrote the American Home Products Presidents' Committee and delegates that he was "sorry to report that District 50 defeated the Meat Cutters overwhelmingly in the La Porte election. . . ."[13] Instead of the promised 25 locals at the next coordinating meeting (or 24, since La Porte was automatically out) only eight made an appearance.[14]

---

[12]Letter from Steven J. Harris to "Dear Amalgamated Meat Cutter Brother and Sister," May 16, 1967, on Industrial Union Department letterhead.

[13]Letter to "American Home Products Presidents' Committee and Delegates" from Steven J. Harris, Assistant Director, Collective Bargaining Section, IUD, June 2, 1967.

[14]See *Attendance List, op. cit.*

The IUD has expressed displeasure at the unwillingness of the Company to extend the scope and breadth of coalition bargaining to new issues and new groups,[15] thereby indicating that there is a possibility of a review and change in Company policy toward dealing with coalitions. There seems, however, to be at least some reluctance on the part of local unions to push the coalition concept. If the Teamsters would cooperate with the IUD, it would become instantly stronger. The IUD group has wooed the Teamsters, and the Teamsters' representatives (or at least those of one Teamster local) have attended IUD meetings, but it is unlikely that any commitment has been made for cooperation. Likewise the Ekco and Brach division groups are not yet part of the coalition movement, although Brach is now covered by the Company pension plan. The existence of both Teamster and Ekco pension plans gives credence to the supposition that American Home is now questioning the uniform approach to benefits. The Company's reluctance to expand coalition bargaining indicates a possible re-examination of its policy toward such bargaining. Its successful insistence that all contract negotiations except for pension and insurance issues be conducted by local management and union representatives, with a minimum of central staff assistance, is further evidence of this point.

In summary, the IUD did manage to gain political advantage and a great deal of valuable publicity as a result of American Home's acquiescence, but the value of the tangible gains resulting from coalition bargaining remain to be demonstrated.

---

[15]"Executive Council Report," *op. cit.*

CHAPTER VI

COALITION BARGAINING IN THE ELECTRICAL EQUIPMENT INDUSTRY: A "UNION VICTORY"?

The negotiations which involved the General Electric Company and the Westinghouse Electric Corporation throughout most of 1966 are touted by the labor movement as a signal victory for coalition bargaining. Although the major union in the effort, the International Union of Electrical, Radio, and Machine Workers (IUE), at first steadfastly denied the existence of any coalition effort, David Lasser, later identified as the Chairman of the GE coordinating committee, hailed the union effort as the greatest success of coalitionism to date.[1] It is of interest here, then, to examine the developments of bargaining in this situation.

Because of the nature of the bargaining relationship, it will be instructive to examine the major case—GE—in some detail and then to

[1]Industrial Union Department, AFL-CIO Collective Bargaining Conference, Washington, D.C., June 27, 28, 1967, which the writer attended.

turn to the events which took place in the Westinghouse situation. Traditionally, General Electric has set the pattern. Such was the situation in 1966. Accordingly, the GE situation will be considered first.

GENERAL ELECTRIC AND BOULWARISM

General Electric Company was incorporated in April 1892 when it acquired the assets and property of Edison General Electric Company, Thompson-Houston Electric Company and Thompson-Houston International Company, the first of which had been founded in 1878 by Thomas A. Edison. The company continued to grow through expansion and acquisition to the point where it is now "the largest and one of the most diversified producers of apparatus, equipment, and appliances used in the generation, transmission, distribution, control and utilization of electricity."[2] Its 1966 income from sales and services amounted to nearly $7.2 billion, with a net income of nearly $340 million from six major operating groups: Aerospace and Defense, Components and Construction Materials, Consumer Products, Electric Utility, Industrial and Information, and International,[3] each of which may be likened in many ways to separate companies. Products divide roughly into four broad classifications by type of market as indicated in Table 6–1. The Company employs nearly 300,000 people in the United States at some 159 plants in 129 cities, and at service locations, warehouses and offices throughout the nation.[4]

LABOR RELATIONS HISTORY

In order better to understand the developments of 1966 and the coalition effort at General Electric, it is first necessary to examine the labor relations history of the Company with an especial look at two significant facets: the Company philosophy known as "Boulwarism," and the role of the IUE in collective bargaining.

Boulwarism

General Electric's approach to collective bargaining, as developed by former Vice-President Lemuel R. Boulware, is basically a marketing

[2]Standard and Poor's, *Standard Corporation Descriptions,* October 31, 1967, pp. 6267–70.
[3]*Ibid.*
[4]*Ibid.*

approach in which the Company researches its employee relations problems, and after having examined all of the facts, makes what it believes to be a fair offer.[5] As part of its evaluation, it considers the demands of the unions, and if the union can demonstrate that the offer of the Company is deficient in some respect and fails to meet the needs of the employees, the offer will be modified. But the Company does not hold back benefits from its offer in order to haggle or to satisfy intraunion political needs, and refuses to be intimidated by threats of force by the unions to expand upon the offer which it considers just.

TABLE 6–1

GENERAL ELECTRIC PRODUCTS BY MARKET GROUPING

Heavy capital goods	Turbine generators, atomic power plants, large electric motors, power and distribution transformers, switchgear, electric locomotives, and jet engines for commercial aircraft.
Consumer goods	Household appliances, radio and television receivers, audio products, small electric housewares, air conditioning equipment, and lamps.
Industrial components and materials	Small electric motors, electric control devices, meters and instruments, plastics, special metals, electrical construction materials, X-ray equipment, computers, and electronic equipment for industrial applications.
Aerospace and defense products	Jet engines, military electronic equipment, missile, space and nuclear propulsion systems.

Source: Standard and Poor's, *Standard Corporation Descriptions,* October 31, 1967, p. 6267.

[5]See Herbert R. Northrup, "Boulwarism v. Coalitionism—the 1966 GE Negotiations," *Management of Personnel Quarterly,* Bureau of Industrial Relations (summer 1966), p. 2–11. Also Herbert R. Northrup, *Boulwarism,* Bureau of Industrial Relations, University of Michigan (Ann Arbor: Bureau of Industrial Relations, 1964), for an extended discussion of General Electric labor policy.

A basic part of the Boulwarism theory lies in communication with the unions and with the employees directly, both upward in ascertaining needs and downward in stating Company viewpoints. Boulware reasoned that if the Company had a good "product," it should make that fact known through all media, written and oral. Another part of the communication theory concerned exchanges with union officials at great length. As part of this program, both Company and unions had a lengthy history of prenegotiation joint conferences with the purpose being to find solutions to key issues and knotty problems. Both sides had likewise often agreed to make use of special bargaining committees which met during negotiations to consider specific problems while main negotiations were concerned with broader issues. Thus, although General Electric's bargaining theory has been characterized as inflexible, the facts would tend to indicate that its position is a carefully chosen one, and one that attempts to reflect fully the needs of its employees as well as those of the Company.

The General Electric philosophy of labor relations also maintains that at least two more principles are of great importance: (1) that the Company "do right" by its employees, and (2) that the Company officials maintain control of the business.

As part of the first tenet, GE, under Boulware's leadership, gradually began to bring most all contract terminations to a single date, which did increase somewhat the individual union's bargaining power, but also insured that all locations would receive contract improvements at about the same time. Likewise, the Company began to evolve benefit plans, including pensions and insurance, that were nearly identical at all locations.[6]

The fact that General Electric insisted upon retaining the sole right to manage the business led to a form of grievance and arbitration that has become unique in American industry, and one that has been a serious bone of contention to the various unions. Basically, the grievance and arbitration clauses that are now contained in GE contracts permit the union to take *certain types* of grievances to arbitration, and gives the employees the right to strike over other types.[7] This system has been under attack by the various unions, both on the legal front and

[6]Northrup, ***Boulwarism, op. cit.***, Chapter 4.

[7]The General Electric attitude toward arbitration is well known. For further explanation, see Northrup, ***Boulwarism, op. cit.***, pp. 139–151.

in negotiations, since the late 1950's. To date, the unions have been unsuccessful in changing the system. In fact, in 1963, the Company succeeded in gaining agreement on a new arbitration clause which nullified court extensions of its duty to arbitrate. A prime demand of the coalition in 1966 was an extension of GE's duty to arbitrate such matters as production standards, wages, and management actions in such areas as subcontracting.

The IUE

The history of the IUE in its dealings with General Electric also presents relevant background in examining the 1966 coalition effort. Because the IUE is the dominant union at GE, and because IUE membership at Company locations represents a substantial portion of the union, GE has always occupied a major portion of the efforts of the union and its leadership—James B. Carey in the past, and Paul Jennings currently. The IUE under Carey's leadership was a militant union which made frequent use of grievance strikes, permitted by contract, to harass and to bring pressure to bear on the Company. Bargaining between the IUE and General Electric evolved into a "regular six-step routine, like the sequence of operations in machining a casting," according to former GE Vice-President Boulware.[8] It began with a great deal of union publicity across the country, but especially in Washington, D.C. and included an economic analysis by IUE director of research David Lasser which was designed to show that union members were being cheated by the Company. Intermediate bargaining steps then followed, and were capped off by step number six—"Bring on the federals," meaning first the Federal Mediation and Conciliation Service, and other federal officials through to the President if possible. Also included here must be the now-frequent intervention sought by the IUE from the National Labor Relations Board (NLRB) in the form of unfair labor practice charges.[9]

The pattern of labor relations between the IUE and General Electric was further complicated by the Carey attitude that he "owed GE a

[8]General Electric Company, *Employee Relations Newsletter*, June 1954.

[9]For further discussion, see Northrup, "Boulwarism v. Coalitionism . . . ," *op. cit.*, p. 6. Note that the IUE has filed refusal to bargain charges against the Company as a part of each negotiation since 1954, and the charges have been accepted by the Board each time since 1960.

strike"[10] in 1960 and the militancy carried with that pronouncement. Carey obtained his strike, but the union was certainly defeated, thereby adding to union political problems, and eventually leading to Carey's downfall as president of the IUE.

In spite of the fact that the IUE constitution is carefully written to prevent challenge to incumbent officers, an effort was launched at the 1964 convention to have Paul Jennings elected as Carey's successor. From the inception of the campaign, charges of fraudulent activity on the part of Carey supporters were made by those who favored Jennings. After the ballots were counted, and Carey proclaimed the victor, the Department of Labor was finally persuaded to enter into the situation under the terms of the Landrum-Griffin Act and found that: "the ballots were miscounted by the [IUE] Trustees . . . instead of winning the election by 2,193 votes, as reported by the Trustees, Carey lost the election by 23,316 votes. . . ."[11]

Past Coalitions

The union that was taken over by Paul Jennings had had a long history of dealing with the General Electric Company, and had had previous experience in participating in coalition efforts against the Company as well. In 1958, for example, all of the 1966 coalition members (see Table 6–2) were brought together by the Industrial Union Department of the AFL-CIO (IUD). The issue at that time involved an effort by GE to introduce a savings and security program which required a rearrangement of already committed wage increases, a factor that made the proposal generally unacceptable to the unions at that time, but involved insufficient interest to become a strike threat.[12]

A second coalition attempt was brought about in 1960 which could have increased pressure to settle on the Company, until Carey's strategy of calling a strike of the IUE locals became apparent. Then, except for a few craft locals in plants where the IUE was the dominant union, the locals of the coalition unions began to settle one by one at a time when the IUE was calling its members off the job.[13]

---

[10]Mr. Carey made this statement as part of an interview with *Steel* magazine, July 27, 1959, p. 71. It was well authenticated despite his later denials. See also Northrup, *Boulwarism, op. cit.*, p. 68.

[11]See U.S. Department of Labor, Office of Labor-Management and Welfare Pension Reports, *Interim Report of Election of National President of International Union of Electrical, Radio and Machine Workers (IUE),* April 5, 1965.

[12]See Northrup, "Boulwarism v. Coalitionism . . . ," *op. cit.*, p. 6.

[13]*Ibid.*

TABLE 6–2

PRINCIPAL UNIONS REPRESENTING GENERAL ELECTRIC EMPLOYEES, 1966

Industrial Union Department Coalition Group	*Estimated Total Membership*	*Approximate Number of Employees in GE*
International Union of Electrical, Radio and Machine Workers (IUE)	270,800	79,400
International Association of Machinists (IAM)	810,000	12,900
United Automobile, Aerospace and Agricultural Implement Workers (UAW)	1,150,000	5,700
Allied Industrial Workers (AIW)	70,000	5,500
International Brotherhood of Electrical Workers (IBEW)	805,000	4,500
Sheet Metal Workers International Alliance (SMWIA)	100,000	3,400
American Federation of Technical Employees (AFTE)	15,000	2,600
American Flint Glass Workers (AFGW)	31,000	125
	Coalition Total	114,125
Non-Coalition Group		
United Electrical, Radio, Machine Workers (UE)	175,000	14,500
International Brotherhood of Teamsters (IBT)	1,300,000	2,500
United Steelworkers of America (USW)	1,000,000	600
Pattern Makers League of North America (PML)	12,700	200
	Grand Total	131,925

Source: Herbert R. Northrup, "Boulwarism v. Coalitionism—the 1966 GE Negotiations," *Management of Personnel Quarterly*, Bureau of Industrial Relations, University of Michigan, Ann Arbor, summer 1965, p. 4.

Bargaining Patterns

Of perhaps greater importance to the background of the 1966 dispute is the overall pattern of collective bargaining that has been established at General Electric. About 130,000 of the Company's 300,000 employees are organized. The Company bargains with some 80 unions for approximately 150 locations.

The IUE, which is the dominant union at GE represents approximately 70 local units and about 79,000 employees. Bargaining over the years between the Company and the union has evolved, by mutual agreement, into the following practice:[14]

1. The Company and the IUE negotiate a national agreement covering such subjects as general wage increases, employee benefits, arbitration, etc., and

2. Local supplements covering local working conditions, layoff procedures, individual job rates, etc., not covered in the national agreement, are negotiated between local management and the local union.

The traditional negotiating committee utilized by the IUE in its national bargaining with the Company is elected from members of the IUE-GE Conference Board, which is itself composed of members elected by the various GE locals of the IUE. In the past, the normal number of elected members on the negotiating committee would be between 10 and 12, and would be augmented by several experts from the IUE staff. At no time in the past did the IUE negotiating committee include representatives from other unions.[15]

In addition to the IUE, this practice of national bargaining is also followed, on the basis of mutual agreement, with the United Electrical, Radio and Machine Workers of America (UE) and the Pattern Makers League of North America. Contracts with all other unions have been conducted on a local basis: local management dealing with local union representatives, according to the units certified by the NLRB.[16]

---

[14]See, for example, "Brief for the Respondent General Electric Company" before the National Labor Relations Board in *General Electric Company and International Union Electrical, Radio and Machine Workers, AFL-CIO,* April 3, 1967, p. 7.

[15]See various briefs for reference. For example, "Post-hearing Brief on Behalf of the Respondent, General Electric Company," in *Ivan C. McLeod* v. *General Electric Company,* 62 LRRM 2809, as reported in *Daily Labor Report,* August 16, 1966, p. D-3.

[16]See "Brief for Respondent . . . ," before the Board, *op. cit.,* p. 8.

The 1966 Negotiations

The three-year agreement between the IUE and General Electric was scheduled to expire on October 2, 1966 and was subject to the following contractual provision:

> Either the Company or the Union may terminate this National Agreement by written notice to the other not more than sixty days and not less than thirty days prior to October 2, 1966 or prior to October 2 of any subsequent year. Not more than 15 days following receipt of such notice, collective bargaining negotiations shall commence between the parties for the purpose of considering the terms of a new agreement, and a proposal for a revision of wages which may be submitted by either the Company or the Union.[17]

Thus the earliest date upon which bargaining was contractually required to begin was August 18, 1966.

The Formation of the Coalition

The IUE and several other unions, however, had begun preparation for the GE and Westinghouse negotiations much earlier, and began to take the first of the "six steps" in mid-October of 1965 when AFL-CIO president George Meany publicly announced the formation of a Committee on Collective Bargaining (CCB).[18] In a statement to the press, Mr. Meany said that the committee was to be composed of the presidents of seven international unions: IUE, International Association of Machinists (IAM), United Automobile, Aerospace and Agricultural Workers International Union (UAW), Allied Industrial Workers of America (AIW), International Brotherhood of Electrical Workers (IBEW), Sheet Metal Workers International Alliance (SMWIA), and the American Federation of Technical Employees (AFTE). The stated function of the CCB was "to coordinate activities with reference to negotiations with the General Electric Company and the Westinghouse Electric Corporation to take place in 1966."[19]

---

[17]*Ibid.*

[18]See for example, "Brief for the National Labor Relations Board" in *Ivan C. McLeod* v. *General Electric Company,* 62 LRRM 2809, before the United States District Court for the Southern District of New York, August 1966, as reported in *Daily Labor Report,* August 12, 1966, p. D-2.

[19]See "Post-hearing Brief . . . ," p. D-3.

A steering committee was also formed at this time under the chairmanship of David Lasser, Assistant to the IUE president, whose job was to pull together research and educational materials to develop a common program and approach for the participating unions. As part of its job, the steering committee assigned various tasks to the research staffs of the several internationals and to the IUD.[20]

Although the GE-Westinghouse coalition effort was not under the direct control of the IUD personnel, as had been the case with many preceding and following efforts, the Industrial Union Department heartily embraced the idea, materially and spiritually. In preparing for its November 1965 convention, the report of Walter P. Reuther, IUD president, noted that the objective for "coordinated bargaining" was "to bring multi-plant companies with several unions into national bargaining on economic items which are national in scope—pensions, insurance, vacations and the like."[21] The Convention went even further, in formulating and adopting a resolution in support of the seven unions involved in the GE-Westinghouse coalition in stating:

> Seven international unions, representing more than 160,000 GE and Westinghouse employees, have joined together to form a common collective bargaining front for the negotiations with those corporations in 1966. They plan to develop national goals which they will jointly support and prevent the corporations from playing one off against the other.
>
> * * *
>
> The experiences of the IUD have shown that in industries in which a number of unions operate, this coordination of collective bargaining is the only way large corporations can be made to face up to their responsibilities. Assistance to affiliated unions to develop such joint collective bargaining activities, in order to deal effectively with giant employers, has been one of the major activities of the IUD. Nowhere are a joint program and a common front more necessary than in dealing with General Electric and Westinghouse.
>
> If either or both of these corporations are permitted to maintain substandard conditions, or to flout the legal obligation to bargain col-

---

[20]Personal Interview, Staff members, Industrial Union Department, AFL-CIO, Summer 1966.

[21]See Walter P. Reuther, *Agenda For Tomorrow,* Report to the Industrial Union Department, AFL-CIO, Sixth Constitutional Convention, Washington, D.C., November 18–19, 1965, p. 71.

lectively, they will exert a drag upon the whole field of collective bargaining.

Therefore, no negotiation in 1966 will be more important than those involving GE and Westinghouse.

NOW, THEREFORE, BE IT RESOLVED:

We pledge the full support and resources of the IUD to the efforts of the Committee on Collective Bargaining, representing the seven unions, to secure justice for their membership in these negotiations, and call upon all affiliated unions to join us in this pledge.[22]

Demand for Joint Bargaining

On November 16, 1965, David Lasser, as Chairman of the CCB, sent a lengthy telegram to Philip D. Moore, Manager of the Company's Employee Relations Service and chief negotiator, noting several requests from the IUE and from the other six unions in the coalition and requesting a joint meeting of the coalition and the Company to discuss pension and insurance items. Mr. Moore politely refused to meet with the group by stating:

> We note that your telegram listed the names of several representatives of other unions. However, this telegram is addressed to you as a

[22] *1965 Proceedings,* Industrial Union Department, AFL-CIO, Sixth Constitutional Convention, Washington, D.C., November 18–19, 1965, pp. 113–114. Note also the speech by IUE President Paul Jennings in support of the motion before the convention (p. 116):

> Mr. President, as one of the seven unions that are part of the committee that was established by President Meany to deal with the upcoming negotiations in 1966, I want to stand on the floor and support these four resolutions and briefly point to their implications, not just for the seven unions involved, but for the entire labor movement.
>
> Just as we discussed yesterday the spillover effect of organizing, so, too, does everybody in this room know that a spillover effect takes place in negotiation. What has happened, unfortunately, down through the years, in the electrical and electronic industry, has not been good for the unions in that industry and, therefore, has not been good for the labor movement and, certainly, has not been good for the nation as a whole.
>
> We have a responsibility, the trade unionists, in this industry to see to it that we have our ranks in order, to see to it that we are able to secure for the members that we represent the benefits and the level of improvement, the level of security, that has been obtained by many other unions in this hall here today.
>
> I feel that what is critical in these resolutions, just as is spelled out on the sign up there, is what we are doing in bringing together autonomous unions, unions that have different drives and different motivations, but basically have one basic responsibility, to advance the interest of their members, to advance the interest of the AFL-CIO. I pledge my union's participation.
>
> While there are many things that I wanted to talk about, Mr. Chairman, I recognize the limit of time. I would just want to make one point very clearly at the end.
>
> I would urge every other union that has any contract with Westinghouse or GE to join the committee that was established by the AFL-CIO to participate with us in this joint collective bargaining program now endorsed, and I am sure it will be endorsed, by the IUD.
>
> We in 1966, I am sure, Mr. Chairman, will come into the negotiations with a drive and with a dedication that will get for our members what they have been entitled to, and that will enhance the image of the AFL-CIO and the IUD and make it possible for other workers to get on board with us in that year. (Applause)

> representative of the IUE since we do not bargain with their unions at the national level. We assume, of course, that these gentlemen will continue to be in touch with their respective local union officials who in turn are always free to discuss appropriate matters covered by their local contracts with local managements.[23]

The Company continued to receive letters and various communications from the coalition group making various requests for joint meetings. GE, on the other hand, was largely unsuccessful in its attempts to get "prenegotiation" meetings, as had been done in 1963 and in other years, under way with the IUE. Whereas the coalition wanted to hold off discussion of all items until such time as the Company would meet with the enlarged committee, General Electric sought to get the meetings started on the subcommittee basis with the IUE on the national level and with other unions locally.[24] Only the UE, a non-coalition union, agreed to GE's procedural proposal.

The "Unity" Movement

On March 15, 1966, the seven coalition unions were joined by the American Flint Glass Workers (AFGW) at a meeting in Washington, D.C. which was to become known as the "Unity Conference." The delegates to the conference were presented with a 47-page booklet prepared by the steering committee entitled "Program for Progress." On its cover it bore a symbol consisting of a circle of links connecting boxes showing the initials of the eight unions. Within the circle appeared the legend: "We unite for a greater measure of justice."[25] The text of the document was preceded by a heading announcing "Joint Union Collective Bargaining Demands for GE-Westinghouse 1966 Negotiations," and was further clarified by a subhead stating: "National Goals adopted by over 300 delegates from the eight International Unions at the Conference on National Collective Bargaining Goals in Washington. . . ."[26] The document then listed and elaborated on a series of three "economic

---

[23]General Electric Company, *Employee Relations News,* November 22, 1965.
[24]*Ibid.,* February 28, 1966.
[25]See "Decision and Opinion" by Judge Marvin Frankel in *McLeod* v. *General Electric Company* (DCSNY) 62 LRRM 2809 at p. 2812.
[26]*Ibid.,* p. 2813.

issues"[27] and six "noneconomic contract clauses"[28] which the unions intended to press on a joint basis. The goals themselves were a composite of individual suggestions made by the representatives of the participating unions resolved in subcommittee and were included in the program only on the basis of unanimous consent of all eight unions, each of which had equal voice, irrespective of membership at GE or Westinghouse.[29]

A conclusion to the booklet was a "Unity Resolution" which was adopted by the delegates and stated in part:

---

[27]As noted by the District Court, the demands were:

"I. Wages

"A. A substantial wage increase to catch up on past wage short-fall, plus an annual improvement factor based on increased productivity and output.

"B. A planned program to end geographical differentials for the same type of work.

"C. A cost of living escalator providing for one percent of wages for each one percent increase in the cost of living.

"II. Holidays and Vacations

"A. Nine paid holidays—double time for holiday work, plus the holiday pay.

"B. A progression schedule on vacations for hourly employees that would provide for a graduated vacation between 1 and 5 years' service, between 5 and 10 years' service, and between 10 and 20 years' service. A proportionate increase in paid vacation benefits for salaried employees.

"C. A vacation bonus of 25 percent of wages.

"III. Income and Employment Security

"A. The SUB (Supplemental Unemployment Benefit) type of layoff benefit plan.

"B. Restrictions on overtime where people are on layoff; double time for all overtime hours.

"C. No contracting out of work historically performed by employees in the bargaining unit when skills, manpower and facilities are available.

"D. The right to move with the job; employees shall have preference over new hires in plants to which their jobs have been moved, or where there is a build-up of operations and a curtailment of job opportunities in the home plant. A reasonable moving expense shall be paid.

"E. A joint labor-management program shall be developed leading to a progressive shortening of the work week and work year.

"F. Provision for 6 days paid sick leave per year for hourly employees. Proportionate increase in paid leave for salaried employees.

[28]The District Court noted the major noneconomic issues as:

5. "I. A full arbitration clause with no restrictions.

"II. The full union shop.

"III. Automation provisions which shall provide for:

"A. Program of retraining of employees to prepare them for new skills that will be needed by changing technology.

"B. Rate retention and/or increases when jobs have become automated.

"C. The maintenance of the bargaining unit against erosion under automation.

"D. Maintenance of job security by some form of attrition clause.

"IV. Continuity of Service. A minimum of two years and time-for-time above two years' service for periods of layoffs.

"V. Anti-Discrimination Clause.

" 'The Company agrees that it will not discriminate against any applicant for employment, or any of the employees, in payment of equal wages, assignment to jobs, seniority, promotions, training, transfer, layoff, discipline, discharge, or any other terms or condition of employment, because of race, color, religion, marital status, sex, age, or national origin.'

"VI. Pension and Insurance Program.

"Details to be found in the Pension & Insurance Fact Sheets."

[29]See "Brief to Board . . . ," *op. cit.*, p. 39.

It is now time for us to convey the details of this program to the membership of our local unions. At the same time we must communicate with the public in a manner which will create sympathetic understanding of our program and of our objectives.

We have developed a sound basis for coordinated negotiations as the result of the spirit of mutual respect and confidence which has been developed to new levels during recent months. . . .

While we come together as representatives of eight different unions accustomed to negotiating with the GE and Westinghouse Corporations on a union by union basis, the companies' representatives have dealt with us and will continue to attempt to deal with us, either locally or nationally, *under a centrally controlled program.* The fact is that even though the companies have opposed company-wide bargaining on any issue they have, in fact, insisted upon the implementation of company-wide policies during contract negotiations.

By the action we have taken here today we intend to confront company-wide policies with a union-wide program.

Our members will know and the companies will know that all bargaining units will be directing their energies toward the same national goals.

Of course, in addition, each union will have an opportunity to pursue additional goals necessary to meeting its own problems.

* * *

We pledge to each other our mutual cooperation, our mutual understanding and our mutual support. (Emphasis added.)[30]

The "Unity" theme was further extended throughout the entire period over which negotiations eventually stretched through the use of a monthly union publication called "Unity" which was to be distributed to all involved GE and Westinghouse workers, and which would keep the various memberships abreast of the developments of the coalition in dealing with the companies.

The unions also attempted to spread the theme of the coalition to the rank and file through a series of 17 "grass-roots" meetings across the country at which the goals of the unions were expounded upon, and where local support was sought. It is reported that at one such meeting the delegates were asked to stand and pledge that no local would sign

[30]"Decision . . . ," *op. cit.*, p. 2813.

with the Company unless agreement was received from other members of the coalition.[31]

A third method of generating rank-and-file support for the union program was brought to the fore on August 16, which was named by the coalition as "Unity Day" at GE. At that time, "Unity" lapel pins, which reproduced the symbol of the cover of "Program for Progress" embraced by the unions in March, and again contained the legend "We unite for a greater measure of justice." At that time Mr. Meany was photographed pinning the buttons on coalition leaders, and acted as spokesman for the group in denouncing the Company.[32] In all, the unions, through the length of the prenegotiation and the negotiation period, maintained a continuous program of employee communication which stressed the unity theme, a theme which boldly proclaimed the existence of a coalition in spite of later periods of denials by union officials.

Events Leading to the Coalition Confrontation

From the exchange of correspondence that began in November of 1965, there continued to be a series of communications between the Company and the unions in the coalition, through the IUE to the Company, each of which alluded to the possibility of joint bargaining on the part of the unions, and each was refused by GE.[33] On March 23, 1966, the eight-union committee decided to abandon its attempts to deal with GE negotiator Moore and elected instead to address a telegram to Company President Fred J. Borch reiterating such points as the following:

> The contracts of our eight unions with GE on the major issues considered by the [Union] conference are the same and we naturally have developed a common program to improve our agreements.
>
> * * *
>
> In order to canvass this whole problem [of a peaceful settlement] facing us jointly as an attempt to lay the groundwork for such collective bargaining, we propose an early meeting with you and your representatives.

---

[31]An extended discussion of the CCB operational procedures is contained in the Company "Brief to Board . . . ," *op. cit.*, pp. 49 ff.

[32]*Employee Relation's News*, August 22, 1966.

[33]See for example, "Decision . . . ," *op. cit.*, pp. 2814–15.

> Such a meeting would be informal and would involve no commitments as to future action by either group.[34]

The request by the unions was rejected by the Company president, and again Moore wrote to various union officials stating his desire to begin prenegotiation meetings and declining to meet with the coalition by stating in part:

> As you know, we are very receptive to appropriate prenegotiation discussions with the IUE, but as we have already elaborated before in greater detail to you and your associates, we do not intend to participate in any eight-union coalition discussions or in any other steps in the direction of industry-wide bargaining. For many reasons we are convinced that such coalition discussions would only be a hindrance to the constructive discussion we hope to get under way.[35]

In response to the Company letter of March 25, John H. Callahan, Chairman of the IUE-GE Conference Board wrote the following on April 13, 1966:

> Your letter of March 25 was presented to our IUE-GE Negotiating Committee and the points in it were duly noted.
>
> The Committee and, we know, our membership were truly disappointed that the officials of General Electric did not find it possible to accept the requests of the eight union presidents for an informal meeting to discuss how we could jointly approach the question of effectively preparing "the way for the kind of collective bargaining that would avoid last minute crises." In supporting the sending of the telegram, it was our conviction that such an informal meeting could be extremely helpful. It could not only have considered the device of using subcommittees, but could have explored any other pre-negotiation activities that might be found useful.
>
> However, it is clear that General Electric is not willing to hold any such joint meeting, even though it may be informal. The IUE did not intend by its telegram any formal request for joint negotiations. Speaking for the IUE-GE Conference Board, *we will not pursue that matter*

---

[34]See for example, "Trial Examiner's Decision," in *General Electric Company and International Union of Electrical, Radio and Machine Workers, AFL-CIO,* June 8, 1967, p. 13. Note also that the union coalition had released the text of the telegram before the Company had received it.

[35]*Employee Relations News,* April 4, 1966.

> *any further and will abandon any suggestions for any such joint meeting or for joint discussions.* (Emphasis added.)[36]

The letter then indicated a willingness to have the IUE engage in subcommittee discussions after ground rules had been established, and suggested a meeting to establish such rules for discussion. The Company quickly responded by suggesting a date and by expressing pleasure at the fact that the "GE-IUE Conference Board is not pursuing the idea of joint meetings or discussions and you have made it clear the IUE was not supporting joint negotiations in the telegram your board sent here recently."[37]

When the Company negotiators entered the meeting room on May 4, 1966, as agreed, to discuss the ground rules for the IUE subcommittee meetings, they found that representatives of each of the seven other coalition unions were present, each wearing lapel buttons reflecting membership in their respective unions. When introduced, each was careful to state that he was representing the IUE, although without conviction in most cases.[38] The IUE maintained that it was merely exercising its right to choose its own representative, and that "all of the individuals present were part of the IUE bargaining team. They had been chosen in order to render their advice and help in the discussions that were to take place on the question of pre-negotiation sub-committees."[39]

The GE bargaining team felt that the presence of the coalition members represented a departure from the agreed-upon conditions for the meeting by stating:

> When we got into this morning's meeting we found that the regular negotiating committee of the IUE was now insisting on having representatives from most of the other seven unions in their coalition group present at the same time, but this was clearly not what we had agreed to. In the face of this subterfuge we recessed our participation

[36]See, for example, *Daily Labor Report,* April 21, 1966, p. A-5.

[37]*Ibid.,* p. A-6.

[38]The *Employee Relations News,* May 9, 1966 notes the following: Members of the GE Negotiating Committee were struck by the obvious amusement of some of the officials of the other coalition unions who were enjoying the charade of posing as members of the IUE Negotiating Committee. In the first two or three minutes of informal handshakes and introductions, some of them, after stating their name, started to identify the coalition union they represented, then remembered the special circumstance, and said—with a wink—"of the IUE."

[39]*Daily Labor Report,* May 14, 1966, p. A-2.

in the meeting until such time as the IUE is ready to deal with us in a sincere effort to form GE-IUE pre-negotiations sub-committees.[40]

Subsequent to that meeting, both sides adhered to their respective positions. GE continued to communicate with the IUE, both publicly and privately, urging it to meet on a good-faith basis; while the unions held steadfast to the position that the makeup of the bargaining committee was solely a matter of union determination.

LEGAL DEVELOPMENTS

Beginning June 8, 1966 General Electric began to file a series of unfair labor practice charges against the IUE and the other seven coalition unions under the terms of Section 8(b) (1) (A) of the National Labor Relations Act. The Company summarized its position by citing five areas in which it felt the unions were acting illegally:

1. In the case of the seven unions in the coalition which have nothing but local certification, it is illegal for them to try to force GE to bargain with them nationally—and this is the course the coalition is following.
2. Even if each of the unions in the coalition were certified to bargain with GE nationally for its locals, it would be illegal for such national unions to bargain with them as a single unit—and this is the course the coalition is following.
3. In addition to the charges identified above, it is illegal for two or more unions to lock themselves together, so that one or more of them cannot bargain freely without the consent of the others—and this is the course the coalition is following.
4. It is illegal for one or more unions to conspire in subterfuges in order to promote other illegal objectives—and this is the course the coalition is following.
5. It is likewise illegal for other union representatives to become conspirators by sitting in with the IUE, claiming they are a part of the IUE Negotiating Committee, and thereby failing to give proper representation to employees at the local level where they are certified—and this is the course the coalition is following.[41]

---

[40] *Ibid.*
[41] *Employee Relations News,* June 13, 1966.

On July 8, the Regional Director of the NLRB wrote the Company announcing his view that there was no basis for the charges brought by GE against the unions, and that at the same time, the General Counsel had authorized the Regional Director to issue a complaint against the Company on the basis of union charges of refusal to bargain on May 4.[42] A complaint was issued on July 13, at which time the IUE promptly asked that Section 10 (j) proceedings be initiated to enjoin the Company from refusing to bargain with the "committee chosen by the IUE."[43] The General Counsel requested the District court to issue such an order two days later.[44]

In four days of testimony before the District Court, the unions argued that the matter of the bargaining committee makeup was strictly a matter of union determination. The General Counsel argued that there existed substantial chance for "serious and unjustifiable interruption of commerce" due to a strike growing out of a refusal to bargain by the Company. The Counsel further stated:

> A prerequisite to the granting of . . . relief is a finding by the District Court that reasonable cause exists to believe that a violation of the Act, as charged, has been committed. The District Court does not have to determine whether in fact, the violation has been committed; the determination with respect to this question is reserved to the Board, subject to review by the courts of appeals.
>
> * * *
>
> [The additional prerequisite is that] the issuance of a temporary injunction is necessary for the protection of the public interest and for the preservation of the status quo.[45]

The Board Counsel then argued that simple failure to meet on the one occasion, before legal bargaining was required, established a *prima facie* case, and that the public interest and status quo should be protected from a strike.

In an *amicus* brief, the National Association of Manufacturers and the Chamber of Commerce of the United States urged the District Court to withhold the injunction sought by the IUE and the Board on

---

[42]See *Daily Labor Report,* July 11, 1966, p. A-5.
[43]*Ibid.,* July 13, 1966, p. A-9.
[44]*Ibid.,* July 15, p. A-11.
[45]See, for example, "Brief for Board . . . ," p. D-5.

the basis that such an injunction would not merely restore the status quo, but would in effect change the relationship between GE and the unions by requiring bargaining with a joint committee and would result in an order "which for all practical purposes would now grant the final relief" which would be anticipated by the unions if the unfair labor practice were litigated to conclusion through Board procedures.[46]

In a 48-page opinion issued on August 18, 1966, District Court Judge Marvin Frankel ordered the Company to bargain with a committee of the union's choosing. The Court accepted the union contention that there was sufficient evidence of a strike threat which would affect commerce and that General Electric had failed to discharge its responsibility by refusing to meet with the union committee. The Court further stated in concluding:

> If it were necessary, the point could be put more strongly. The parties have made a detailed record. Despite respondent's proposed inferences about secret motives and hidden plots, there is little in the way of material dispute concerning the facts. The points of controversy are essentially legal rather than factual. Without meaning to usurp the Board's primary role, but merely to explicate the court's conclusions, it may be said that the decision would go for the petitioner as a matter of independent judgment if such a judgment were either required or permissible.[47]

On appeal, however, the Circuit Court severely chastised both the District Court and the Board. It stated in part:

> It is black-letter law that the issuance of an injunction is an extraordinary remedy indeed. This is especially true in the labor field. . . .
>
> * * *
>
> We are not convinced that the facts in the present case reveal those special circumstances which must be present before a court will intervene and issue an injunction prior to the Board's hearing and decision. The Board has not demonstrated that an injunction is necessary to preserve the status quo or to prevent any irreparable harm. Moreover, the basic legal question underlying its conduct—the very same question presented in the *American Radiator* case, 155 NLRB

[46]*Daily Labor Report,* July 25, 1966, p. A-1.
[47]See "Decision . . . ," *op. cit.,* at p. 2824.

No. 69 (1965) in which the Board did not see fit to seek an injunction —is a very difficult one to resolve and one which no court has considered. It would be more in keeping with the scheme intended by Congress to have this case, particularly because of its unusual characteristics, follow the path of Board hearing and decision on the unfair labor practice charges, rather than to short-circuit the established administrative design. The Board cannot abdicate one of the prime purposes for which it was created and thus deprive the Court of the expertise which would be available to it in reviewing the Board's holding in an enforcement proceeding. . . .

* * *

. . . It is difficult to imagine a case that presented more vividly the need for prompt action by the Labor Board. For reasons that escape us, the Board decided not to utilize with dispatch its adjudicatory machinery but to proceed instead at cross purpose with that envisaged by Congress in the National Labor Relations Act.[48]

On application to Supreme Court Justice Harlan by the Board, a stay of the Second Circuit's dissolution of the injunction was granted by the Justice. Subsequent to the settlement of the 1966 negotiations the High Court declined to review the legality of the NLRB's use of an injunction to force the Company to bargain. The Court agreed with GE that the matter was moot in light of the contract which had been agreed to in the interim. The Court, in effect, wiped the slate clean and put all previous court actions aside by referring the matter back to the District Court.[49] Up to this point, neither the IUE nor the Board have demonstrated interest in reopening the case.

A finding by the NLRB trial examiner on June 8, 1967 found the Company guilty of a refusal to bargain charge, basically reflecting the fact that the examiner was bound at that time by the Board's decision in *American-Standard*. General Electric appealed the decision.

On October 24, 1968, the Board, in a four to one decision, followed the recommendations of its trial examiner and found the Company in violation of the law in refusing to meet with an expanded committee, thereby upholding the union practice of permitting "outsiders" to participate in collective bargaining negotiations.

---

[48]Decision of the United States Court of Appeals for the Second Circuit, No. 476, September Term 1965 in *McLeod* v. *General Electric Company,* 63 LRRM 2065, September 8, 1966.

[49]*Employee Relations News,* January 23, 1967.

The Board majority, in supporting the unions' position recognized the potential impact of coalition bargaining, but minimized its implications by stating in part:

> Such representatives could attempt to bargain for their unions while serving on the negotiating committee of another, or they might claim to be bargaining for one union when, in fact, they were locked into an understanding that no union would sign an agreement unless all unions did.
>
> But to recognize the possibility of abuse is quite different from concluding, as does our dissenting colleague [Board Member Jenkins], that abuse is inherent in any attempt at coordinated bargaining.
>
> We do not believe that the mere possibility of such abuse, without substantial evidence of ulterior motive or bad faith, justifies qualification of a union's right to select the persons who will represent it at the negotiating table.[50]

General Electric Company has appealed the decision of the Board.

THE COALITION IN ACTION

In spite of repeated denials of any sort of joint effort or bargaining coalition by union leaders before the Board and the Courts, the actions of the unions during and after the General Electric negotiations demonstrated amply that the unions were effectively working together in an attempt to extract a greater settlement from the Company.

For economic and pragmatic reasons, GE refused to deal with the coalition until forced to do so. (Table 6–3) For equally pragmatic reasons, the coalition elected to pursue joint bargaining by use of every means at its command. When it became obvious that General Electric would not participate in joint bargaining on the demands set forth by the CCB, the unions began to implement a plan whereby it hoped to achieve the same end in spite of a refusal by GE to negotiate a Company-wide contract on the coalition issues. In addition to the information exchange which it hoped to gain through the presence of the outsiders at the IUE table, the union group also set up a regional communication system that utilized 17 regional coordinators who were connected by a network of teletype machines to key negotiation centers in

---

[50]Reported in the *New York Times*, October 24, 1968. See also "Trial Examiner's Decision . . . ," *op. cit.*, pp. 26–27.

New York, Washington and Pittsburgh. Bargaining developments, Company statements and local union actions were gathered by the coordinators, fed into Washington, then digested and disseminated back to the coordinators and through them to the locals.[51]

TABLE 6–3

WHY WE DO NOT ACCEPT COALITION BARGAINING

For many months we have been trying to make it clear that for many good reasons—affecting the Company, employees, the public, and unions—we oppose the idea of bargaining with a coalition of unions. Summing up, here are the reasons:

1. We are convinced that the basic strategy of the union coalition is to present a "united front" for unanimously rejecting any Company proposals (no matter how good) in favor of forcing a broad-scale strike. The purpose of this strike would be to test whether General Electric can be forced to enlarge its offer solely to avert or end such a strike. This could be a very expensive experiment which would benefit no one.

2. For many years General Electric has stood firmly for the principle of negotiating in a forthright manner which holds nothing back simply to be able to make last-minute, strike-threat concessions. In this year's negotiations we intend to bargain in the same way because we believe it really serves everyone best in the long run.

3. In the end, the coalition stands as little more than an outright strike-broadening and strike-lengthening effort, and we do not see how that can be good for anyone.

4. Various aspects of preliminary "coordinated" bargaining—such as unions pooling research and information, improving communications with one another and with their membership, analyzing the long-range impact of their demands and strategies, etc.—are not basically a concern to General Electric provided these are not merely instruments of enforcing strike discipline on locals whether they want to strike or not.

5. Beyond the immediate concern of a 1966 strike we are also concerned with the obvious long-term strategy of the coalition to bring about conditions for industry-wide bargaining in the electrical industry. Here again

[51]See David Lasser, "A Victory for Coordinated Bargaining," *AFL-CIO American Federationist,* April 1967, p. 16.

TABLE 6–3

WHY WE DO NOT ACCEPT COALITION BARGAINING (Continued)

it is clear that an industry where strikes have been rare and where wages and working conditions are good needs no new instrument for imposing industry-wide strikes or economic settlements that would impair growth and competitive health in world-wide markets. No other industry is more exposed today to the disciplines of the international market place.

6. Coalition officials have made no secret of the fact that they are intent on shattering the wage guidepost even though it has been endorsed by the public as a means to avoid further domestic inflation.

7. It is all too clear that the strike-bound coalition intends to turn its back on the negotiating table in favor of seeking a settlement through government intervention. This is damaging to the whole collective bargaining process and encourages the excesses already evident in such debacles as we have seen in other negotiations.

8. By trying to centralize negotiations that have been traditionally localized, the coalition inevitably would submerge the varying needs and concerns of employees in more than 100 different General Electric businesses. This risks the now common danger of inviting local strikes even after national strikes are settled. This has been happening in other industries where big unions have centralized their bargaining and overlooked the concerns of their local memberships. In some of these industries there is already a trend away from such centralized bargaining.

9. Lastly, but perhaps the very best reason for rejecting coalition bargaining, is the fact that traditional relationships rather than the new coalition experiment have provided a 33-year bargaining history of sound and peaceful contract settlements which is unmatched by any other major manufacturing concern. In sharp contrast with earlier years, this year's bargaining picture is already badly clouded by the coalition's unwillingness to engage in normal prenegotiations meetings and the coalition's new course of local strikes, NLRB charges, law suits, and other tactics. What the coalition has done so far, as well as what it has *not* done so far, toward constructive collective bargaining is evidence enough that we must reject the course of the coalition.

Source: General Electric Company, *Employee Relations News,* No. 66–28, July 25, 1966, p. 1.

Prior to August 18 when Judge Frankel issued the injunction ordering GE to bargain with the coalition, there had been no meetings between the Company and any of the coalition unions. Negotiations had, however, been under way with the UE, and progress was being made. On August 23 negotiations began with the IUE at which time representatives of the other 10 unions were present[52] and accepted by the Company as representatives of the IUE. When the order was reversed, but the injunction dissolution stayed by Justice Harlan, the outsiders remained, but GE negotiators simply refused to acknowledge their presence, and ignored them in discussions.[53]

Bargaining continued with some progress apparent throughout the latter part of August and early September. Four days before the IUE contract was set to expire, however, the unions staged a second "Unity Conference" in Washington. "Each bargaining unit was asked to poll its membership on the crucial questions—to accept GE's offer, to authorize a strike or simply to continue bargaining."[54] The coalition also prepared a new set of national goals to present at the conference.

Apparently, the poll of the membership gave the leadership support in its view that the Company offer was not sufficient, because a unanimous conference statement stated:

> We want a settlement, not a strike. But we want to make it clear to GE that the offer now before us is not acceptable; and that we do not accept the Boulware philosophy that it cannot be improved.
>
> It must be improved—by midnight, October 2.[55]

Despite the brave words, it was apparent that at least the union with the most members at General Electric, the IUE, was in no mood for a strike. The Company had put a generous offer on the table: a three-year contract with increases of 4 percent the first year, and 3 percent each of the next two years, plus a three cent annual cost-of-living adjustment and improvements in holidays, pensions, insurance and other benefits.[56]

The memories of the 1960 situation when a strike was last tried on

---

[52]By this time, the coalition had added three more unions to its ranks: The International Brotherhood of Electrical Workers (IBEW), United Association of Journeymen Plumbers and Steamfitters of the United States and Canada, and United Steelworkers of America (USW).

[53]Lasser, *op. cit.*, p. 18.

[54]*Ibid.*, p. 16.

[55]*Ibid.*

[56]Personal Interviews with General Electric Company Officials, Fall 1967.

a company-wide basis was still fresh in the minds of many IUE negotiators. The IUE Conference Board was reported actually moving to accept the GE offer when George Meany again stepped into the situation.[57] He reiterated his support for turning down the GE offer, and after he visited the White House, President Johnson called the parties to Washington. The status quo was extended for two weeks while negotiations continued under a panel consisting of Labor Secretary Wirtz, Defense Secretary McNamara, and Commerce Secretary Connor together with Chief Mediator Simkin.

General Electric, unlike many companies which have been called to Washington, declined to cease communicating and to alter its basic approach to labor relations. Despite heavy pressure from the government, it soon became apparent that if there was to be settlement it had to come on terms close to those offered by the company which publicly announced it was "out of proposal ideas."[58]

Toward the end of the two-week contract extension period, General Electric offered a way out for the union coalition by a technique which it has often utilized before—a rearrangement of contract terms. It proposed a cost-of-living "shared-risk" formula instead of the three cent per year (1 percent) guarantee. This was accepted by the IUE and by most other unions with which General Electric deals. Under this arrangement cost-of-living payments could be slightly higher or lower than the three cents originally proposed by the Company (see Table 6–4) depending upon the movement in the Consumer Price Index. In 1968, General Electric employees received a 1 percent cost-of-living adjustment which averaged three cents.

General Electric did, however, experience some local strikes after the IUE settlement. At Schenectady a threatened work stoppage occurred revolving around downward adjustments previously made in a runaway incentive situation—a noncoalition issue which had been in process for about two years. At Evendale, Ohio, the UAW and the IAM struck the huge jet engine plant in an attempt to gain a contract superior to the one agreed upon in Washington. President Johnson secured a Taft-Hartley 80-day injunction to end the Evendale strike.[59] Before the 80 days were over, both the IAM and the UAW settled with

[57] *Ibid.*
[58] *Employee Relations News,* October 3, 1966.
[59] *Employee Relations News,* October 24, 1966.

the Company without enriching the Company's offer and with a different contract expiration date than that affecting the IUE. Apparently, the unions did not wish to risk a Taft-Hartley vote on the Company's last offer.[60]

TABLE 6–4

GENERAL ELECTRIC—IUE
COST-OF-LIVING ADJUSTMENT FORMULA

6. (a) Cost-of-Living Adjustments, based on the National Consumer Price Index (Base 1957–1959=100) as published by the United States Bureau of Labor Statistics, will be made effective for salaried and hourly employees on the dates indicated for the following two measurement periods and using the formula listed below:

As of October 2, 1967, based on the percentage change in the Index for October 1967 from the Index for October 1966.

As of September 30, 1968, based on the percentage change in the Index for October 1968 from the Index for October 1967.

Each of these Cost-of-Living Adjustments, to be added to salary rates and to hourly rates and, in the case of incentive workers, to the earnings thereof, shall be:

(1) One half of one percent (0.5%) if the Index increases by less than 2% (or even if the Index decreases), or

(2) One per cent (1.0%) if the Index increases by at least 2% but less than 3%, or

(3) One and one-half per cent (1½%) if the Index increases by at least 3% but less than 3½%, or

(4) One and three quarters per cent (1¾%) if the Index increases by 3½% or more.

(b) As soon as practical after the Index for October 1967 and for October 1968 is released by the Bureau of Labor Statistics, the appropriate percentage increase as determined from (a) above will be applied after the application of Section 3(a) above for the appropriate date and in the manner described in Section 3(b) above.

(c) No adjustment, retroactive or otherwise, shall be made in pay or benefits as a result of any revision which later may be made in the published

[60]Personal Interviews, *op. cit.*

TABLE 6–4

GENERAL ELECTRIC—IUE
COST-OF-LIVING ADJUSTMENT FORMULA
(Continued)

figures for the Index for any month on the basis of which the cost-of-living calculation shall have been determined.

(d) In the event the Bureau of Labor Statistics issues a revised Index with a conversion table by which the present Index can be made applicable to any change in said Index, the Union and the Company agree to accept such conversion table. If no such conversion table is issued following any revision of the Index, the parties will promptly undertake negotiations solely with respect to agreeing upon a substitute formula for determining a comparable cost-of-living adjustment and failing agreement in such negotiations, the Union and the Locals shall, upon giving 10 days' notice, have the right to strike solely with respect to such issue.

Source: 1966–1969 GE-IUE (AFL-CIO) National Agreement, Wage Agreement, October 28, 1966, pp. 6–7.

The UAW also struck GE's metallurgical products plant in Detroit, staying out ten weeks before returning to work without additional economic gains. This contract provided for a termination date of December 28, 1969, instead of the IUE and general date of October 26th.[61]

COALITION RESULTS AT GENERAL ELECTRIC

In evaluating its gains, the unions cite three areas in which they feel that coalitionism reaped benefits:

> 1. The 1966 agreements were better than the total of the two preceding contracts, covering 1960–1966. Important benefits lost in 1960 were restored. The annual wage increase was won on a more adequate level, a partial cost-of-living escalator was established and inequity adjustments for day, skilled, and salaried workers were negotiated . . . pension, insurance and vacation agreements, closed until 1968, were not only reopened, but substantially improved.
>
> 2. Equally important was that the GE philosophy of "one and only one offer" was shattered. The final agreement for 36 months and

[61] *Ibid.*

3 weeks increased the value of the earlier offer by 5 to 7 cents an hour.

The "wage guideline" that GE had said was "too high" was effectively destroyed.

3. The most far-reaching result was membership recognition that coordinated bargaining, in spite of its complexities and difficulties, has completely proved itself and must continue as a permanent feature of GE and Westinghouse negotiations. This led to the cooperation . . . between unions on strike at a given plant; and the support given by non-striking to striking locals where companies tried to move production from one plant to another.

While there was only one year to prepare for 1966 negotiations, there are nearly three years to prepare for 1969. With what has been learned, with harmonious inter-union relations and stronger membership support, a much better job can be done.[62]

The Company, as might be expected, disagrees with this assessment.[63]

1. It is true that the 1966 contract provided more liberal economic terms than those of the previous two contracts. General Electric, however, has always geared its economic package to market conditions, and in 1966 it in effect met the market after the airline strike smashed the guidelines. The cost-of-living provisions, so widely heralded by IUE, again met market conditions, but unlike those in contracts in the 1950's, carefully limited the Company's total liability. Other adjustments were neither unusual or departures from previous company policies.

2. General Electric has never confined itself to one offer except in 1949, the first year of Boulware's active direction of Company labor relations.[64] Actually, General Electric did what it usually does to gain final agreement—rearranged its basic offer.

3. The union drive to alter General Electric's limited arbitration of grievances failed completely. No significant change in this aspect of the contract was made.

4. Whether coalition bargaining has "proved itself" to General Electric employees remains to be demonstrated. The IUE, in particular,

---

[62]Lasser, *op. cit.*, p. 19.
[63]The following section was developed from Personal Interviews, *op. cit.*
[64]See Northrup, *Boulwarism, op. cit.*, Chapter 6.

obviously did not desire a test, and the UAW's two strikes gained it nothing of significance.

To the outside observer it would seem that the union claim of victory is at best premature. Despite considerable governmental attempts at assistance, General Electric achieved largely peaceful settlement without recognizing the coalition. The largest strike—the Schenectady one—was probably likely regardless of the structure of bargaining. The UAW strikes resulted in contract expiration dates that will make future coalition attempts more difficult.

On the other hand, future coalition attempts, like this one, have been made easier because Paul Jennings, president of the IUE, is much more inclined to cooperate with other unions, and to work with them than was his predecessor, James B. Carey. George Meany, president of the AFL-CIO has put his prestige on the line favoring coalition bargaining, and the precedent for White House intervention has been established. Moreover, the returns to employees, whether dictated by coalition power or by General Electric market recognition, were high. All this argues for more coalition attempts at General Electric in 1969.

WESTINGHOUSE

The Westinghouse Electric Corporation is the oldest and second largest manufacturer of electrical apparatus and appliances. It was incorporated in Pennsylvania in January 1886 as Westinghouse Electric Company and became the Westinghouse Electric & Manufacturing Company in 1889 when it purchased the Chartiers Improvement Company. By 1966, the Company had grown to the point where it employed about 125,000 people at 75 manufacturing locations and 47 repair shops. In 1966, it generated a net income of about $292 million on net sales of $2.58 billion. Westinghouse products are highly diversified and are used by nearly all electric power companies, railroads, city transit systems and industrial plants. They also include propulsion and electrical equipment for the Navy and the marine industry in general, and certain electrical equipment for the aviation industry.[65] (See Table 6–5.) Some of these products, such as motors and control devices, are sold to other manufacturers for application to their products.

---

[65]Standard and Poor's, *Standard Corporation Descriptions,* July 31, 1967, pp. 1359–63.

TABLE 6–5

WESTINGHOUSE ELECTRIC COMPANY

	Products
Electrical Industrial Apparatus	Air conditioning, air handling, transportation, and vehicular temperature control equipment, controls, electronic tubes; electric stairways, elevators, fluorescent and incandescent lamps, gear and gear motors, industrial ceramics and computer systems, integrated circuits, lighting fixtures, motors, plastics, rectifiers, regulators, semiconductor devices, switchboards, wiring devices, and X-ray apparatus.
Electrical Generation, Transmission and Distribution Equipment	Atomic power systems, atomic fuel, capacitors and lightning arresters, electrical measuring instruments, high voltage power circuit breakers, insulators, large generators and motors, meters, reduction gears, relays, steam and gas turbines, steam condensers, switch gear and transformers.
Household Appliances	Air conditioners, cabinets and vanities, clothes dryers and washers, dishwashers, electric ranges, heating equipment, lamps, portable appliances, radio receivers, refrigerators, stereo phonographs and television receivers.
Aerospace & Defense Equipment	Airborne weapon control systems, aircraft electric power equipment and systems, communication systems, marine propulsion and auxiliary equipment, missile launching and handling equipment, ocean science and engineering equipment and services, reconnaissance and surveillance systems, space propulsion and power systems, underwater search and detection equipment, and underwater weapons systems.

Source: Standard and Poor's, *Standard Corporation Descriptions*, July 31, 1967, p. 1359.

In addition to its broad line of products for industrial application, Westinghouse participates in numerous efforts for the U.S. government atomic energy and other defense related programs; is a leading producer of home appliances; is a forerunner in the design and manufacture of water desalting plants; and through its broadcast subsidiaries, operates seven radio and five television broadcast stations.

LABOR RELATIONS BACKGROUND

In certain respects the labor relations situation at Westinghouse has been influenced by developments at General Electric. There is, however, a very definite separate set of circumstances that has brought about the evolution of labor relations at Westinghouse. Like GE, Westinghouse has a national agreement which covers the 38,000 employees represented by the IUE; but unlike General Electric, Westinghouse also maintains national, or company-wide, contracts with the Federation of Westinghouse Independent Salaried Unions (15,000); the UE (7,500) and a contract with the IBEW for its 700 repair shop members. The IBEW also represents another 15,000 plant people, with separate agreements for each plant location.[66]

Westinghouse, like General Electric, had also evolved a pattern of bargaining under which three of its national contracts had expired at the same time, with the IBEW contract continuing for an additional month. Accordingly, master negotiations were conducted in Pittsburgh and most of the union representatives stayed in the same hotel. Because the same general settlement was accorded to all of the unions, there was apparently a long history of informal "coordination" among the various Westinghouse unions.[67] Evidence tends to indicate that all phases of contract settlement have been thoroughly discussed by all of the involved unions.

THE WESTINGHOUSE COALITION

Traditionally, labor contracts at Westinghouse have expired about two weeks after those at General Electric. And like GE, the lead in bargaining was usually assumed by the IUE, representing the largest number of workers.

---

[66]Personal Interviews with Westinghouse Electric Corporation Officials, November 9, 1967 and April 5, 1968.

[67]*Ibid.*

In a situation that was similar in both electrical manufacturers, Westinghouse was subjected to an extended series of requests for joint bargaining by the coalition unions, the first of which occurred on March 24, 1966 in a telegram from the coalition to Westinghouse President D. C. Burnham. The response to this effort, and the several that followed, was much the same as was GE's—a polite refusal to enlarge the negotiations beyond that which existed at the time.

When negotiations finally began—after having been delayed by various charges by the unions of unfair labor practices—the Company found that representatives of the IBEW and the IAM appeared at an IUE negotiating meeting. At that time, Westinghouse agreed to let the outsiders remain during the meetings but retained the right to protest, or reconsider its decision at a later date. When IBEW negotiations began, IUE and IAM representatives were present and each group presented the same extensive set of contract demands—some of which seemed to be inappropriate to the union making them. In all, the three unions attended sessions of the others, but apparently seldom attempted to participate, and were, at most ineffectual.[68] It soon became apparent that the outsiders were of little value, and they ceased attending meetings. Unlike the GE situation, and in spite of union publicity to the contrary, there was little interest expressed by the other Westinghouse unions in participating in the GE-Westinghouse coalition effort.

In bargaining, it has been noted that the IUE was the largest of the coalition unions, and the one that traditionally set the pattern for settlement. In the 1966 negotiations, however, it would appear that the IBEW took a more militant stand, it demanded both a single national contract to include all IBEW represented plants and an end to area wage differentials which both General Electric and Westinghouse have always maintained as a result of geographic and product diversity and the competitive markets in which they operate.[69]

Although bargaining at Westinghouse continued with all unions, as in the past, and with periodic participation of outsiders in negotiating sessions, apparently little progress was made on economic issues until settlement was reached by the IUE at General Electric. At that time, the IUE announced that it was prepared to settle for the same pattern,

---

[68]*Ibid.*
[69]*Ibid.* See also *Business Week,* November 5, 1966, pp. 50–51.

and did so, effectively abandoning the other coalition unions, and thereby ending the threat of a company-wide shutdown.

Three of the larger IBEW manufacturing locals elected to strike the Company in anticipation of a larger settlement. After six months, each of the three returned to work under essentially the same terms as had been offered to the other locations.[70]

ANALYSIS

Although labor leaders hailed the coalition effort at Westinghouse in the same glowing terms as were used for the GE settlement,[71] a closer look at the results would tend to indicate that little, if anything, was gained by the effort. The unions did get a settlement that was fully equivalent to the General Electric agreement, and a settlement that was substantially better than the one reached in 1963. It is noted, however, that the settlements reached by Westinghouse and its unions have nearly always followed the GE pattern; and that it differed from earlier contracts for much the same reasons of economics that the GE settlement was richer: generally higher levels of wage increases throughout American industry. Moreover, the quick acceptance of contract terms based on the GE agreement by the IUE and in contrast, the long strike by IBEW locals, cannot have enhanced cooperation between these unions.

Thus, in spite of the tremendous amount of publicity generated by the Westinghouse coalition leaders, and by AFL-CIO President Meany, it would seem that little in the way of tangible gain was made to advance the cause of coalition bargaining at Westinghouse Electric Corporation.

---

[70]The IBEW manufacturing locals that struck were at Dover, New Jersey; Athens, Georgia; and Bloomington, Indiana. The strikes were ended at essentially the same terms as had been offered at the outset, although slight adjustments in non-wage areas were made. The IBEW was likewise unable to eliminate or narrow area wage differentials.

[71]Lasser, *op. cit.*, pp. 13, 19.

CHAPTER VII

UNION CARBIDE: A CASE OF THE FAILURE OF THE COALITION APPROACH

The effort of the AFL-CIO's Industrial Union Department (IUD) to compel the Union Carbide Corporation to bargain with a coalition of unions was, by its own admission, its greatest failure to date.[1] This failure was not attributed so much to any ineptness or lack of planning by the IUD, but was rather the result of a massive sustained effort by the Company to prevent any significant future coalition efforts on the part of the unions with which it deals.

The study of the Carbide situation amply demonstrates that the coalition movement can be defeated if the company is able and willing to bear the necessary costs.

[1]Taken from statements made by several IUD and international union officials made at the IUD Collective Bargaining Conference in Washington, D.C., June 27–29, 1967.

THE COMPANY

Union Carbide Corporation is one of the most diversified giants of American industry. Its total assets at the end of 1966 were $2.4 billion, sales $2.2 billion, and profit almost $231 million.[2] The Company employs over 80,000 people in the United States, Canada and Puerto Rico and has 46,000 employees in unconsolidated foreign subsidiaries.

The firm as it now exists was incorporated in November 1917 in New York when it acquired the properties of the Union Carbide Company, National Carbon Company, Inc., the Linde Air Products Company, and the Prest-O-Lite Company, Inc., as well as the subsidiaries of those predecessors. It has continued to expand through growth and acquisition to the point where it now operates about 280 plants in the United States and Canada and maintains some 174 sales offices and 412 warehouses in principal domestic industrial centers. Company operations also include 30 subsidiaries throughout the world and a transportation system of four ocean-going ships, 120 barges, 4,300 private railroad cars and a fleet of especially constructed highway trailers for transporting cryogenic fluids.[3]

Because of its size, Union Carbide is divided into various operating groups: metals, chemicals, carbons, industrial gases, and plastics. Table 7–1 shows the range of the Company's operations by product grouping.[4]

TABLE 7–1

OPERATIONS OF UNION CARBIDE CORPORATION BY PRODUCT GROUPING

Product Groups	*Illustrative Examples of Products*
Metals & minerals	Ferroalloys, alloying metals, refractory metals and compounds; titanium master alloys and composites, special alloys, metal

[2]Much of the information in this section is taken from Standard and Poor's, *Standard Corporation Descriptions*, July 31, 1967, pp. 1230–1233. (See also *Fortune*, December 1965, which described Union Carbide as the "most conglomerate of all chemical companies" and, behind General Electric and Westinghouse, the third "most conglomerate" business in the United States. Although Carbide may not now occupy "third place," it certainly remains as one of the most diversified American corporations, and therefore a prime target of the IUD.)

[3]Standard and Poor's, *loc. cit.*

[4]*Ibid.*

	ceramics, boron and silicon nitrides, grid wire, ores and concentrates including chromium, manganese, asbestos and zirconium diboride.
Carbon products	Activated carbon, aerospace graphite, anodes for electrolytic cells, brushes for electric motors and generators, chemical processing equipment, electrical and mechanical specialities, fabrics, fibers and foils, furnace electrodes and linings, lighting carbons, molten metal processing equipment, nuclear graphite and fuel elements, pipe slides, pyrotechnic graphite, spectroscopic electrodes and powders, structural shapes.
Chemical products	Synthetic organic chemicals including solvents, intermediates, monomers, plasticizers, lubricants, humectants, pesticides, corrosion inhibitors, fluorocarbon propellants and refrigerants, fungistants, fumigants, water-soluble resins, silicone chemicals and products, molecular sieves, synthetic crystals, automotive chemicals, latexes, urethane foam chemicals, detergent alkylates and intermediates, coatings, and chemicals.
Gases and equipment	Oxygen, hydrogen, nitrogen, argon, helium and other atmospheric gases, calcium carbide and acetylene; welding, cutting and surfacing equipment, flame plating, steel conditioning machines, rock-piercing and shearing equipment, cryogenic fluids and equipment and Polarstream in-transit refrigeration of food.
Food products	Food casings and specialty films for the food industry.

TABLE 7–1

OPERATIONS OF UNION CARBIDE CORPORATION BY PRODUCT GROUPING
(Continued)

Product Groups	*Illustrative Examples of Products*
Textile materials	Dynel modacrylic fibers, Fiberboard non-woven materials, Vileau vinyl fabrics.
Plastics	Acrylonitrile-butadiene-styrene (ABS) plastics, acrylic, epoxy, parylene, phenolic phenoxy, polyethylene, polypropylene, polystyrene, polysulfane and vinyl resins and components; film and sheeting bags, bottles and other containers.
Consumer products	Batteries for clocks, flashlights, photoflash, portable radios and television sets, hearing aids, toys, military equipment and cordless appliances; flashlights, miniature bulbs, automotive antifreezes, car care products, medical oxygen, synthetic star sapphires, rubies and emeralds, swim products, mattresses and sofa beds, baby and juvenile plastic products, straws, bags and wrap.
Nuclear products	Radio isotopes and stable isotopes, uranium ores and concentrates, irradiation and other nuclear services. Also operates Atomic Energy Commission installations at Oak Ridge, Tennessee and Paducah, Kentucky.
Research	Union Carbide employs more than 2,000 scientists and engineers in research and development activity at 24 laboratories in the United States, Canada and Europe.

Source: Standard and Poor's, *Standard Corporation Descriptions,* July 31, 1967, pp. 1230.

Labor Policy

Union Carbide has long pursued a consistent policy of labor relations which it described as "pro-employee," a policy that has proved to be viable by almost any measure. The Company believes that the wishes of the employees may be best expressed without an "intermediary" in the form of a labor union, but has always felt that once a union has been selected to bargain for its employees it should then bargain in good faith with that union. Although less than half of Carbide's employees have chosen union representation, Union Carbide is a party to more than 100 labor contracts which have each been locally negotiated (see Table 7–2). The plants deal with some 24 international unions and one independent local union. With one exception inherited from a corporate acquisition, the union has been certified or recognized as the collective bargaining agent for each plant locally.[5]

TABLE 7–2

UNION AFFILIATION—EMPLOYEES OF UNION CARBIDE CORPORATION

December 31, 1966

35,200—Total Number of Hourly Employees

- 22,950—Hourly Employees Represented by Unions (65 percent)
  - 6,300—Represented by OCAW
  - 4,000—Represented by USW
  - 3,700—Represented by IAM
  - 1,900—Represented by 2 Local Trades Councils
  - 3,650—Represented by 12 other international unions affiliated with AFL-CIO
  - 1,800—Represented by 7 other internationals not affiliated with AFL-CIO
  - 1,600—Represented by 1 independent local union

Source: Union Carbide Corporation

Prior to 1966, Carbide labor negotiations were usually concluded in a satisfactory manner without resorting to either strikes or lockouts,

[5] *Union Carbide's Experience with the IUD's Coordinated Bargaining Program*, prepared by Union Carbide, March 1, 1967, p. 1.

as demonstrated by a lost time record as a percent of hours worked that was considerably lower than the national average. There were only two years prior to 1966 when strike losses approached or exceeded the national average: in 1957 and 1959. In both of these years, losses were the direct result of international unions attempting to force the Company to bargain on a multiplant basis and of the company's refusal to agree to such a position. In 1957, the Oil, Chemical and Atomic Workers (OCAW) struck five Linde plants seeking joint negotiations; and in 1959 the United Steelworkers of America (USW) sought joint negotiations for three ferroalloy plants.[6] Neither effort was successful, and neither effort approached the magnitude of the effort of the Industrial Union Department of the AFL-CIO (IUD) that came about in 1966.

The Company has always bargained on a local basis and attempted to maintain wages that compared favorably with those in the area or industry. It has never followed a policy of company wage uniformity. Its pension and group insurance plans have, however, with some time lags, as will be described below, tended to be fairly uniform throughout the country—a fact that the coalition proponents seized upon to support their case.

COALITION HISTORY

Because of the fact that Union Carbide has been—from its very inception—more of a holding company than an operating entity, all dealings with local unions were on a strictly local basis. It was not until the middle 1940's that staff functions such as industrial relations were made an integral part of the operations of the Company. In fact, it was not until the middle 1950's that all components of the Corporation agreed to use "Union Carbide" on their letterheads, and a Corporate reorganization in 1963 and 1964 made these components operating divisions responsible to the office of the President of the Company.[7]

Early Union Attempts at Coalition Bargaining

The roots of joint bargaining efforts at Union Carbide go back as far as October 1945 when the first meeting of what was to become

---

[6] *Ibid.*, p. 2.

[7] "Union Carbide's 1966 IUD Story," a report prepared by Union Carbide's Law Department, July 1967, p. 2.

known as the "Carbide Council" was held. This first "policy conference" was attended by representatives of the United Electrical Workers (UE) and the Gas, Coke and Chemical Workers (which later became part of the Oil, Chemical and Atomic Workers Union—OCAW). Out of this first meeting came an invitation to other Carbide locals in New York, New Jersey, Ohio, and West Virginia; and in December of that year, the Council formally requested corporation-wide bargaining at Union Carbide.[8]

The Company refused to negotiate with this first coalition, but by 1949 had begun to meet informally with the group for discussion of mutual problems. These meetings began on an annual basis in the late 1950's, and were conducted with a clear understanding that no negotiations would take place at the meeting. The company made such understanding a condition for the meetings.

The Early Effort of the IUD

When a separate Collective Bargaining Services Section was formed by the IUD in April 1964 with the express purpose of promoting coalition bargaining, the Union Carbide Council was one of the first to cooperate with the IUD officials at a Washington meeting. Although the Council maintained a separate identity at that time, published reports indicated that the Council and the IUD were about to form an alliance.[9] When the Collective Bargaining Services Section made its report to the IUD Convention in November of 1965, it stated that:

> Eight international unions are represented on this [Union Carbide] committee: Machinists, Chemical Workers, IUE, OCAW, Transport Workers, UAW, Steelworkers, and Glass and Ceramic Workers. In the past, the committee has been purely informational. In December 1965, however, the IUD and a steering committee of the major unions will hold a top level meeting with company representatives to discuss the possibility of national negotiations of the company-wide pension plan. Also to be discussed is the current 50 percent employees' contribution under the hospital-medical-surgical program. At the very least, it is expected that bargaining goals will be worked out with the company

[8] *Ibid.*

[9] See for example: "Teaming up for Wage Talks," *Chemical Week,* November 20, 1965, pp. 23–24.

which can then be spread to each local union whose contracts expire in 1966.[10]

Although the referred to meeting never occurred, the IUD continued to work quickly and efficiently in attempting to weld the various key Carbide locals into a coalition for bargaining in 1966. By March of that year, the IUD Coordinator for the Union Carbide Committee, Steve Harris, had sent a memorandum to each committee member outlining a proposed set of bargaining demands and enclosing a resolution to be passed by each local which would bind that union to the IUD program. The resolution stated that each local whose contract with the Company expired in 1966 "will participate in coordinated bargaining with the Company. . . . Each local union participating in the 1966 coordinated bargaining will consult the IUD-Union Carbide Steering Committee, and consider its views and advice before accepting any final Company proposal."[11]

The unions had decided that the Mining and Metals Division of the Company would be the primary target for the first round of coalition bargaining since four of the five ferroalloy plants of the division had contracts that expired within a space of two months during July and August. At the annual meeting of the Company and the Carbide Council in April 1966, there was a greater-than-usual number of people in attendance; and a new spirit of militancy was apparent. At this meeting, Harris, the IUD coordinator, stated the unions' desire to engage in multiunit bargaining on pension and insurance as well as on certain other "national economic demands." Harris even went so far as to promise that Company that "You're in for trouble this year—by August or September a bunch of plants will be down."[12] This meeting was followed by a visit to Carbide's New York offices by Jack Conway, Executive Director of the IUD, who suggested that a dialogue be initi-

[10]*Agenda for Tomorrow,* Report to the Industrial Union Department, AFL-CIO, Sixth Constitutional Convention, Washington, D.C., November 18–19, 1965 by Walter P. Reuther, President, p. 70. The Unions referred to are: International Association of Machinists and Aerospace Workers (IAM), International Chemical Workers Union (ICWU), International Union of Electrical, Radio and Machine Workers (IUE), Oil, Chemical and Atomic Workers International Union (OCAW), Transport Workers Union (TWU), International Union, United Automobile, Aerospace and Agricultural Implement Workers of America (UAW), United Steelworkers of America (USW), and United Glass and Ceramic Workers of North America (UGCW).

[11]Letter from Steve Harris, Coordinator, Collective Bargaining Services Section, Industrial Union Department, AFL-CIO to Union Carbide Committee, March 7, 1966.

[12]Personal Interview with Earl L. Engle, General Manager—Industrial Relations, Union Carbide Corporation, New York, August 7, 1967.

ated between top officials of Union Carbide, the IUD, and the international union officers involved in the coalition program.[13]

At each turn, the Company firmly told the unions that it had no intention of bargaining on any basis except that as certified by the National Labor Relations Borad (NLRB), that is, on an individual plant-by-plant basis. The Company stated its belief that local bargaining is best for employee and employer, and that confining the negotiations to local issues, the needs of the employees at the particular location would be best met.

The Two-Contract System

Union Carbide has traditionally maintained two separate agreements with each of the unions that have been certified to represent employees at any given location. The first of these is the usual labor agreement which delineates work rules, seniority, wage rates and other conditions of employment. The length of such an agreement is typically from one to three years. There is also a second agreement at each location, specified to run for a period of five years which sets forth the terms of pension and insurance plans (life, sickness and accident coverage) applicable to the employees. In general, all such plans are very nearly identical. The Company ordinarily reviews its policies in the pension and insurance areas every two to three years; and when deemed appropriate, improvements are made. First benefits are extended to the salaried and nonunion hourly employees, then, as labor agreements become open for negotiation or as unions ask for the improvements, the Company usually makes these improvements available to the bargaining unit—without deducting the cost from the expected wage increases—and extends the term of the pension and insurance agreement for another five-year period.[14]

This dual contract arrangement seemed to the IUD a sound basis for its efforts to build a strong coalition at Union Carbide. Indeed, by the spring of 1966, the IUD had formulated a program to force coalition bargaining on the Company:

> The committee had agreed to a double approach. First to coordinated bargaining to secure the best economic proposal possible for those

[13]*Ibid.*
[14]*Union Carbide's Experience*, p. 1.

> locals whose contracts expired between July and November 1966 and to prepare for national bargaining of the company-wide pension and life insurance plans in 1967.
>
> A common set of goals was prepared by the local unions in the metals division plus other locals whose contracts expired in the second half of 1966. Representatives of the coordinating locals attended negotiations at several plant locations and also attended local membership meetings. Local unions pledged to work together until a decent settlement had been secured always keeping in mind that the major effect would occur in 1967 when 25,000 members were available to strike while in 1966 only 7,000 would be available.[15]

It is therefore evident that the IUD was prepared to take on Carbide, and the first test of the coalition came when bargaining began at the Alloy, West Virginia, metals plant.

THE 1966 NEGOTIATIONS

Although the Company began negotiating new labor agreements in the early part of 1966 on the same basis as it had in the past, and was successful in reaching satisfactory settlements at some locations, it soon became obvious that the IUD was indeed becoming involved in Carbide bargaining, that a coalition was attempting to change the structure of bargaining, and that the "spearhead" of this attempt was aimed at the ferroalloy plants (Alloy, Ashtabula, Portland, Marietta, and Sheffield). The bargaining strategy of the IUD first became operative at Alloy, West Virginia, when the OCAW local there engaged in delaying tactics and where, as we shall note, the Company locked out the employees on July 2. It was apparent to the Company that the Alloy union was willing to let the situation drag on until it was in a position to join other locations in a multiunit effort. Carbide's calendar of negotiations at major plants during the second half of 1966 is shown below:

Deadline	*Plant*	*Union*
July 2	Alloy, West Virginia	OCAW
July 13	Ashtabula, Ohio	USW
*August 1	Niagara Falls, New York	OCAW
August 15	Portland, Oregon	USW

---

[15] *Ibid.*, p. 2 ff.

August 22	East Chicago, Indiana	OCAW
August 27	Marietta, Ohio	OCAW
September 1	Sistersville, West Virginia	ICWU
September 29	Kokomo, Indiana	USW
October 1	Speedway, Indiana	OCAW
October 1	Whiting, Indiana	OCAW
*October 28	Fostoria, Ohio	IUE
November 1	Sheffield, Alabama	USW

(*Plants where settlements were made without strikes.)

Alloy, West Virginia

The July 2, 1966, contract deadline at Alloy was the first of the ferroalloy plants that the IUD had included in its program. The OCAW, with the IUD's Harris directing strategy but not the bargaining table, advanced the demands of the IUD committee and "sat on its hands as the deadline approached. It was plain that the Union wanted to work past the deadline without a contract, and later join other plants in a simultaneous work stoppage."[16]

The Company, in its attempt to get meaningful negotiations under way, offered the union an improved vacation plan which had been granted to salaried and some other union represented units and certain changes in the pension and insurance plans. Tied to these proposals was a Company demand that the pension and insurance agreement be amended to run for another five-year period. This proposal did not meet with the IUD plans for a total effort in 1967 and brought, on June 10, the filing by the Union of an unfair labor practice charge.[17] The Company made no note in negotiating sessions of the receipt of the charges, and strangely enough, the Union also failed to make mention of the charges.

Throughout the negotiating meetings, the Company found it extremely difficult to engage the Union in meaningful bargaining, even on non-economic issues which were to be settled prior to the economic matters. In light of the Union objection to the inclusion of pension,

[16]*Union Carbide's Experience, op. cit.,* p. 6.

[17]See Trial Examiner's Decision. 165 NLRB No. 26, Union Carbide Corporation, Mining and Metals Division and Oil, Chemical and Atomic Workers International Union, Local 3–89, AFL-CIO, October 14, 1966. Also Findings of Fact and Conclusions of Law in *Farkes* vs. *Union Carbide Corporation,* Civil No. 3487, U.S. District Court, Southern District of West Virginia at Charleston, August 12, 1966.

insurance and benefit proposals, a second package proposal for settlement was presented by Carbide on June 28. The second package was silent on the "objectional" pension and insurance proposals and did not provide improvements in the vacation plan, but increased the wage offer by one cent per hour.[18] A third and final offer was presented to the union on June 29 as the contract deadline approached, again including increased pension, insurance and vacation benefits. For the third time, the Union failed to respond with any counteroffer and simply rejected the Company proposals.

After communicating the proposed settlement to the employees so that they would understand its offer and what the reason was for the impasse, as well as the seriousness of the situation, the Company shut down the plant and locked out its employees.

Legal Maneuvers

The filing of the already noted unfair labor practice charge by OCAW of the coalition was just the first of many legal efforts that were made by both sides to settle the impasse and to bring about the successful consummation of a new contract. Some of the highlights are discussed below.

On July 7, 1966, five days after the lockout began at Alloy, Carbide filed unfair labor practice charges with the Board based on the Company contention that the union had failed to bargain in good faith by refusing even to respond to the three Company offers with any counterproposals.[19] On July 22, while a Board field investigator was taking and reviewing affidavits on the merits of the Company charge, a telegram was sent by the Cincinnati office of the Board to management stating that the Company charges were to be dismissed and that the Union charge would result in a complaint being filed against the Company. The NLRB also stated that it was instituting injunction proceedings under the terms of Section 10(j) of the National Labor Relations Act.[20]

In attempting to secure a 10(j) injunction, a Board attorney first tried on July 27 to have an *ex parte* order issued to reopen the Alloy

[18]See *Case Study, op. cit.*, p. 3.
[19]Engle Interview, *loc. cit.*
[20]Telegram to Union Carbide from Acting Regional Board Director Emil Farkes, July 22, 1966, 5:20 P.M.

plant. A federal court judge in Bluefield, West Virginia, refused to grant an *ex parte* order, but set a hearing for August 1 on the injunction petition before Federal District Court Judge J. A. Field, Jr., in Charleston.[21] After some two and a half days of testimony between August 1 and August 3, the judge denied the NLRB move for an injunction, voicing the opinion that the lockout was entirely legal and that there was no basis for the Board's contention that the Company had committed an unfair labor practice.[22]

(Ed: This was one of the several times that the Board has failed to gain the use of the injunction to support coalition programs involving various companies.)

At that point, the Board proceeded to press its charge of an unfair labor practice against the Company in a one-day hearing on August 29, 1966, before Trial Examiner George J. Bott. The entire proceedings of the District Court were stipulated into the record, and little else was introduced in the form of new evidence. The Trial Examiner Bott, nevertheless, found that the lockout was illegal. Bott recommended that the Company be found guilty of the charge, and that the workers be "made whole for any loss of pay suffered by them."[23]

A three-member panel of the Board, however, did not adopt the recommendations of the Trial Examiner. In its Decision and Order, of June 9, 1967, the panel stated, in part:

> . . . Accordingly, it has not been established that Respondent [Union Carbide] insisted on the nonmandatory bargaining demand to the point

[21]On July 27, a Board attorney traveled approximately 120 miles to a Federal District Court in Bluefield, West Virginia and told the Court that he expected the Company attorneys to be there shortly. Because no attorney had been notified of the hearing, none appeared, and the Board attorney asked the Court to issue a temporary restraining order, *ex parte,* which was denied.

[22]See "Findings of Fact and Conclusions and Law," *op. cit.* Also letter from Judge John A. Field, Jr., Chief Judge, to Stanley A. Mestel, NLRB and David P. Johnson, representing Carbide.

The entire thrust and argument of the unfair labor practice charge in the Alloy situation centered around the question of whether or not Carbide was forcing an impasse on a nonmandatory subject of bargaining: the pension and insurance agreement which did not expire until a year later.

The Unions and the General Counsel contended that the final Company offer containing the improvements in pensions, holidays and insurance was one that precluded a lockout because the unions had not agreed to reopen the pension and insurance agreement; and that the impasse was forced through a nonbargainable issue.

Carbide argued that it had indeed made three offers which were rejected by, but still available to the Union, and that there was no insistence upon the Union taking all of the items offered and that the impasse and thus the lockout was legal.

[23]See Trial Examiner's Decision, *Union Carbide,* 165 NLRB, No. 26, June 15, 1967.

> of impasse. And, we are equally convinced that Respondent did not employ the subsequent lockout for the unlawful purpose of obtaining the nonmandatory bargaining item or otherwise to frustrate or undermine the Union's position as the bargaining representative of Respondent's employees.
>
> Having found that the Respondent's conduct during the negotiations, including the lockout after impasse in bargaining was reached, was not unlawful, we shall dismiss the complaint in its entirety.[24]

The OCAW appealed this decision of the panel to the full Board for reconsideration, but the Board reaffirmed its order.[25] The case currently is before the Circuit Court for the District of Columbia on the Union's appeal from the Board's orders.

While these legal maneuverings were in process and after the lockout had been in progress at Alloy for twelve weeks, the Company invited the employees back to work, but since other locations were then striking against Carbide and the IUD demands had not been met, the OCAW and the IUD then officially called a strike at the Alloy plant.[26] It lasted until some other strikes in the Company were settled.

Ashtabula, Ohio

The Steelworker contract at Ashtabula bore a termination date of July 13, and contract negotiations there followed the same general pattern as had been established at Alloy: there seemed to be no real interest in bargaining until several plants could be shut down in a simultaneous effort. Perhaps the USW expected to be locked out at Ashtabula in the same manner as had occurred at Alloy, but the Company apparently felt that production was needed and that a second lockout would not add materially to its bargaining strength.[27] Ohio Law also provides for immediate payment of unemployment compensation benefits when workers are locked out. Thus, negotiations continued past the contract deadline.

Agreement was reached on July 28 in an off-the-record informal meeting with the District Director of the Steelworkers, after several concessions by the Carbide representative, but the agreement was repu-

---

[24]The three-man panel of the Board consisted of members Fanning, Brown, and Jenkins.
[25]See Order Denying Motion, 165 NLRB, No. 26, July 19, 1967.
[26]Engle Interview, *loc. cit.*
[27]Engle Interview, *loc. cit.*

diated the next day.[28] On August 27, the Ashtabula local joined with other coalition members in multiplant strikes that would run for up to 246 calendar days.

Marietta, Ohio

The situation at Marietta is illustrative of the power that the IUD had in the Carbide situation. The plant has two separately certified locals of the OCAW: one at the steam station having about 75 employees, and a production unit of about 1000 workers.

The strike was called by the IUD and OCAW on August 27, the same day that the strikes were called at East Chicago, Ashtabula and Portland, Oregon. (Sistersville, West Virginia, struck on August 31.) The steam station at Marietta, however, by a narrow vote decided to remain at work, while the production unit joined the other strikers.

In the process of bargaining, the Carbide negotiators claim that it became apparent to them that the local union leaders and the rank and file did not fully support the programs espoused by the international and the IUD. In fact, they allege that local union leadership indicated a willingness to settle the strike called by the IUD by approaching the Company with a proposition for an off-the-record accord. It is reported that five of the seven members of the local committee agreed to recommend the settlement at a membership ratification meeting. Three days later, when a local meeting was held across the Ohio River at Parkersburg, West Virginia, to vote on the proposed agreement, the local officials found the dais filled with members of other unions, the IUD coordinator, and the International President of the OCAW. When the International took over the meeting, the membership was "reminded of its responsibility" to the coalition effort and told, in effect, that the meeting was not in order. No vote was taken.[29]

This usurpation, however, led to what was soon to become a back-to-work movement when the employees began to realize that the local had lost control of its own bargaining. Since the IUD describes the situation in January 1967 as "the weaknesses that were developing at Marietta,"[30] it is believed that this local IUD friction did exist and was

[28] *Ibid.*
[29] See *Case Study, loc. cit.*
[30] *Ibid.*

a factor in the coalition defeat. The strike was called off on January 27, 1967.

Sheffield, Alabama

The Sheffield situation provides another example of the manner in which the coalition dominated the situation. The USW international union is the certified bargaining agent for the Sheffield plant of Carbide's Mining and Metals Division. As negotiations proceeded on the wage reopener at that plant, it became evident that agreement could be reached. Terms were agreed upon, the membership voted to accept the new settlement, and local officials signed the agreement. The international representative however, refused to sign the stipulation in spite of alleged previous open statements that he would do so if the agreement were ratified by the membership and signed by local officials. On November 9, upon instructions from the Steelworkers International, a picket line was established at Sheffield.

Just prior to Thanksgiving day, however, a back-to-work movement had started when 34 of the 320 employees at the plant crossed the international picket line and renewed some limited production. By Christmas sufficient pressure was put on the international by some 130 members who were crossing the picket line that it was forced to come to terms with the Company.

Union Carbide viewed the USW picket line as an act in violation of the law, and filed an unfair labor practice charge with the Atlanta Regional Board office and asked the Board to seek 10(j) proceedings against the Union so as to reopen the plant by having the picketing enjoined. Both of these applications were held in a state of suspension by the NLRB for some two and a half months, at which time it dismissed the charge, explaining that now the strike had ended, the wage reopening agreement had been signed by the international union, and, moreover, the union's alleged violation of the no-strike provision had been referred to arbitration.[31] The Company had filed a grievance against the international union at Sheffield, claiming a violation of the no-strike clause. However, in a decision rendered in August 1967, arbitrator Carl Warns dismissed the grievance. He rationalized that since the international was the certified bargaining agent, it could not be

[31]Engle Interview, *loc. cit.*

bound by a wage reopening settlement (which would shut off the right to strike) that it had not signed.

Kokomo, Indiana

The situation at the Kokomo metals plant was different from the others in two respects: much of the production there was of a labor-intensive nature, and some of the products manufactured were defense components for use in aerospace equipment.

The IUD looked at the situation at Kokomo as the key to forcing Union Carbide into national bargaining, either through an attempt to have the defense aspect force a Taft-Hartley injunction to cover all of the struck operations, or through use of the "good offices" of federal officials. At the time that the Kokomo plant was struck, union negotiators were insisting that only national bargaining would settle the various strikes; and Kokomo was to be the focal point of this bargaining. The Company, however, insisted that bargaining be continued on a local basis, and continued to reaffirm its position that no strike, with the exception of Kokomo, was having any serious effect on the national welfare.[32]

Carbide felt that the offer made to the employees at the Kokomo plant would have been accepted if it had been put to a secret vote, but this the union refused to do, insisting instead that the negotiations be moved to Washington. Finally, at the insistence of the Secretary of Labor, Carbide did agree to a bargaining session in Secretary Wirtz's office, but insisted successfully that such negotiations be confined to the wage reopener at Kokomo only.

When this Washington session got under way, the local Kokomo management was prepared to settle, but the union, represented by officials of the IUD and three internationals, amply demonstrated that they would not on a local basis. In view of this impasse, the Secretary of Labor recommended that an 80-day injunction be issued to send just this plant back to work. The President sought the injunction, and it was issued by the federal district court for the District of Columbia. Bargaining continued for about seven more weeks before the union accepted an amended Company offer. The Company believes that the union was worried that the "last offer" would be accepted by the mem-

[32]*Ibid.*

bership in the event of a vote provided by the Taft-Hartley machinery and chose to reach a negotiated settlement instead.[33]

It is clear from the union activities with regard to the Kokomo situation that the main thrust of the efforts by the IUD were directed toward extralegal reshaping of the bargaining unit to embrace nation-wide bargaining. It was a great disappointment to the unions when Carbide was successful in insisting on local bargaining, despite union pressure exerted on the office of the Secretary of Labor in Washington.

The Traveling Circus

After September 1 (by which time work stoppages had occurred at Alloy, Ashtabula, Portland, East Chicago, Marietta, and Sistersville), there were several occasions when numerous "outsiders" (i.e., representatives of other local and international unions) showed up at the bargaining table. This first occurred at a negotiating meeting for the Marietta plant in nearby Parkersburg, West Virginia, on September 9. A similar situation almost developed in Parkersburg on September 14 at a meeting for the Sistersville plant. In this case, the "outsiders" were in the immediate vicinity, but did not actually enter the room where the bargaining table was. Also, when negotiations were reconvened for the Alloy unit on September 21, "outsiders" were present. Further evidence of the existence of the coalition was presented by the October 5 meeting of the Carbide Council at Ashtabula, Ohio, which coincided in time and place with negotiations called by the Federal Mediation and Conciliation Service. An across-the-table confrontation did not occur at Ashtabula, however, for FMCS personnel met with each of the negotiating committees separately. Meetings at which "outsiders" appeared came to

---

[33]The IUD *Case Study, op. cit.*, describes the Kokomo situation a little differently (p. 4 ff):

Repeated efforts were made by the IUD steering committee which included representatives of USA, OCAW, and IUD through Bill Simkin, Director of Federal Mediation Conciliation Service, Jim Reynolds, Assistant Secretary of Labor and finally Willard Wirtz, the Secretary of Labor, to force the company to meet with the steering committee at one place to settle all strikes. The company resisted all efforts by these government officials.

Finally, when a Taft-Hartley 80-day injunction became imminent at the largest of the struck plants at Kokomo, Indiana, W. Wirtz, made one last attempt to bring the parties to Washington. The Kokomo local union committee was augmented by the IUD steering committee at a special Sunday morning session. The company unfortunately sent the same Kokomo plant negotiations [sic] who had handled local negotiations during six months of fruitless bargaining. Bargaining made fruitless because of their lack of authority to make decisions on any important issue.

The company had once again thumbed its nose at the United States government. Secretary Wirtz had sent the same telegram to the company which was sent to the international presidents. This wire requested that both sides be represented by those who could make decisions for the corporations and the unions. The unions had such representatives there, the company did not.

be known as the "traveling circus." The ringmaster was Steve Harris of the IUD, although he did not appear in person at these meetings.

The Carbide position on the presence of "outsiders" was simply this: The local union was free to choose any negotiating committee it wished; and as long as the local claimed that the "outsiders" were representing it and that they were there to bargain on only a contract for that particular plant, then there could be no valid objection. The Company asked only the spokesman for the certified local if the "outsiders" were the local's representatives. However, the Company frequently expressed the conviction that these persons for the most part did not help the local committee, but that they usually impeded progress of the meeting.[34]

Wherever the circus occurred, the union bargaining committee set forth the IUD-formulated demands as the major part of the total package to be bargained. However, the union committees were less than willing to engage in any real bargaining on a single plant basis. In fact, after this one round by the traveling circus, the Company found it difficult to get the union for any one plant to come to the bargaining table. In the fall of 1966 and continuing into the winter, unions and the IUD were disposed to let the economic pressures build on the company in the belief that eventually it would engage in coalition bargaining.

Analysis

As the data in Table 7–3 show, the employees represented by 11 unions lost from 44 to 246 calendar days of work involving some 7,200 employees and totaling about 6.0 million hours. The Company suffered an after tax loss in profit of some $17 million.[35]

At the time that the work interruption began at Alloy, the highest increase in the area was then granted by a nonunion duPont Company plant, an increase which was estimated to have been about 11 cents per hour.[36] The Carbide proposal had been between 8.5 and 10.5 cents with "still a little to give,"[37] and if the vacation improvement is included, a total of 14.5 to 16.5 cents would be the estimated cost. This amounted to about 3.5 percent in wages or 4 to 5 percent for the package.

---

[34]Engle Interview, *loc. cit.*
[35]*Case Study, loc. cit.*
[36]Engle Interview, *loc. cit.*
[37]*Ibid.*

Table 7–3

IUD STRIKES AT UNION CARBIDE
1966–1967

Location	*Union*	*Contract Expired*	*Strike Began/Ended/Length*	*New Contract Expires*	*Remarks*
Alloy, West Virginia 1,200 employees	OCAW	July 2, 1966	Lockout—July 2, 1966 Strike—Sept. 26, 1966 —February 12, 1967 226 days	Feb. 13, 1969	
Ashtabula, Ohio 900 employees	USW	July 13, 1966	August 28, 1966 —April 2, 1967 218 days	March 31, 1970	
Portland, Oregon 100 employees	USW	Aug. 15, 1966	August 28, 1966 —April 30, 1967 246 days	July 1, 1970	
East Chicago, Indiana 115 employees	OCAW	Aug. 22, 1966	August 28, 1966 —March 26, 1967 210 days	April 1, 1970	
Marietta, Ohio 1,250 employees	OCAW	Aug. 27, 1966	August 28, 1966 —January 27, 1967 152 days	Aug. 27, 1969	
Sistersville-Long Reach, W. Va. 250 employees	ICWU	Sept. 1, 1966	September 1, 1966 —March 19, 1967 200 days	Sept. 15, 1969	

Kokomo, Indiana 2,150 employees	USW	Wage Reopener– Sept. 29, 1966	September 30, 1966 —December 23, 1966 85 days	March 29, 1968	Returned to work per Taft-Hartley Injunction; negotiated settlement reached Feb. 1967, extending contract from Sept. 29, 1967 to March 29, 1968
Speedway, Indiana 440 employees	OCAW	Sept. 30, 1966	October 1, 1966 —March 19, 1967 170 days	Mar. 23, 1970	
*Whiting, Indiana 420 employees	OCAW	Wage Reopener– Oct. 1, 1966	October 1, 1966 —April 6, 1967 188 days	April 6, 1969	New contract negotiated existing contract would have expired August 1, 1967
*Whiting, Indiana 30 employees	OCAW	Nov. 1, 1966	November 4, 1966 —April 14, 1967 164 days	April 15, 1970	
Sheffield, Alabama 300 employees	USW	Wage Reopener– Nov. 1, 1966	November 9, 1966 —December 23, 1966 44 days	Nov. 1, 1967	Local union signed wage reopening settlement Oct. 31, 1966, but International Union set up picket line Nov. 9, 1966; extension of contract was negotiated in April, 1967 so that it now expires November 1, 1968

*There were two separate establishments at Whiting (Chemicals Plant; Hydrogen Plant). The same OCAW Local Union represented employees at both such plants plus employees at the East Chicago Plant.

Source: Union Carbide Corporation records, January 1968.

Between the time bargaining began at Alloy and the time of settlement, several agreements of national impact[38] had changed the expected basis of settlement. In fact, the general pattern established at the various Carbide plants was one of about 15 cents the first year, 10 cents the second, and 10 cents per hour the third year on contracts that ranged in length from 12 to 38 months for an average increase of between 4.5 and 5 percent of the base rates then in effect.[39]

The contract expiration dates are now more disparate than those in effect at the time when the IUD began its effort, and the pension and insurance agreements have been again extended for five-year periods. The IUD admits that this encounter is its major defeat up to this point, but claims that it has not given up the effort. It states:

> During the next few years the 14 international unions in Union Carbide will be concentrating on an effort to organize the large number of United States and Canadian plants of the corporation.
>
> . . . Attempts will also be made to coordinate activities with the European labor movement which represents a large number of Union Carbide plants. The next effort with Union Carbide must be a broad-based fully coordinated strike which includes an effective consumer boycott of the company's principal product lines. Anything less would provide only the same type draw which resulted from the 1966–67 round of coordination.
>
> The company, in order to avoid a larger coordinated effort in 1967 which would have included approximately 25,000 employees, took the initiative and locked out the Alloy membership. The Company expected that this group would crumble and that the pattern would be established before other locals could legally strike. When this did not happen and the other plants did strike as their contracts expired, the company . . . fought to the bitter end. Fortunately, with the exception of a few weaknesses, the unions were able to battle the company in a strike which was financed on a shoe string. Between the Alloy lockout and the Portland settlement there were 10 months of heartache and deprivation. The members in these 11 plants will not be able by them-

---

[38]During this period, agreements had been concluded in airlines, construction and in the General Electric-Westinghouse encounter with coalition bargaining. All of these helped lay to rest the 3.2 percent guidepost figure that had been a target at the start of the Alloy negotiations.

[39]See *Union Carbide's Experience, loc cit.* It is also interesting to note that of 7,200 employees who were out of work during the strike and lockout period, including many skilled tradesmen, only about 200 failed to return to work when the strikes were settled—a number far less than might have been expected from normal rates of attrition.

> selves to take on the Union Carbide giant again. It must be a broad-based cooperative effort which includes all of the unions which will gain the fruits of this effort.[40]

Union Carbide remains opposed to coalition bargaining, and has now negotiated a sizable number of its contracts to expire over a broad spectrum of time. The employees won somewhat greater benefits as a result of the coalition attempt, and of developments in collective bargaining which occurred elsewhere during the last half of 1966. For these gains, they paid a high price in strikes, lockouts, and time lost from work. The IUD must convince them that another attempt is worth the efforts. In view of the experience and its costs, this is not likely to prove an easy task for the coalition proponents.

[40]*Case Study, op. cit.,* p. 7.

CHAPTER VIII

COALITION BARGAINING AT 3M: THE OBJECTIVES BECOME CLEAR

The effort of the Industrial Union Department of the AFL-CIO (IUD) to engage Minnesota Mining and Manufacturing Company (3M) in a coalition effort in 1967 was an effort that cannot be regarded as a real success by the unions, but it is a situation wherein the subterfuge was removed, and the real objectives of the coalition program were brought to the fore.

Although the ultimate move toward coalition bargaining directly involved only two participating locals, the 3M situation reflects one that had been underway for several years, where numerous locals had been active in the IUD program, and where the coalition was in many ways quite advanced in its development.

THE COMPANY

The Minnesota Mining and Manufacturing Company was first incorporated in 1902, and reincorporated in June 1929 under Delaware law.[1] Originally, the Company produced bonding materials for coated abrasives. Operations have continually expanded since that time, largely through the development of new products, but also through acquisition of other companies. 3M currently manufactures and markets a highly diversified range of products that includes about 25,000 separate items in 40 major product lines.

The Company and its subsidiaries operate about 113 plants, with 70 in the United States, 26 in Great Britain and Eastern Europe, and the remainder spread throughout the free world. Additionally, 3M has about 285 sales offices of which 128 are in the United States and the remainder in 140 cities in 32 foreign countries.

The more than 53,000 employees of the 3M Company helped to make it one of the leaders in the fields of pressure sensitive tapes, adhesive products, coated abrasives, copying machines, electrical insulating materials, reflective materials, magnetic recording tapes, roofing materials, photographic supplies, and printing materials. (See Table 8–1). Its sales for 1967 amounted to more than $1.2 billion, with a net income of more than $147 million.

LABOR RELATIONS BACKGROUND

At the 70 plants that are operated by 3M in the United States, the Company maintains about 50 separate collective bargaining agreements with some 19 separate international unions. (See Table 8–2). The history of the 3M labor relations and Company policy has amply supported the contention that contracts have always been conducted on a plant-by-plant basis, and that there has never been national or company-wide bargaining of any nature—despite claims to the contrary by the IUD.[2] A single exception to the strictly local bargaining rule came about in 1955 when the Company and two Oil, Chemical and Atomic Workers International Union (OCAW) locals at Hastings (Chemolite) and St. Paul, Minnesota voluntarily agreed to negotiate certain major cost items on a joint basis. The agreement to negotiate these items for the two locals only—located about 15 miles apart—has continued to date.

---

[1]Standard and Poor's, *Standard Corporation Descriptions,* September 14, 1967, p. 8359.

[2]Personal interviews with 3M Company officers, Summer 1967 and Spring 1968, Philadelphia, Pennsylvania and St. Paul, Minnesota.

TABLE 8–1

3M COMPANY
PRODUCTS BY GROUP

Group	*Products*
Tape and allied products	Pressure-sensitive adhesive tapes for industrial, commercial and home use, automatic and manual tape dispensers, reinforced plastics, gummed tapes for carton sealing, specialty items, including surgical tapes, surgical drapes, hospital masks, and dental restorative materials; decorative ribbons, non-woven fabrics.
Abrasives, adhesives and chemicals	Coated abrasives and related products, non-slip floor coverings, non-woven abrasive materials for cleaning, scouring and finishing, adhesives, coatings and sealers for joining, protecting and sealing, industrial resins, fluro-chemicals for fabric protection, coolants, surficants; fluorinated plastics, gyro fluids, oils, greases and waxes, industrial chemicals.
Graphic systems	Infrared dry copying machines, dry photocopying machines, and copy papers, overhead projectors, and curriculum materials, microfilm processor-cameras, reader-printers and aperature cards, action paper (used for business machine use and produces an image upon impact without carbons, coatings, ribbons or ink), glassine and greaseproof papers, lithographic offset printing plates, printing chemicals and specialty items, a self-contained, fully automatic background music system; Fastax high-speed cameras.

TABLE 8–1

3M COMPANY
PRODUCTS BY GROUP
(Continued)

Electrical products	Pressure-sensitive tapes for holding, insulating, protecting, resins for encapsulating, impregnating, and splicing, electrical connectors, flexible electrical insulations, mica paper, electrical and mechanical laminates, technical ceramics, heat-sealable and plain polyester films for a variety of industrial and commercial applications, magnetic sound, video, computer and instrumentation tapes and tape recorders, instrumentation and video-band recorders-reproducers, thermoelectric elements and generators, electric radiant heating systems.
Advertising services and protective products	Reflective sheeting, tapes, compounds and paints, emblem film, light-diffusing, glare-free paints, aluminized fabric, lane-marking products, woodgrained vinyl finishes, nationwide display advertising service, colored roofing granules, mechanical plating and finishing products, commercial sand, quarry and crushed stone, ready-mix concrete.
Photographic Products	Still and movie films in color and black-and-white for amateur, professional and industrial markets, photographic papers, chemicals and other products, microfilm, photographic equipment. Wholly-owned Dynacolor Corp. also processes 8mm and 35mm color films at processing stations thruout the U.S.

Source: Standard and Poor's *Standard Corporation Descriptions,* September 14, 1967, p. 8359.

TABLE 8–2

UNION REPRESENTATION AT 3M COMPANY

Union	*Number of Bargaining Units*	*Estimated Total 3M Membership*
American Federation of Grain Millers (AFGM)	1	500
Allied Industrial Workers of American International Union (AIW)	1	600
International Union of United Brewery, Flour, Cereal, Soft Drink & Distillery Workers (UBW)	1	65
United Cement, Lime & Gypsum Workers International Union (UCLG)	1	50
International Association of Machinists & Aerospace Workers (IAM)	3	450
International Chemical Workers Union (ICWU)	1	40
International Union of Operating Engineers (IUDE)	6	400
Oil, Chemical & Atomic Workers International Union (OCAW)	9	4,560
International Brotherhood of Pulp, Sulphite & Paper Mill Workers of the United States and Canada (PSPW)	1	540
International Brotherhood of Teamsters, Chauffeurs, Warehousemen & Helpers of America (IBT)	5	600
United Automobile, Aerospace & Agricultural Implement Workers of America (UAW)	1	275
United Electrical, Radio & Machine Workers of America (Independent) (UE)	1	185
United Glass & Ceramic Workers of North America (UGCW)	1	420
District 50, United Mine Workers of America (Independent) (D-50)	6	N.A.
United Papermakers & Paperworkers (UPP)	1	90
Other AFL-CIO Affiliated Unions	12	N.A.

Source: Industrial Union Department, AFL-CIO, Report to 3M-IUD Committee at a Conference, Washington, D.C., April 14, 1967, pp. B1–B4.

All other negotiations for the remainder of the plants are under direct supervision of local management and local union officials with central staff assistance when required.[3] In such negotiations, the local plant manager is practically in an autonomous position; preparation for negotiations with a particular bargaining unit begin with the plant manager securing recommendations and suggestions from his foremen, personnel manager, and department superintendents. The manager, key department heads, and an industrial relations representative review the requests and develop a proposal, but the decision of the plant manager is a paramount factor in developing a negotiating posture for 3M local bargaining. Pensions and insurance arrangements are similar in most 3M plants, but are negotiated locally. There are also some plants which have unique pension and insurance agreements.[4]

DEVELOPMENT OF THE COALITION

The early development of a coalition at 3M came about in a manner similar to those in other situations, when a group of OCAW locals joined together to form a 3M Council for the purpose of exchanging information and discussing problems of mutual interest. As in other cases, meetings were informal, infrequent, and without real direction or objective. Since 1957 the OCAW 3M Council had frequently presented the Company with demands for Company-wide bargaining on certain major economic issues.[5]

At no time, however, has 3M ever given encouragement to the OCAW demands for enlargement of the bargaining unit and/or for national bargaining.

The Beginning of the IUD Program

Late in 1961, at a time when the IUD was beginning to develop its goals for "coordinated" bargaining, the OCAW was also beginning to prepare for its 3M negotiations at St. Paul and Hastings, Minnesota. In

[3]See for example, Respondent's Brief, "Appeal to the Board" in Minnesota Mining & Manufacturing Company and Oil, Chemical and Atomic Workers International Union, AFL-CIO, —— NLRB No. ——, p. 3.

[4]See for example, "Appellant's Brief," in *Minnesota Mining & Manufacturing Company* v. *Clarence A. Meter,* LRRM, p. 5; also *Record* in the United States Court of Appeals for the Eighth Circuit in *Minnesota Mining* v. *Clarance A. Meter,* pp. 139, 142.

[5]See for example, "Respondent's Brief," in *Clarence A. Meter* v. *Minnesota Mining & Manufacturing Company,* United States District Court for the District of Minnesota Third Division, p. 2.

light of the interest shown by the OCAW in coalition bargaining with several other firms, it apparently decided to permit the IUD to assume leadership in bargaining with 3M.[6]

In February 1962, the Industrial Department conducted its first meeting designed to acquaint 3M local unions, and the parent internationals with its program of coalition bargaining and what might be expected in the way of gains from 3M. As part of the preparation for that meeting, the IUD presented those attending with a 29-page analysis of Company operations, plant locations, financial, stock, salary data, and a comparative contract analysis for many plants.[7] A second meeting was held in February 1964, and a third in March 1965.[8]

Following the 1962 meeting, however, the IUD made its first attempts to bring about coalition bargaining at 3M. At that time, Stephen Harris, then a pension expert for the IUD, approached the Company informally to request national bargaining on the pension question. When 3M refused to meet on such a basis, Harris attended negotiating meetings at various locations to act as an advisor to the local committees.[9] The Company made no effort to prevent such participation by an expert called by the local.

As a second part of the effort to bring about coalition bargaining at that time, however, "the IUD invited representatives from other unions to sit in a separate room and advise the negotiating committee . . . . The final settlement was reached after consultation with the representatives of all other unions."[10] Following the 1964 negotiations, the IUD took further credit for negotiated changes in the 3M insurance plan at St. Paul and Chemolite.[11]

---

[6]The *Agenda for Tomorrow,* Report to the Industrial Union Department, AFL-CIO Sixth Constitutional Convention, Washington, D.C., November 18–19, 1968, is a report by IUD president Walter P. Reuther which lists companies such as Union Carbide, American Home Products, Rohm and Haas, Olin-Matheson, Johns-Manville and others as having been engaged in "coordinated bargaining" prior to that time, pp. 67–70.

[7]Industrial Union Department, AFL-CIO, Research Section, Analysis of *Minnesota Mining & Manufacturing Company,* for presentation at the IUD-Minnesota Mining Conference, Washington, D.C., February 19, 1962.

[8]Reports similar to that noted in footnote 7 above were presented at the 1964 and 1965 meetings which corrected and updated previous data. In addition, attendance lists were prepared which showed in 1964 that 36 people attended representing eight internationals and 11 locals (three international unions had no locals represented). In 1965, 39 delegates were present, with 10 internationals and 11 locals (two internationals had no local represented). Three IUD representatives attended each meeting.

[9]*Agenda for Tomorrow, op. cit.,* p. 68.

[10]See "Sample Case Study for IUD Collective Bargaining Conference," held at Washington, D.C., June 28, 1967.

[11]*Agenda for Tomorrow, loc. cit.*

In continuing to develop coalition bargaining at 3M, the IUD began to increase the frequency of meetings with the various unions, and in March 1965 reported that "the delegates decided that after three years of meeting, the Committee should establish bargaining goals which the local unions negotiating over the next two or three years should try to achieve . . . ."[12] Among the demands were those for a union shop, general economic improvements, and one for coterminous expiration dates on pension and insurance programs. Immediately, too, the IUD began to increase the volume of communication from Coordinator Harris to the coalition members, reporting many demands, settlements, arbitration awards, etc., all of which was designed to stimulate locals into taking similar, if not identical, positions on a wide range of topics affecting 3M employees across the nation.[13]

TABLE 8–3

SUMMARY OF COALITION DEMANDS AS OF MARCH 1965

1. Union Shop
2. Elimination of the use of an area wage survey
3. Increase in shift premium to 25 cents per hour
4. Vacation improvements
5. Increase in holidays to ten
6. Supplementary Unemployment Benefits (SUB)
7. Sick leave improvements
8. Increase in sickness and accident coverage
9. Long-term disability plan
10. Free life insurance and increase in contributory plan
11. Coterminous expiration of pension and insurance plans
12. Non-contributory pension in 1967

Source: *Memorandum* to "All 3M-IUD Committee Delegates," from Stephen J. Harris, Assistant Director of the Collective Bargaining Section, IUD, March 15, 1965.

[12]See *Memorandum* to "All 3M-IUD Committee Delegates," from Stephen J. Harris, Assistant Director of the Collective Bargaining Section, IUD, March 15, 1965. It is amusing to note that certain seeds of dissention were evident within the group at that point. Pictures were taken of the group, the availability of which was noted as:

#A79565—Entire group
#A79566—All non-OCAW
#A79567—All OCAW

[13]See for example, Harris *Memoranda,* dated March 15, 1965, April 21, May 5, May 18, June 3, July 1, etc. to 3M-IUD Committee Delegates. The Memorandum of May 18 devotes special discussion to the subject of "orthopedic bras"—apparently a vital interest of the coalition.

The IUD continued to hold periodic meetings of all those international and local unions interested in coalition bargaining, and continued to maintain regular communication with the locals. It was, however, at a meeting in April 1967, when preparing for a major effort at 3M, that the IUD began to commit itself fully, and apparently submitted a plan to the delegates, which when approved, led to the confrontation at 3M.[14]

The President's Committee

Following their experiences with Union Carbide, the IUD Executive Board took steps to "avoid mistakes that sometimes allowed promising situations to wither away." Therefore, "when the time for bargaining coordinations draws near a president's committee is convened so that each [international] president or his representative may be aware of, and in agreement with the overall approach [of the coalition]."[15]

The first meeting of the 3M President's Committee was held in June 1967 when designated representatives of eight international unions, along with four other union officers met with Harris. The report of the meeting noted: (Also see Table 8–4)

> It was unanimously decided by this committee that all unions would be invited to St. Paul to participate as part of the St. Paul-Hastings Committee during pension bargaining in July and August. It is likely that the company will resist these attempts. Other companies such as G.E. and American Standard have also resisted such efforts in the past. In these cases the NLRB has found that the union has the right to include in its bargaining committee representatives of its choice. Two weeks ago, Anaconda, which has fought unions for years, accepted representatives of other unions in its Butte, Montana local negotiations. Obviously more and more companies are now accepting the realities of this type of bargaining. It is hoped that 3M will also do so without a fight. If the company decides not to, the unions involved have decided to use whatever weapons are available to them.

* * *

---

[14]At a Washington meeting on April 14, 1967, the IUD presented the delegates with a legal-sized document whose 58 pages of detail spelled out specifics of a 3M financial analysis, plant location list, contract expiration dates, contract analysis, and pension and insurance analysis. See also, Harris *Memoranda* dated May 14, 1967, June 5, June 28, and July 28.

[15]See for example, Section of AFL-CIO Executive Council Report to AFL-CIO Convention Summarizing Activities of Industrial Union Department, as reported in *Daily Labor Report,* December 6, 1967, p. D-1.

> As soon as the first negotiating sessions are scheduled at St. Paul we will notify each of the President's Committee representatives and they in turn will notify other representatives who ought to be in attendance. We are enclosing a copy of the economic items which will be proposed at St. Paul and Hastings. We will keep you informed.[16]

At that point, Harris continued to make arrangements to buttress the decision of the President's committee, and to force 3M to begin bargaining on the issues which the IUD considered to be national in scope, namely pensions and insurance, as well as other issues still considered to be coalition demands.[17]

TABLE 8–4

UNIONS PARTICIPATING IN IUD—3M COALITION EFFORT 1967

International Union	*Locals Participating*
*Allied Industrial Workers of America	0
*American Federation of Grain Millers	1
*Brotherhood of Painters, Decorators and Paperhangers	1
International Brotherhood of Pulp, Sulphite and Paper Mill Workers	1
*International Brotherhood of Teamsters	1
International Union of Operating Engineers	0
Laborers International Union	1
*Oil, Chemical and Atomic Workers	6
*United Automobile Workers	1
*United Glass and Ceramic Workers	1

*Represented at President's Committee meeting.

Source: Memorandum to "3M President's Committee Representatives & International & Local Delegates," from Stephen J. Harris, Assistant Director, Collective Bargaining Section, Industrial Union Department, Washington, D.C., June 28, 1967.

Coalition Bargaining History

As has been previously noted 3M had consistently refused to agree to any expansion of the bargaining structure and would not consent to

[16]Harris *Memorandum,* June 28, 1967.

[17]The Harris *Memorandum* of July 10, 1967 indicated that he had met with the St. Paul and Hastings committees and indicated that they would not begin bargaining until 3M agreed to meet with outsiders present.

meet with the IUD or any unions with respect to national bargaining. It did, as also noted, permit Harris to attend meetings and act as spokesman for the local committee on matters relating to pension and insurance where he appeared as an expert or consultant, apparently at the invitation of the local and international concerned.

The coalition, at the behest of the IUD did in fact make one unsuccessful attempt to have "outsiders" attend bargaining sessions for the Bristol, Pennsylvania, Glass Workers local in the spring of 1965. At that time, Company and local union representatives were bargaining for a new contract when the union unexpectedly made significant reductions in its demands. When the Company responded with what it considered to be a "good" offer, the union called a caucus. At that time, it is reported that Harris telegraphed other coalition members that the Bristol local needed assistance, and that the presence of the other union officials was required. When the IUD tried to lead the others into the meeting, 3M refused to meet with the expanded group. A federal mediator was used as an intermediary for three days until the outsiders left, meetings were resumed, and agreement was reached shortly thereafter.[18]

The 1967 Coalition Attempt

The effort brought about by the IUD in 1967 to bring the various 3M-IUD coalition unions into a program of national bargaining was one that resulted in a direct confrontation, a damaging strike at St. Paul and Hastings and a serious setback to the unions' cause. The Oil, Chemical and Atomic Workers International Union (OCAW) holds representation rights for the 3M employees at its St. Paul and Hastings (Chemolite), Minnesota plants which employed about 2,450 and 850, respectively. The bargaining relationship at St. Paul has existed for 20 years, and that at Chemolite for 17 years, and has resulted in only small work stoppages after an organizational strike before the recognition of the Hastings union.[19] As previously noted, since 1955, some economic items were jointly negotiated for these groups, although separate bargaining was conducted for the remainder of the contract, and separate agreements were maintained, which bore common termination dates.

---

[18]Personal Interview, *loc. cit.*
[19]"Appeal to the Board," *op. cit.*, p. 2.

The events leading to the confrontation actually began early in the spring of 1967 when Harris telephoned Mr. Lyle H. Fisher, 3M Vice-President for Personnel and Industrial Relations, in an effort to have the Company cooperate in a program to engage in national pension bargaining beginning with the Bristol, Pennsylvania negotiations, and extending to other coalition locations. The Company agreed to meet on an off-the-record basis again to express its feelings toward coalition bargaining. A top level meeting was held, attended by 3M and international union officials, at which time both parties expressed determination to maintain their respective positions. Harris later announced that the IUD committee was resolute in its demand for coalition bargaining, especially at the two key Minnesota locations.[20]

When negotiations did get under way at Bristol, 3M experienced difficulty in engaging the union in meaningful bargaining. Although the Glass Workers were reluctant to negotiate on specific items, the area of greatest concern seemed to be that of pensions, where negotiations were apparently under the direction of the IUD's Harris. The Company agreed that if after one year 3M and the Glass Workers at Bristol could agree to a new pension plan, the plan would be installed in lieu of part of a deferred wage increase.[21]

With Bristol negotiations settled, the IUD and the coalition was then ready to turn to the more critical matter of the St. Paul-Hastings bargaining, where contracts were set to expire at 12:01 A.M. August 27, 1967.[22] In spite of the fact that 3M had repeatedly stated that it would not meet with a local committee in the presence of outsiders, when the OCAW sent the required reopening letter to the Company for St. Paul and Chemolite, it stated in part:

> We also wish to inform you that our negotiating Committee for the forthcoming Negotiations will at times include certain Members or

---

[20]Personal Interview, *loc. cit.*

[21]The IUD has used this method in other situations whereby it gains agreement with an employer to extend improvements "backward" to units that have otherwise completed negotiations. It is then possible to make a key set of negotiations have an impact upon both future and past negotiations.

The "Case Study" *op. cit.* couches such an agreement in different terms:

. . . [3M] does not make fringe benefit changes in any location until it is forced to do so in St. Paul-Hastings negotiations. In fact, the recent Bristol, Pennsylvania settlement actually includes language which will provide the pension and vacation changes to this group after it is negotiated elsewhere. This local union of 400 members therefore has no voice in these plans [sic].

[22]Contractual terms as shown in *Record, op. cit.*, p. 200.

> Officers of other Labor Organizations. These individuals, when they participate in our Negotiations, will be part of our Bargaining Committee, and we shall be Negotiating only for our Bargaining Unit. We have been advised that we have the Legal Right to include such persons on our Negotiating Committee. If you have any objections to their participation, please let me know immediately so that we can attempt to come to some understanding about this matter before the Negotiations commence.[23]

Telephone conversations then took place between the OCAW District Director, and Mr. Charles Tourek, 3M Director of Industrial Relations, who repeated Company objections to "members of officers of other labor organizations."

The Company formally responded on July 10, by stating:

> In accordance with our recent telephone conversation, we are prepared to meet under the same conditions as in the past at any time which is mutually convenient to work out a new agreement for St. Paul and Chemolite.[24]

Upon receipt of the 3M correspondence, the OCAW District Director contacted Harris at the IUD for instructions,[25] and later that day wrote to 3M agreeing to a meeting under the terms suggested by the Company.[26] Negotiating sessions were then scheduled for July 14. Before the meetings, however, the Company was further assured by the OCAW that no outsiders would be present, and even went so far as to cite specifically those individuals who would be in attendance—including Harris.[27]

A meeting did take place on the scheduled date, at which time all of the union representatives that had been expected were in attendance. The union negotiators appeared to be under the direction of Harris and bargaining was conducted in an ostensible atmosphere of friendliness and trust for about an hour and a half.[28] At a certain point, apparently

[23]Letter to "Mr. Chuck Tourek," Director of Industrial Relations, 3M, from Lyman Covert, Director, District 6, OCAW, St. Paul, Minnesota, June 23, 1967.

[24]Response to Covert from C. F. Tourek as shown in *Record, op. cit.*, p. 203, July 10, 1967.

[25]Harris, *Memorandum,* July 17, 1967.

[26]See "Appellant's Brief," *op. cit.*, p. 8.

[27]See, "Brief for Trial Examiner," Respondent's Brief in *Minnesota Mining & Manufacturing Company and Oil, Chemical and Atomic Workers International Union, AFL-CIO,*—NLRB No.—, p. 3.

[28]Personal Interview, *loc. cit.*

on cue, two representatives of other labor organizations entered the room and attempted to join in the negotiations.[29]

A communication from Harris to coalition members provides some amplification of the day's developments:

> On July 11th [OCAW District Director Lyman] Covert contacted me and we agreed to accept the company's conditions for a *preliminary* meeting to resolve procedural matters on July 14th. At this preliminary meeting only the OCAW committees, district director, international representative and myself would be present for the unions. It was further agreed that we would bring two representatives of other unions into St. Paul to participate in a negotiating session which would immediately follow the preliminary session. At this session we would present the company with the union's pension proposals. Although all other economic and non-economic proposals had already been submitted in writing the pension proposals had not.
>
> * * *
>
> At the St. Paul preliminary negotiating session which began at 10 a.m. on July 14th the company indicated that it was willing to negotiate on pensions for two days each week, local non-economic on a plant level two days a week and the other economic items one day each week. Tourek indicated that he was quite pleased that negotiations had begun even though they had been delayed in the beginning.
>
> The unions then indicated that they were unwilling to meet to discuss pensions unless the company agreed that they could include in their bargaining committee representatives of their choice. Tourek indicated that he was unwilling to discuss this matter since unfair labor practice charges were before the NLRB and that if the unions held to this position pensions could not be negotiated until the Board and the courts had made a decision on this matter. We then indicated to Tourek that until the company was willing to meet with a committee of the union's choice there would be no negotiations on any item since pensions had to be an integral part of this year's settlement.
>
> There was some debate concerning the agreement reached at Bristol. Tourek indicated that in order to clarify this he would bring his representative in from Bristol in order to explain to us what the understanding had actually been. We indicated to him that this was

[29] "Respondent's Brief," *op. cit.*, p. 3.

precisely why we want to bring in representatives of the OCAW local unions' choice as part of their bargaining committee. If he was going to bring in a representative who had attended Bristol negotiations we would have every right to do the same thing.

Since the preliminary meeting had ended, we indicated we were prepared to submit pension demands to the company. At the same time Chuck Kline and Don Cagle, Research Director of the Allied Industrial Workers from Milwaukee, entered the room. . . . At this point Tourek rose and indicated that the meeting was at an end. We reiterated once more that since our bargaining committee was now all present we were prepared to submit pension demands and begin negotiations on that issue and on all other issues. With that Tourek led his committee of 21 representatives from the room.

* * *

After the short negotiating session we met with David R. Hols, NLRB Attorney in Minneapolis. He took an affidavit from me concerning the events of that morning and indicated that he was sending a report to Washington this week. We expect that the NLRB General Council will attempt to secure a 10-J Taft-Hartley injunction as soon as possible. We will keep all delegates informed.[30]

True to Mr. Harris' prediction, the NLRB moved quickly into the District Court where a 10(j) injunction was obtained. The Court of Appeals, however, later overruled the lower court as will be discussed below.

It was the Company position at that time that the legality of being forced to deal with outsiders had not yet been fully established by the courts; that it had refused to meet on that basis previously; and that it would refuse to do so unless specifically ordered to do otherwise. The 3M negotiating committee withdrew from negotiations on July 14, not

---

[30]Harris *Memorandum,* July 17, 1967. At that time, Harris also called for an emergency assembly of coalition representatives, the notice for which stated:

URGENT MEETING

Because of the company's refusal to bargain, the St. Paul and Hastings local unions will hold a special joint emergency membership meeting beginning at 10 a.m. on Sunday, July 30, 1967. The meeting will be held at the St. Paul City Auditorium. In order to show the solidarity of all unions in 3M we are requesting that as many local and international representatives as possible plan to attend this special meeting. The IUD Presidents and Delegates Committees will meet with the St. Paul and Hastings negotiating committees beginning at 1 p.m. at the Hotel Lowry in downtown St. Paul on the same day. . . . It is urgent that as many delegates as possible attend both meetings. We will meet in the lobby of the Lowry at 9:15 a.m. Sunday to go to the Auditorium together.

only for those reasons, but also because it considered the union to have acted in bad faith by attempting to bring outsiders into the bargaining despite earlier promises to refrain from so doing.[31] The IUD's claim that two separate meetings were involved was given little credance by 3M.

Following the interruption of bargaining for the St. Paul and Hastings OCAW local unions in July, there were no further meetings conducted by the parties until more than a month later, August 16. This meeting was requested by the OCAW which stated (again) specifically that no outsiders would be present. The two-hour meeting was held, and conducted without the presence of any but the negotiating committees that had been present in past bargaining sessions.[32]

A third meeting was held the following day, at which time union leadership was assumed by Harris of the IUD, and later by Richard Prosten, another IUD coordinator. The union proposed that both parties agree to the ruling of the District Court (discussed below) with respect to the matter of outsiders, and that the contract be extended until September 17, in order to permit the OCAW representatives to attend the union international convention. The Company agreed to meet this request, and the parties began to negotiate on local issues, apparently with little progress because of a union desire to await the decision of the District Court.[33]

When the District Court granted the National Labor Relations Board (NLRB) a temporary injunction ordering 3M to bargain with three outsiders present, bargaining recommenced despite a Company appeal, with Harris acting as spokesman for all issues. There was little movement on the part of the IUD-OCAW group on any major economic or non-economic issues, although limited progress was made on local items. In two weeks of negotiating, the unions made only one counteroffer—which was concerned only with pension proposals. Conduct at the bargaining table, and elsewhere seemed to indicate that the IUD and the OCAW were determined to create an impasse and a work stoppage at St. Paul and Chemolite.[34] In fact, the unions did not wait until the Company's final offer was extended before a combined mem-

[31]See "Respondent's Brief," *op. cit.*, p. 4. Also *Record, op. cit.*, pp. 156–157.
[32]*Record, op. cit.*, pp. 157–159.
[33]Personal Interview, *loc. cit.*
[34]*Ibid.*

bership meeting was held on September 10 where rejection of a proposal and strike authorization was overwhelmingly granted.[35]

Bargaining continued with less than a week until the extended deadline, but with the unions still refusing to extend a counteroffer in any areas other than pensions. It is reported that each time agreement seemed imminent on any particular issue, a "red herring" would be introduced which prevented any sort of accord.[36] On the day before the contract expired, a final Company offer was introduced; shortly thereafter, the unions made a counteroffer, considered to be unrealistic by 3M. A strike began at St. Paul and Hastings the next day, September 17, 1967.[37]

While the strikes were in progress at St. Paul and Chemolite, 3M opened negotiations at Fairmont, Minnesota, 130 miles southwest of St. Paul, where the work force is represented by another OCAW local. When meetings there began, three outsiders entered the sessions, at which time 3M filed an unfair labor practice charge, with the union counterfiling.[38] Because the Fairmont contract specifically designated the union bargaining committee, the OCAW was induced to resume negotiations, and a settlement was reached without further evidence of the IUD or the coalition. The agreement reached was for a total package not significantly different from that eventually accepted by the St. Paul and Hastings locals when they later voted to end their strikes.[39]

After the work stoppage was begun by the coalition unions, no bargaining sessions were held for more than a month until October 20. After that, they were continued for nearly another month before agreement was finally reached. Progress was made only after Elwood Swisher, OCAW International Vice-President, began to take charge of the union bargaining teams.[40] At that time too, Harris began to with-

---

[35]*Ibid.* Also Harris *Memorandum,* September 11, 1967. The reported vote was 1648 to 25 in favor of a strike.

[36]Personal Interview, *loc. cit.*

[37]It is reported that when the membership gathered to hear the 3M Company offer, that Harris participated in the meeting. As each member entered the hall, he was given a printed copy of the offer. After a prolonged discussion of coalition bargaining, and a protracted discussion of the offer, a speaker is said to have ripped the offer in two, and several in the audience did the same. Soon most followed suit, and a vote rejected the offer by a wide margin.

[38]The Company charge was based on the alleged illegality of coalition aims and the specific contract language. The OCAW charge was a simple refusal-to-bargain charge. Both sides were induced by the Board to withdraw charges when settlement was reached. OCAW local 6–505 at Fairmont had been listed as a coalition member, and sent delegates to several IUD-3M Committee meetings.

[39]Personal Interview, *loc. cit.*

[40]It is reported that Harris attended only two of the last 14 or 15 bargaining sessions prior to agreement, and that those appearances were not toward the end of the meeting period.

draw from the situation and outsiders were no longer present. After Swisher had apparently regained control of the situation, he named Les Van Toll, OCAW international representative, as chief union spokesman, who concluded a satisfactory contract.[41]

On November 21, 1967, after nine and a half weeks of striking, the 3,400 OCAW union members voted, at separate membership meetings, and agreed to return to work at terms quite similar to those offered before the walk-out.[42] Slight improvements were made in shift differentials and vacations; and an adjustment was made in the offer for second year wage increases, based on area wage surveys.[43]

LEGAL DEVELOPMENTS

As a result of the 1967 IUD coalition effort at 3M, several legal developments have transpired that are of interest here. The first was the result of an unfair labor practice charge and request for injunctive relief under the terms of Section 10(j) of the National Labor Relations Act, and the second concerns the Board proceedings growing from that charge.

The 10(j) Proceedings

Based upon telephone conversations with 3M officials indicating an unwillingness to meet with any coalition bargaining committee, the OCAW filed an unfair labor practice charge with the NLRB on July 10, 1967.[44] When 3M left the first negotiating session on July 14 upon the appearance of "Members or Officers of other Labor Organizations," the charge was amended, by including a request for injunctive relief. On August 10, the Board issued a compliant,[45] and filed a Petition for Injunction under 10(j) of the Act the following day.[46]

The thrust of the Company argument centered about two issues before the District Court: 1) that the dispute in question was not one

---

[41]Personal Interview, *loc. cit.* It is also noted that OCAW President A. F. Grospiron also participated in some bargaining sessions prior to settlement.

[42]It is noted that agreement was reached by the UAW and Ford during the period of the 3M strike. Because Harris apparently made an issue of the Ford settlement, it is reasonable to assume that the 3M strike was prolonged due to raised levels of expectations on the part of the strikers.

[43]See *Stipulation of Agreement,* reached by the parties November 21, 1967.

[44]See "Charge Against Employer," Case No. 18-CA-2443, July 10, 1967 as shown in *Record, op. cit.,* p.1.

[45]*Record, op. cit.,* p. 3.

[46]*Ibid.,* p. 8.

properly subject to injunctive measures,[47] and 2) that the unions were indeed engaging in a coalition effort where goals went far beyond the scope of legitimate bargaining at St. Paul and Hastings.[48] (See discussion of union objectives below). The General Counsel maintained that injunctive relief under section 10(j) was indeed proper and just.

The District Court on September 5, in granting a temporary injunction ordering the Company to bargain, noted the testimony presented by 3M, and in fact agreed that:

> . . . there can be little question but that some of the members and leaders of the union would desire, and it is their ultimate objective to attain in the future nationalized or multi-plant bargaining. . . .[49]

Nevertheless, the Court felt that the Board had presented a *prima facie* case that the Company had indeed refused to bargain, and therefore concluded:

> . . . Since it is more than reasonably clear that in all probability such will finally be determined to be their legal right, failure to adjudicate accordingly at this stage will be irreplaceable, will be lost forever and will be something the union cannot achieve or retrieve two or three years from now when the contract again is up for renewal. This can be said to constitute irreparable harm and injury to the union and its members by the deprivation of its legal rights, for the protection of which it has no place to turn except this court. . . .[50]

The Court then continued in its exploration of the reasoning behind the granting of the injunction and stated:

> In conclusion, the court has attempted to balance the equities to determine the harm to 3M when an injunction issues. It would seem that nothing irreparable can come to 3M if the Board ultimately decides on the merits in its favor and thus the injunction becomes dissolved. Even though in 1967, three additional people sat at the bargaining table with no vote, and negotiated only for the two locals involved, no great injury can have occurred. Perhaps 3M feels that if it proceeded to a bargaining session with the "outsiders" present without

[47]"Respondent's Brief," *op. cit.*, pp. 4–16.

[48]*Ibid.*, pp. 2–4, also, *Record, op. cit.*, pp. 147–79, 122–28, 128–36.

[49]Decision of U.S. District Court, District of Minnesota in *Meter* v. *Minnesota Mining & Manufacturing Company*, September 5, 1967, LRRM, as reported in the *Daily Labor Report*, September 13, 1967, p. D-4.

[50]*Ibid.*, p. D-6.

a court injunction, it would in some way be consenting to such practice, could in some way be waiving a right by altering an established pattern. If so, its reluctance to do so is understandable. Both sides agree that nationwide or multi-plant bargaining cannot take place without consent of the parties and would be illegal if attempted to be forced by the union. Thus perhaps, the unwillingness of 3M to be deemed to have consented since it objects to any such format. Obeying an injunction of course cannot be deemed in any way a consent on the part of 3M should the Board ultimately uphold 3M's position.

The injunction should provide that:

(1) It shall be in force and effect only until a final disposition of the case before the Board or a determination by the Board (and the courts if appealed) on the merits of the issues involved and shall automatically then be dissolved.

(2) It shall restrict the two local unions to the presence at negotiations of not more than three selected officers or members of other unions plus, as in the past, a representative of the Industrial Union Development Department of AFL-CIO and the usual member or number of members of OCAW International. The case has arisen in this court because of the presence of two men brought into negotiating sessions by the union; apparently a third had been expected. The court bases its temporary injunction on the presentation of these facts. Perhaps the Board ultimately will allow more in attendance, but for the interim and until a decision on the merits the number should be limited to the facts presented before the court.

(3) It shall be limited and apply only to negotiations with the St. Paul and Hastings locals and have no application to other 3M plants or locations.

(4) It shall prohibit other union members sitting with the bargaining committees from having any vote on acceptance or rejection of proposals and shall confine their activities solely to assisting and advising and negotiating for the two local unions and not for their own unions.[51]

When bargaining began under the terms of the injunction, the IUD all but made a sham of the order. Whereas the Court had ordered that no more than three outsiders be present at any meeting, the coalition immediately began to rotate its members through the negotiating ses-

[51] *Ibid.*, p. D-7.

sions. There was not more than three present, but seldom were the same three in attendance.[52]

Upon appeal to the Eighth Circuit Court of Appeals immediately following the September 6 injunction, 3M argued on essentially the same basis as it had in the District court, *viz:* That injunctive relief was improper,[53] and that the union's unlawful objective negated the reasonable cause issue that would lead to a prima facie case for the Board.[54]

In reversing the decision of the District Court, the Circuit Court indicated that it did:

> . . . not quarrel with its [the District Court] determination that there is 'reasonable cause' to believe that 3M has violated Section 8(a) (1) and (5) . . . [but]
>
> * * *
>
> A careful analysis of the record convinces us that this case presents nothing more than a showing of 'reasonable cause' to believe the Act was violated.[55]

Whereas the District Court had pointed to a new set of standards which it applied as the appropriate basis for relief under Section 10(j), the higher court disagreed almost entirely. In reversing the order, it stated:

> The district judge in part predicated his order of injunctive relief upon a finding that the situation created by 3M's refusal to bargain posed a serious threat " 'upon the public interest . . . grave enough to justify swifter connective action . . .' than the Board can mete." The problem with the district court's finding, however, is that the record is devoid of any evidence which would support it. The Board has utterly failed to present any factual data which would remotely suggest that the public interest is or may be affected by the alleged unfair labor practices.
>
> Moreover, we find the district court's determination that the OCAW and its affiliated Locals will suffer irreparable harm unless

---

[52]Personal Interview, *loc. cit.* On one occasion, the unions did attempt to bring more than three outsiders. When the Company noted that the Court order specifically limited the number to three, Harris grumbled to the effect that 3M was more interested in who was present than it was in bargaining.

[53]"Appelant's Brief," *op. cit.*, pp. 15–36.

[54]*Ibid.*, pp. 37–41.

[55]*Minnesota Mining & Manufacturing Company* v. *Meter,* 66 LRRM 2203, 273 F.Supp 659 (D.Minn., 1967).

relief is granted equally untenable in light of the record before us. The court based its finding of irreparable harm on the rationale that if it was ultimately determined that the Union had a right to the presence of temporary union representatives at its negotiating sessions, it would have been deprived of a clearly determined legal right, for which compensatory damages would have proved an inadequate redress. This reasoning can apply with equal force to other 8(a)(5) situations, where a union's right to compel the employer to bargain with it in good faith is ultimately vindicated through the regular Board channels. The record, however, refutes the contention that the OCAW would suffer irreparable consequences by the absence of other union advisors. Negotiations between the Union and 3M have culminated in successive collective bargaining agreements for a period of almost two decades. All of these contracts have been realized without the presence of "outsiders" to advise the Union. Only in recent months has the OCAW strenuously urged that it has been required to bargain on disadvantageous terms with the Company because of the absence of other union representatives. In view of the past history of acceptable contracts negotiated between 3M and the OCAW, we find it highly unlikely that the OCAW will sustain any injury in its bargaining position if it retains the present composition of its negotiating committee pending a determination on the merits of this labor dispute.

The district court also determined that injunctive relief was necessary to maintain the status quo. It concluded that by reason of the long history of amicable collective bargaining there existed a harmonious relationship between the parties and that:

> "it might well be determined that the status quo which the court is called upon to preserve is that peaceable, desirable, continuing relationship and status which has lasted for so many years and that failure to grant the injunction for that for which there is reasonable cause to believe the union has a legal right, may disrupt the status quo in this sense."

No authority is cited to support the court's concept of status quo. We agree with 3M that the status quo consists of the bargaining position of the parties prior to the attempt by the OCAW to include representatives of other labor organizations as a part of its negotiating committee.[56]

---

[56]*Ibid.*, p. D-4.

Thus, the court of Appeals reversed the decision of the lower court, vacated the injunction, and left the matter of the unfair labor practice to be decided by the Board through its normal procedures. The General Counsel did not appeal this decision to the United States Supreme Court.

The decision of the appellate court was announced on November 8, thirteen days before the parties finally came to agreement, but at a time when the negotiations were apparently no longer under the direction of the IUD, and at a time when the outsiders had ceased attending negotiating sessions for the striking locals.

NLRB Proceedings

In proceedings before the NLRB Trial Examiner on the basic issue of the refusal to bargain charge, both parties agreed to waive a hearing, substituting instead the Record before the District Court. In his decision, the Trial Examiner also cited the decisions of the District and Appeals Courts. In presenting the Case for the Company, 3M pointed to two issues, namely: 1) that an employer may not be forced to bargain on a company-wide basis, and 2) that the program of "coordinated bargaining" that the unions had embarked upon had as its ultimate goal an unlawful objective.[57]

The Trial Examiner's Decision treats with the subject of IUD and coalition union objectives at length, and states in part:

> The Company contends that the Union's ultimate aim is "coordinated bargaining," that is, bargaining which will embrace more than the single unit the Union represents, and which will settle terms for other units and at other plants. The record does establish that this is an ultimate objective of the Union, and the presence of representatives of other labor organizations in the St. Paul and Hastings negotiations may well be an opening wedge in this hoped-for development. *The Company perhaps should not be blamed for trying to keep the union camel from sticking its nose under the tent. But whatever may be the Company's fears, and howsoever accurate its prognostication and its discernment of the Union's ultimate aims, the Company here and now is under a duty to bargain with the Union, and this encompasses a duty to bargain with whatever representatives the Union chooses to send.*

[57]"Brief for Trial Examiner," *op. cit.*

The mere possibility of future abuse (which indeed the Union disclaims), is no justification for an anticipatory refusal to bargain. . . . On this record the General Counsel established that the Union's negotiators, including those who normally represented other labor organizations, were to engage solely in bargaining on behalf of the St. Paul and Hastings units. The Company could not, therefore, lawfully refuse to negotiate with them. (Emphasis added).[58]

The Trial Examiner then continued, bound by Board precedent set in the *American Radiator*[59] case existing at the time to find 3M guilty of refusing to bargain with a union committee which "included among its negotiators representatives who were members of, and normally represented, other labor organizations . . . ."[60]

The Company currently has appealed to the Board for review of the decision of the Trial Examiner. In arguing that it has no duty to bargain with a labor organization that has illegal motives as its goal, it summarizes its position by stating:

. . . What the coordinated bargaining program amounts to is nothing more than an attempt to bypass the requirement that bargaining be confined to an appropriate unit and to seek an expansion going beyond such unit. This is not to say that information exchange is in any manner inappropriate or unlawful in collective bargaining, nor has Respondent [3M] ever sought to impede or prevent such exchange. But there is a vast difference between devising techniques for the purpose of obtaining the maximum possible facts to engage in effective collective bargaining as contrasted to a program admittedly designed to force an employer to bargain on a national basis.

The basic issue present here relates to a question of motive and intent. Did the union commence negotiation with the motive of forcing Respondent to bargain beyond the appropriate unit? An analysis of all the surrounding circumstances, including the statements made as to objective and intent, the testimony given and the reasons therefore, establishes that the answer to this question is "yes." Such a conclusion was recognized by the Trial Examiner by virtue of his finding that coordinated bargaining indeed was the ultimate goal of the Union and

---

[58]"Trial Examiner's Decision," in *Minnesota Mining & Manufacturing Company* and *Oil, Chemical and Atomic Workers International Union AFL-CIO*, November 16, 1967,—NLRB No.—, pp. 7–8.

[59]*American Radiator Corporation* v. *NLRB*, 65 LRRM 3071.

[60]"Trial Examiner's Decision," *op. cit.*, p. 8.

> that the designation of the outside representatives may be the opening wedge in obtaining such goal. Placed in such a position with full knowledge of the Union's motive, the Company should not be required to "sit back and wait" until the goal is reached. The defensive action taken by the Company was completely justifiable under these particular circumstances.[61]

In view of the NLRB's decision in the *General Electric* case, the Board as expected did uphold the trial examiner's ruling against 3M.

The Objective of the IUD Coalition

The 3M Company was in a better position than any other Company to date except perhaps those in the nonferrous metals industry, to demonstrate through documentary proof and through court testimony what the real aims and objectives of the IUD and the 3M union coalition are. It is reasonable to assume that the same goals are sought by each such IUD committee, and is therefore instructive to examine the evidence compiled in this situation.

Official IUD Documents

As part of the normal activity connected with the formation and encouragement of a company committee, the IUD makes good use of various channels of communication to union members in order to elicit and maintain interest in its coalition programs. One of the most effective of these channels is the IUD *Agenda,* the Department's official publication. Since the formation of the 3M committee in 1962, the *Agenda* has made frequent reference to that committee and its dealings with the Company, especially in citing the goals of the coalition.

For example, in the February 1965 issue of *Agenda* the IUD made its first claim with respect to 3M when it stated:

> *In two cases, the IUD has been successful because of its committees in securing national bargaining with large companies.* At Minnesota Mining and Manufacturing the company agreed to negotiate changes in its national pension plan (a plan which had never previously been negotiated with any union) for two plants of the OCAW. With cooperation of the IUD and with representatives of 10 other international unions consulting with the negotiators, changes were successfully negotiated.

[61]"Appeal to the Board," *op. cit.*, pp. 27–28.

The changes were approved by the other union representatives before they were accepted by the OCAW. (Emphasis added).[62]

A second specific reference to coalition activity at 3M was noted in the *Agenda* of December 1965 when the IUD spokesman noted:

> A second move in this area took place late in 1961 when eight international unions having bargaining rights with Minnesota Mining and Manufacturing Co. met under IUD sponsorship to decide on techniques for approaching the company on a national pension plan. The union with the largest membership was the Oil, Chemical and Atomic Workers.
>
> The unions met with the company, which agreed to work out a pattern settlement [*sic*] for the workers at its OCAW plants at St. Paul and Hastings, Minn. Representatives of other unions involved served on a steering committee which advised the negotiators and concurred in the final settlement. The negotiated pattern was then offered to the other unions as their contracts expired. In 1964 this was extended to new insurance patterns, including long-term disability insurance.
>
> * * *
>
> The objective at 3M is uniformity of expiration dates on contracts, and complete coordinated bargaining by 1967.
>
> * * *
>
> In some of the coordinated bargaining committees, a steering committee made up of representatives of coordinating locals is established to participate in local negotiations.
>
> The representatives of other unions, at times, have been able to correct or contradict statements made by company representatives concerning practices in their home plants. *The ultimate goal of coordinated bargaining is to force companies to negotiate major economic items on a national level.* (Emphasis added).[63]

In spite of the fact that Harris denied that any element of force was inherent in the coalition program, it is noted that the Executive Director of the IUD has been quoted on numerous occasions as having made the statement that "The ultimate goal of coordinated bargaining

---

[62]"Collective Bargaining Newsletter," IUD *Agenda,* February 1965, as reported in the *Record, op. cit.,* p. 216.

[63]"Modern Union Policy . . . Co-ordinate," IUD *Agenda,* February 1965, as shown in the *Record, op. cit.,* p. 206.

is to force companies to negotiate major economic items on a national level."[64]

The IUD, in continuing to prepare for the 1967 negotiations began to prepare 3M union membership for the campaign by stating:

> The year 1967 promises to be one of considerable collective bargaining activity throughout the nation. Expectations also are that coordinated collective bargaining techniques will gain increased attention during the year.
>
> At Minnesota Mining & Manufacturing, representatives of all plants are expected to join in negotiations on a pension plan for which the first negotiated improvements were won four and a half years ago. Several major collective bargaining agreements covering 3M employee groups also will come up for negotiations during the first part of the year.[65]

A letter to the 3M coalition members amply illustrated the aims of the IUD group when it prepared to begin bargaining for the OCAW locals at St. Paul and Chemolite. It stated:

> Since the President's Committee unanimously decided that they would insist that all unions participate in St. Paul-Hastings pension negotiations this year, the company was notified of the intention of the two OCAW locals.
>
> Last Wednesday, July 5th, while I was in St. Paul on other business I met with the St. Paul and Hastings negotiating committees. All but two or three of the 18 members were present. They unanimously voted that there would be no meetings held with the company on either economic [or] non-economic proposals until the company agreed to the inclusion of other unions as part of the OCAW bargaining committee. This decision was reported to Chuck Tourek by [OCAW District Director] Lyman Covert on Friday, July 7th. Tourek then indicated that the company would be unwilling to meet under such circumstances. The union is filing unfair labor practice charges against the company.
>
> In the meantime it is expected that the company will, through letters, ads, and telephone communications, attempt to pressure the

[64]See testimony shown in the *Record, op. cit.*, pp. 122–126, 180–191.

[65]"Collective Bargaining Newsletter," IUD *Agenda,* January 1967, as shown in the *Record, op. cit.*, p. 218.

OCAW committees and membership into negotiations. At the moment the committees and membership appear very strong even with the possibility that there will be no real negotiations in advance of the contract expiration date. As soon as a meeting date is set up we will be notifying all of the members of the presidents' committee. We will also keep you informed concerning all future developments.[66]

Court Testimony

In addition to the various documents cited, both published and unpublished which alluded the IUD aims, testimony presented before the District Court in the 10(j) proceedings also gave light to the ultimate objective of coalition bargaining at 3M. For example, in his deposition for the Court, IUD coordinator Harris made the following statement:

> We realized that our long term goal, because, you know, our hope is to get the law changed to permit us to have national bargaining on national issues with companies like GE and Westinghouse and others which have a single pension and single insurance.
>
> Until the law is changed we know, unless the company agrees to these things, we can't do it. The law is specific. Even in the Standard Oil—I mean the American Standard decision it says the General Counsel admits that the Company could not be forced into international bargaining. All right. That's the law. Our hope is to get the law changed some day.
>
> * * *
>
> Q. Referring to a statement which appears on page 12 of Deposition Exhibit No. 2, reading as follows, "The ultimate goal of coordinated bargaining is to force companies to negotiate major economic items on a national level." Does that statement correctly set forth the position of the IUD relating to the goal of coordinated bargaining?
>
> A. Well, except for the word "force." I would say that the ultimate goal of coordinated bargaining is to get national bargaining with corporations that are national corporations on the issues which are determined nationally by the corporation itself either by getting an agreement as we did with American Home Products, to do it that way, or by getting the law—by convincing congress that the law ought to be changed.[67]

---

[66]Harris *Memorandum,* July 10, 1967.
[67]*Record, op. cit.,* pp. 189–192.

Testimony presented at the hearing also brought forth some remarkable inconsistencies on the part of union witnesses. For example, OCAW International Representative Lloyd E. Bristow testified that he had no knowledge of the 3M-IUD Coordinated Bargaining Program, was only vaguely aware of the 1962 participation of the IUD in negotiations, and in general that he was unaware of any program of coalition bargaining.[68] All this was despite the fact that he had been named "Assistant Coordinator for the 3M-IUD Coordinated Program,"[69] and that his name appeared consistently on the "Attendance Lists" of the IUD coalition group meetings.[70]

Likewise, although the OCAW reopening letter for the St. Paul and Hastings locals stated that outsiders would be negotiating only for those two local bargaining units, the testimony offered by St. Paul local president presented a conflicting point of view as shown in the Record. He testified in response to questions of the Counsel for the Board:

> Q. I just have a few questions here. I believe that you testified these representatives from other international unions were not a part of your bargaining committee this year.
> A. Yes.
>
> Q. Do you mean the formal committee of nine?
> A. Right.
>
> Q. They were not to be a part of that committee?
> A. That's right.
>
> Q. Were they to be a part of the bargaining committee informally?
> A. No. *They are not going to be no part of the bargaining committee whatsoever.* (Emphasis added.)[71]

If the other representatives were not to be a part of either a formal or informal bargaining committee, one might ask what function these other representatives were to perform, and who, in fact, they were representing during the St. Paul and Hastings negotiations. If these individuals were not representing the local unions, as claimed in the OCAW reopening letter, but were instead representing their own union, this

[68] *Ibid.*, pp. 73–96.
[69] OCAW Intra-Organization Communication from Lyman Covert, District 6 Director to Chic St. Croix, Research Director, June 26, 1967, shown in the *Record, op. cit.*, p. 205.
[70] See various "Attendance Lists."
[71] *Record, op. cit.*, p. 194.

would present clear evidence that their designation at other bargaining sessions was again part of the overall plan to force 3M to negotiate on a company-wide basis. Further testimony by the St. Paul local president is critical. He stated as follows:

> Q. These representatives or their unions also have collective bargaining agreements with 3M at other plants, isn't that true?
>
> A. True.
>
> Q. And they would have an interest in the 3M negotiations because of the fact that they also have contracts, isn't that true?
>
> A. True.
>
> Q. *So that when they appear during the course of the 3M negotiations they are actually representing their own local unions rather than the Oil, Chemical and Atomic Workers, right?*
>
> A. *Right.* (Emphasis added).[72]

Another Unfair Labor Practice Charge

A situation arose at 3M's Bedford Park, Illinois plant that gave further evidence of the IUD's goal in having outsiders present at key negotiating meetings. The local contract at that location specifically provided that a leave of absence could be granted to a local union member to facilitate the affairs of that local or international union.[73] When the local president requested "time off to attend IUD meetings with the 3M Company in St. Paul, Minnesota on July 14,"[74] the Company refused to grant his leave as being inconsistent with the contract provisions.

In a letter to the Plant Personnel Manager, the local president stated that 3M Regional Industrial Relations Manager, James Keely, was:

> . . . working under direct orders from his 3M superiors. His orders are to wreck this IUD meeting in St. Paul no matter what the cost. The cost, if the 3M upper echelon has its way, will be staggering in more ways than one. For every action the 3M Company takes in this matter will be met with a reaction by all 3M Local Unions.[75]

---

[72]*Ibid.*, p. 195–96.

[73]See "Brief for Trial Examiner," *op. cit.*, p. 18.

[74]Letter to Mr. Peter Becker, Personnel Manager of 3M's Bedford Park Plant from Anthony Lattanzio, President, Local 232, American Federation of Grain Millers, Chicago, July 13, 1967.

[75]*Ibid.*, p. 2.

When the Company refused to alter its posture with regard to granting a leave of absence, the local filed an unfair labor practice charge with the local Board, and stated as the Basis of the Charge:

> *With the object of frustrating effective coordinated bargaining, especially concerning company-wide pension program, in behalf of all its employees working in 3M establishments covered by labor agreements with AFL-CIO unions,* on July 13, 1967, employer [3M] denied a brief leave of absence, under threat of discharge, to Anthony Lattanzio, president of local 232, American Federation of Grain Millers, AFL-CIO, bargaining agent at above plant, *to enable him to attend bargaining conferences in behalf of 3M employees of its St. Paul-Hastings, Minnesota operations. Employer was advised and well knew that said Lattanzio was then and there a member of OCAW bargaining committee for St. Paul-Hastings employees.* Employer had ample opportunity to arrange for a work substitute for Lattanzio. By this and other misconduct, employer has violated and continues to violate the Act. (Emphasis added).[76]

UNITY OF THE COALITION

There are at least five instances of note to demonstrate that the local and international unions who had been a party to the IUD plans and programs were not at all times in agreement with the manner in which the Industrial Union Department was proceeding.

In January 1966, Harris reported to the coalition delegates that District 50 which was not a part of this committee, had elicited enough support from employees at the 3M Bedford Park plant to gain a Board decertification election. Although the incumbent Grain Millers were successful in staving off the raid, Harris noted that certain sentiment had been developed to discuss the possibility of having coalition members conduct raids on the six 3M plants represented by District 50.[77]

A situation developed at Bristol, Pennsylvania, however, which pitted two coalition unions against each other: the Glass Workers and the Teamsters. Following a wildcat strike at the Glass Workers plant, Harris announced that the Teamsters were raiding that local.[78] He appeared to be further piqued by the fact that communications had

[76]Charge Against Employer, Case No. 13-CA-7965, July 18, 1967, as shown in the *Record, op. cit.*, p. 231.
[77]Harris *Memorandum,* January 25, 1966.
[78]*Ibid.,* March 11, March 23, 1966.

ceased to flow from the local there and noted that, "We can only assume that the local officers have been reporting directly to the interested locals."[79]

It has already been noted that the OCAW local at Fairmount, Minnesota, a coalition supporter, settled without any serious attempt to engage in joint bargaining, despite the fact that it was in a position to join with the St. Paul-Chemolite group in the multi-plant strike already in progress.

Evidence is also strong to support the fact that the OCAW international union had become disenchanted with the manner in which negotiations were being guided by the IUD. It is apparent that Harris had exceeded the bargaining authority granted him in the strike situation, and that when the international office became aware of the problems that had been created by the coalition program, it stepped in to regain control of the negotiations and of the locals. Once the OCAW did regain control, negotiations got off dead-center, and significant progress was made for the first time.[80]

Throughout the nine and one-half week strike period, it was apparent that there was little in the way of substantial monetary support for the St. Paul and Hastings locals from other coalition unions. It appeared that most 3M locals failed to support the position of the striking unions after the initial flurry of support for the coalition.[81] Company negotiators reported that there also seemed to be a general lack of agreement as to goals and means between the two "coordinating" locals, and that a sense of mistrust pervaded the relationship. It is reported that Harris sent a letter to all locals upon settlement of the contracts which detailed the results of the negotiations, but also stated that the coalition was strong with the exception of certain "weaknesses"

---

[79]*Ibid.*, April 13, 1966.

[80]Personal Interview, *loc. cit.*

[81]*Ibid.* It is also instructive to note that many 3M employees work under a bonus system which rewards production. Apparently one of the goals of the IUD Committee is to eliminate such plans, as described by Harris in a Memorandum of February 18, 1966 when detailing a settlement at Bedford Park:

> A major breakthrough providing that the production of employees on each shift will be combined in determining the production bonus within that group. Previously the company paid group bonus to each shift separately.
>
> It played one shift against the other. When bonus increased, the company would restudy the jobs, change the standards, and reduce the bonus. In the future, if one shift wishes to work very hard and the other shift desires to make just average, both groups will get incentive earnings calculated on a combination of the bonus from the first shift and the standard rate from the second shift. This means that the hard working group will not get rewarded for their added effort. It is hoped that this will cut down on the eager beaver's production.

that had developed. The officers of the St. Paul local apparently felt that the entire tenor of the negotiations had been misrepresented. They then sent a separate letter to the coalition members which noted a desire to cooperate, but then severely criticized the IUD for its handling of the entire situation.[82]

Analysis

The IUD has maintained a 3M committee for more than five years, and has *claimed* that it has been engaging the company-wide bargaining on pensions since 1962. Despite these claims, it is doubtful that significant gains may be attributed to the program. The most notable development, albeit dubious, may be the fact that the IUD caused 3400 people to lose nine and a half weeks work.

When the IUD first began to take an interest in pension negotiations in 1962, 3M agreed to let Harris participate in such bargaining because of his expertise in such matters. The first such pension agreement was reached at one plant, and then extended to others as they requested it upon reopening of contracts. In each instance where the plan was extended, the pension negotiations were part of the total contract bargaining, and 3M received credit for the plan in the final package. The IUD has now made this matter a key point in its publicity program by implying that 3M automatically extended the plan to each coalition effort. Such was simply not the case.[83]

When the full coalition bargaining attempt was made by the IUD in 1967, 3M apparently considered filing an unfair labor practice charge against the unions, but in light of the Union Carbide experience before the Board, elected not to do so.[84] The Company instead decided that the IUD publicity effort to extend coalitionism, and indeed the program itself, had grown beyond the bounds of propriety and should be halted before it got out of hand. 3M felt that there was a strong legal basis to refuse to meet with a coalition group, and that a stand had to be taken on the union subterfuge of pretending to be bargaining locally while in fact positioning for joint, national bargaining.[85]

The two plant coalition strike did not result in substantial gains for

---

[82]Personal Interview, *loc. cit.*
[83]*Ibid.*
[84]*Ibid.*
[85]*Ibid.*

the unions. The workers returned to their jobs on the basis of a settlement that was only slightly different from those offered by 3M prior to the walkout, and other improvements were not significant. In fact, it seems likely that the 1967 effort caused a setback, rather than a gain, for coalition bargaining.

CHAPTER IX

THE NONFERROUS INDUSTRY: THE GREAT CONFRONTATION

The long strike in the nonferrous metal industry, popularly called the copper industry, which began in the summer of 1967, may come to be known as the classic case in the study of coalition bargaining. Evident here were nearly all of the techniques developed by the AFL-CIO's Industrial Union Department (IUD): the bringing together of a union coalition, the charades, strangers, and coalition maneuvering, the direct confrontation with four major producers representing the bulk of the industry in an extended work stoppage, government intervention, and finally a new pattern of bargaining for the copper producers and their unions—though not the one sought by the coalition. It is, however, instructive to examine the events which commenced with efforts of the IUD to organize the copper and brass industry committee early in 1966. First, however, it is necessary to summarize the industry and its labor relations picture as background.

THE NONFERROUS INDUSTRY

That segment of American industry which is variously referred to as the "nonferrous" or "copper" industry is actually a rather diverse one, from the standpoint both of product and process. In addition to copper and brass, the industry also mines and processes gold, silver, molybdenum, zinc, lead, cadmium, arsenic, and other metals which are often by-products of the production of the basic copper, lead and zinc. From the process standpoint, the industry includes mining, both open-pit and underground, smelting, refining, fabricating, plating, secondary metals operations, (scrap), and numerous other smaller activities.

The bulk of the primary production of copper in the United States is located in the five Western states of Arizona, New Mexico, Utah, Nevada, and Montana. Although it is in these states where both open-pit and underground mines and smelters are located, the major copper producers also operate smelters, refineries and fabricating plants across the country.

Copper, being a metal available in many places throughout the world, is subject to competition on the world market, where its price is generally determined on the London Metals Exchange. In the recent past, most American producers have attempted to maintain domestic copper prices at a level substantially below world quotations in order to avoid potential shifts by users to competitive materials.[1] In the absence of major work stoppages or disturbances in foreign countries producing copper, makes it appear to some that the world production of copper ore and refined copper may be substantially in excess of total demand, a situation that will be compounded with the opening of new mines in Africa and South America.[2]

Currently, most domestic copper is mined from large low-grade ore deposits. American producers have attempted to maintain a competitive edge over imported metal by utilizing larger and more efficient equipment, new means of mining, and new technology which will permit the smelting and refining of a lower grade ore. Many U.S. mines are now operating beyond the former date of predicted obsolescence, because of constant advances of technology in the industry.

---

[1]See, for example, "Situation Facing Companies in Present Copper Strike," Copper Strike Information Bureau, New York, November 1967, pp. 9–10. The Copper Strike Information Bureau is a service provided by the major nonferrous producers.

[2]Personal interviews with officials of the Anaconda Company, May 1968. New York City.

A few domestic copper producing locations which are at best marginal have been kept productive by firms which have extensive operations elsewhere within and without the United States. The purpose is to maintain as strong a production base as possible, to satisfy customer needs, and to be able to supply U.S. defense requirements in time of national emergency or world disruption of the international copper supply.[3]

The importance of copper to the national economy at this time cannot be understated. Because of its mechanical, chemical, and physical properties, it is used extensively in various alloys, in most all of the wire used for electrical transmission, electronics, water, and other tubing, and in a multitude of other applications. The conflict in Southeast Asia and its related defense activities has created an unprecedented demand for copper. The Industrial Union Department of the AFL-CIO estimated that copper consumption for military-related uses in 1967 would amount to more than 600 million pounds—enough to build 15.5 million new automobiles.[4] Because of its strategic importance, the federal government has established a "national stockpile" of copper, and has further instituted a previously unheard of 10 to 29 percent "set aside" of all U.S. copper production for defense purposes, in order to ensure that a sufficient amount of the production would be diverted to defense uses.

Although there are numerous companies which might be classified as having the bulk of their activities in the nonferrous industry, and others which have a partial or substantial interest in copper and copper-related operations, about 90 percent of the mining, smelting, and refining of copper is carried on in the United States by four companies: American Smelting and Refining Company, Anaconda Company, Kennecott Copper Corporation, and Phelps Dodge Corporation, all of which also produce lead and zinc.[5] It was these four that were the primary target of the coalition unions in the 1967–1968 copper conflict. A brief sketch of each of the companies follows. (See Table 9–1 for comparisons)

---

[3]"Situation Facing Companies . . . ," *op. cit.*, p. 10.

[4]See "Copper and Brass Conference," a three-volume document prepared by the Industrial Union Department, AFL-CIO for presentation to a meeting in Chicago, Illinois, October 26–28, 1966, pp. A1–A5.

[5]Among the other firms listed by the IUD for the Copper and Brass Industry were: Calumet and Hecla, Cerro, Magma Copper, National Distillers, Revere Copper and Brass, Scovill Manufacturing.

American Smelting and Refining Company

The Company, also known as ASARCO, was founded in 1899. It is one of the largest smelters and refiners of metal ores and scrap in the nation. It has mining interests throughout the world which include lead, zinc, copper, gold, and silver. ASARCO also derives revenue through the sale of arsenic, nickel-sulphate, sulphuric acid, zinc dust, bismuth, cadmium, platinum, and other by-products of smelting and refining operations. The Company is also one of the largest in the "secondary metals" industry, which involves the reclaiming of valuable metals through the melting and refining of scrap for re-use.

TABLE 9–1

COMPARISONS OF TOP FOUR COPPER PRODUCERS, 1966

	Net Sales (thousand dollars)	*Net Income* (thousand dollars)	*Copper Produced* (tons)	*Silver Produced* (thousand ounces)	*Gold Produced* (ounces)
ASARCO	653,787	69,234	482,530	76,217	773,943
Anaconda	1,234,640	132,408	772,525	13,453	82,000
Kennecott	739,714	125,375	682,219	4,847	388,000
Phelps Dodge	553,958	82,619	590,412	3,681	130,000

Source: Standard and Poor's, *Standard Corporation Descriptions*, pp. 6190–6529, 1967.

ASARCO, in 1966, employed some 13,300 people in its primary operations and subsidiaries, at mines, smelters, and refining locations. In that same year, the Company produced more than 482,000 tons of copper, 155,650 tons of zinc, 224,830 tons of lead as well as 773,943 ounces of gold and 76,216,974 of silver, which when added to other operations resulted in net sales in excess of $650 million and a net income after depletion of more than $69 million.[6] In the Western states it has smelters and mines, with refineries on both the West and East Coasts where imported copper is also processed. Additionally, ASARCO owns majority interest in Mt. Isa Mines, Ltd. (Australia) and Southern Peru Copper Corporation, and owns substantial minority interest in General Cable Corporation, Revere Copper and Brass Incorporated as well as ASARCO Mexicana (Mexico).

[6]Standard and Poor's, *Standard Corporation Descriptions*, June 12, 1967, pp. 6475–78.

Anaconda Company

Founded in 1895, the Anaconda Company, with its subsidiaries, had nearly 45,000 employees in 1966 in operations that made it the largest producer of copper and a major factor in zinc, fabricated copper, brass, and copper-base alloy products. Operations embrace the mining and smelting of copper, zinc, lead, and manganese ores, the refining of the metal by-products such as gold, silver, the refining of metal on a toll or purchase basis for other producers, and the manufacture and distribution of semifinished copper, brass, and alloy products. Recently, Anaconda has expanded into the mining and processing of uranium, production of primary aluminum, and fabrication of aluminum products.

The Company is substantially integrated with operations and subsidiaries throughout the world. In fact, in 1966 net income from foreign sources represented about 57 percent of consolidated net, primarily from South American mining operations. In that year, Anaconda had total sales of about $1.2 billion which yielded a net income of about $132 million, through the production of 772,525 tons of copper, 180,652 tons of zinc, 105,821 tons of aluminum, substantial amounts of other metals, as well as about 125 million board feet of lumber through one of its subsidiaries in Montana.[7]

Although Anaconda operations are substantially integrated in some respects, it is apparent that each of the subsidiary operations enjoys a certain amount of managerial freedom and individual autonomy to perform under "profit center" evaluation by the parent Anaconda Company. This becomes especially evident when examining subsidiaries such as Anaconda American Brass, Anaconda Wire & Cable, Anaconda Astrodata, Anaconda Aluminum, or the Butte, Anaconda & Pacific Railway, each of which deals in a specific market, has different input factors, different economic structures, and different operations. Thus, the very basic structure of the Company was to become a stumbling block for coalition unions, as discussed below.

Kennecott Copper Corporation

Kennecott, founded in 1915, is the second largest producer of copper in the world. The annual productive capacity of its operating

[7]*Ibid.*, October 31, 1967, pp. 6190–93.

properties is in excess of one billion pounds of copper, about 74 percent of which is obtained from domestic mines, with the remainder from Chile. It is the second largest producer of molybdenum, an alloy used in steel, and also produces sizable quantities of gold, silver, and other metals through recovery in its copper operations.

Kennecott's domestic mining operations are conducted through four divisions: the Utah property, the Nevada mines, Ray mines in Arizona, and the Chino mines in New Mexico. The Chilean mines operated by the Company are the only sizable operation which makes use of underground methods, but the grade of the imported ore is higher than that obtained by the domestic open-pit methods, so that the costs are somewhat offset. In 1966, the Utah property, the most efficient of the domestic operations, contributed about 39 percent of Kennecott's copper production, Chino 17 percent, Ray 12 percent, Nevada 6 percent, and Chile about 26 percent.

The Company also operates subsidiaries such as Kennecott Sales Corporation, Kennecott Refining Corporation, Chase Brass & Copper Company, and a railroad, which are structured to function in a manner in order to serve special purpose objectives within the parent corporation. In 1966, Kennecott employed an average of nearly 25,000 people in producing and selling 616,668 tons of copper, 338,000 ounces of gold, 4,847,000 ounces of silver, 17,932,000 pounds of molybdenum and other materials for a total operating revenue of more than $739 million, and net income before depletion of about $125 million.[8]

Phelps Dodge Corporation

Phelps Dodge, founded in 1885 as Copper Queen Consolidated Mining Company, is now the third largest domestic producer of copper, an important custom smelter-refiner and ranks among the largest of the domestic wire manufacturers. Phelps Dodge maintains the bulk of its mining and smelting operations in Arizona where four large groups of properties are owned, and where production costs are relatively low because of the comparatively high gold-silver content of the ore, and because the bulk of the ore is obtained through working of large open-pit mines. All of the Company's ore is treated at its two electrolytic plants which also operate on a toll basis for other producers. In addi-

[8]*Ibid.*, May 23, 1967, pp. 6527–30.

tion to the normal copper by-products noted above, Phelps Dodge also recovers copper sulphate, copper oxide, nickel sulphate, platinum, palladium, selenium, and tellurium through copper refining operations.

In addition to the production of primary metals, Phelps Dodge also operates subsidiaries which are engaged in the production of fabricated copper products including copper and alloy rods, tubes, wire and cable, pipes, coils and transformers, electronic products, specialty tubing, and magnet wire; aluminum fabrication; and the operation of railroads and retail outlets. Many of these operations are conducted as separate subsidiary corporations on a basis that gives relative freedom of operation from the parent copper corporation.

In 1966, Phelps Dodge employed more than 15,000 people in operations that resulted in sales and operating revenue of nearly $554 million and a net income of about $82 million. It did so through the production of about 590,412 tons of copper, 3,680,000 ounces of silver, and 130,000 ounces of gold, as well as through the operations of its various subsidiaries.[9]

Copper Industry Industrial Relations

In order to understand the situation that developed into a nine-month copper strike, it is first necessary to examine the labor relations picture with respect to the unions involved and some background therein, and to examine the bargaining relationships and patterns that had evolved in the copper industry.

The Copper Unions

The unions in the copper industry have had stormy careers. The so-called "hard rock" mines were the backbone of that unique pre-World War I American radical group, the Industrial Workers of the World, which believed in, and engaged in, direct action to achieve its objectives. Later the Miners withdrew from the IWW, took the name International Union of Mine, Mill and Smelter Workers, and affiliated with the AFL. Mine-Mill (or M-M) as it is popularly called, followed John L. Lewis out of the AFL as a charter member of the CIO in 1935. By then, and substantially for many years, it had allegedly become Com-

[9]*Ibid.*, October 31, 1967, pp. 6203–06.

munist infiltrated and was a member of the pro-Communist bloc within the CIO until its expulsion from that federation in 1950.

Besides M-M, a host of craft unions have bargaining rights in the nonferrous industry. In addition, after the expulsion of Mine-Mill from the CIO, the United Steelworkers were given jurisdiction, first by the CIO, and later by the merged AFL-CIO. Even before Mine-Mill was expelled, a large defection from Mine-Mill ranks had occurred. In the "brass valley" of Connecticut, for example, most employees transferred their allegiance from M-M to the United Automobile Workers in the late forties.[10]

Mine-Mill thus brought neither great union strength nor stability to the copper industry. In addition to its divisive radicalism, the union was hindered by rival unionism, poor financing, employer opposition to organization, the structural characteristics and geographic dispersion of the industry.[11]

Through passage of time, the problems of M-M tended to increase. The United Steelworkers, especially, kept attempting to take away bargaining rights at all M-M locations. District 50, formerly of the United Mine Workers, the Teamsters, and the various craft unions also considered the membership of the expelled M-M fair organizational game. In most cases Mine-Mill held onto its bargaining rights: old loyalties of the miners to the successor of the IWW did not die easily. But the costs of repelling raiders ate up the union treasury and weakened its efforts to organize elsewhere, and technology, new processes, and some loss to rivals caused membership decline.

In the wake of its expulsion from the CIO, Mine-Mill began to cast about for a merger partner but without success. During the late fifties the union, as noted, was declining in terms of membership, finances and reputation. It was being strained not only by rival unionism, but also by trials growing out of the Communist-domination charges. There seemed to be little prospect for growth of the union. At one point, Mine-Mill had agreed with the Teamsters to enter a mutual assistance pact which provided M-M with a loan of funds and immunity

[10]See, for example, Vernon H. Jensen, *Collective Bargaining in the Nonferrous Industry,* Institute of Industrial Relations (Berkeley: University of California, 1955) for a more complete discussion of the labor relations industry.

[11]For a thorough discussion of the union history, see: Vernon H. Jensen, *Nonferrous Metals Industry Unionism 1932–1954,* New York State School of Industrial and Labor Relations (Ithaca, New York: Cornell University, 1954).

from raiding by the IBT, but merger talks never produced results perhaps because of the Communist issue.[12]

During the early sixties, the Steelworkers continued its attempts to gain a more secure foothold in the copper industry through an intensive organizational and raiding campaign under the direction of a former M-M vice-president. The USW did win some plant elections, but encountered substantial difficulties imposed by the National Labor Relations Board's (NLRB) contract bar rule where three-year contracts had become common, also from a basic distrust of the USW by ethnic-oriented workers in the Southwest, and from vigorous counter campaigns by Mine-Mill. During the period of 1963–1965 when more contracts reopened, and were thus opened for raiding, M-M succeeded in winning some bargaining units back from the Steelworkers.[13] It is evident, therefore, that although the Mine, Mill and Smelter union was continuing to decay financially and in overall strength, it had not yet given in to the attempts of the USW to take over the Mine-Mill union on a local-by-local basis, and it still had substantial membership support.

In 1966, a series of legal events resulted in the disposal or dropping of all charges that had been pending, or under appeal, with regard to the Communist issue effecting the Mine-Mill union and its officers, thereby largely neutralizing the "taint" from M-M.[14] At that time the United Steelworkers of America engaged the officials of M-M in negotiations which were to result in its absorption into the USW, and which would make USW the dominant union in the industry.[15] The merger announcement was made on January 18, 1967 but was to become effective July 1, 1967, coincidentally the day on which a substantial portion of the copper industry labor agreements would be open.[16]

Bargaining Relationships

Contrary to other situations where coalitions have been formed to force a company to deal with more than representatives of a single bargaining unit for purposes of joint bargaining, all of the copper com-

[12]*Ibid.*
[13]*Ibid.*
[14]*Ibid.*
[15]There was some move among the M-M membership, in continuing its historical opposition to the USW, to prevent the merger, but it had no success.
[16]*Daily Labor Report,* January 18, 1967, p. A-5.

panies had dealt, at one time or another, with groups of local unions on a multiunit basis. In some cases this had been done voluntarily where either side was theoretically free to break away from the group if it so desired, although ASARCO always bargained with its M-M Council of 12 to 13 plants under protest, and refused to add additional units.

The copper industry has been engaged in various forms of joint bargaining since the War Labor Board, in attempting to settle labor disputes during World War II, granted several separate bargaining units common termination dates. Since that time, the various companies have engaged in various forms of joint bargaining, but have always maintained separate contacts with each bargaining unit.

Phelps Dodge, for example, typically bargained for its Arizona properties at sessions where representatives of its unions met in joint sessions to negotiate separate but similar contracts for Phelps Dodge employees. It is of note, however, that the four locations: Bisbee, where there are: maintenance facilities, an underground mine, an open-pit mine, and a concentrator; Douglas, where there are: maintenance shops and a smelter; Morenci, where there are: maintenance facilities, an open-pit mine, a concentrator, a precipitator, and a smelter; and Ajo, where there are: maintenance shops, an open-pit mine, a concentrator, and a smelter: all which share the same general economic constraints, are located in the same area of the country, and are all engaged in essentially similar operations. The agreement to conduct joint negotiations was one that was arrived at voluntarily, and one that provided a convenience for both Company and unions. In no case did Phelps Dodge permit these negotiations to be expanded to include operations outside either the region under the management of the Western Operations group, or outside the specific segment of the industry concerned.[17]

At Anaconda, a somewhat analogous situation existed. The Company's metal mining, milling, smelting, and refining operations at four separate locations in Western Montana are regarded as a somewhat integrated operation under the direction of the management of the Montana Operations group of the parent company. Prior to the 1967–1968 confrontation, Anaconda dealt with the unions representing

[17]See transcript of *Proceedings of the Special Panel Appointed to Assist in Settlement of the Copper Dispute* (Taylor Panel), January 30–February 2, 1968, Washington, D.C. Vol. 1, pp. 100–143.

its workers either on an individual or a coalition basis and executed agreements either on a single or multiple unit arrangement. For example, Anaconda often met with the four local unions represented by M-M and would execute a single agreement covering those workers. At times, the various craft unions would deal with the Company as a council which sought a single agreement; and at times, the unions would seek to bargain on an individual basis.

The Company stated that it had expressed a willingness during the 1967 negotiations to negotiate a master agreement, which would replace the individual agreements, signed according to NLRB certification and which would apply to all locals involved in primary metal production in Montana. It noted that because of the integrated nature of the operation, the relative geographic proximity, the single international union—M-M at that time—and the interdependent nature of the continuous operation, that it would be more convenient to operate under such a single contract arrangement. Anaconda was also quite clear, however, that it had no desire to include other types of operations, new mining ventures, or other locals from locations outside of Montana in such a master contract. Specifically excluded were such groups as the Anaconda-owned railroad, water company, lumber operation, wire mills, brass plants, and all others, except for the four which it cited explicitly.[18]

At American Smelting and Refining, a different type of situation developed, which the coalition unions attempted to enlarge into company-wide bargaining. Over the course of bargaining, 12 Mine, Mill and Smelter locals banded together in a loose confederation which became known as the ASARCO Council whose purpose was to tie together, as much as possible, the various locals in seeking to gain common settlements from the Company. Originally, there were 13 local unions in the Council—representing employees in diverse operations of the Company—but the number was reduced to 12 when ASARCO shut down one location as uneconomic, partially because of high costs. (Later, the Company's Groundhog underground lead-zinc mine suffered the same fate.) Because of the common contract termination dates for the Mine-Mill unions which had been imposed by the War Labor Board, ASARCO was in a position where it found it difficult to maintain

[18] *Ibid.*, Vol. 3, pp. 275–338.

separate contracts, wage differentials, and local provisions to reflect differences that existed among these plants whose local unions attempted to bargain through the ASARCO Council.

The Company never did engage in company-wide bargaining, but rather conducted simultaneous negotiations with the M-M council members, which usually resulted in quite similar packages. These individual agreements, however, reflected the differences inherent in different geographical locations, as well as differences in operations of the various types of plants represented in the Council. One result of Council activity was the evolution of a single pension plan covering the employees of the 12 plants, and a narrowing of differences in health and welfare plans for the group.[19] ASARCO was emphatic in emphasizing the point that it had not engaged in joint bargaining as proposed by the 1967 Steelworker coalition, despite union claims to the contrary.[20]

It is Kennecott Copper Corporation which engaged in joint bargaining to the greatest degree in the nonferrous industry. The Company operates four major mining and process locations as part of its Western Mining Divisions. Beginning in the mid-fifties Mine-Mill, which then represented about half of the Kennecott employees, and the Company agreed to bargain with other unions jointly on a four-division basis which covered the mining properties. This grouping of unions, which was known as the Unity Council, also included two locals of the USW and although the international union remained aloof to this marriage to the M-M at that time, the Steelworkers' locals were willing to join Mine-Mill and other unions who chose to participate in the joint effort.

Thus, through the Unity Council, the Western properties of Kennecott began to engage in a pattern of joint bargaining. When the merger of Mine-Mill and the Steelworkers appeared to be forthcoming, the Company began to encourage all of the unions representing workers at the Western mining properties to form a coalition for bargaining purposes, and was successful to the point where 97 percent of the represented employees at those locations have banded together for joint bargaining.[21] The reasons for such a decision were apparently based upon the observation that the properties had many parallel elements:

---

[19] *Ibid.*, Vol. 4, pp. 402–504.
[20] *Ibid.*, pp. 436–441.
[21] *Ibid.*, p. 177.

job requirements, products, geographic homogenity, and economics, and that joint bargaining would eliminate whipsawing. Kennecott, however, adds a caveat:

> . . . We have learned that the economics are not so parallel, and that it may not be wise to put all seemingly alike properties in the same bargaining group.
>
> Equalization of pay rates and fringe benefits among the four copper properties has resulted in labor costs at the Nevada Mines Division which threaten to shorten the life of that property. It is a low yield property now, and the forecast for the future, when recognizing the likelihood of a sizable settlement this year, is that it may or may not continue operations through its earlier expected life.
>
> It is axiomatic that when you approach the end of a known ore body, the higher wages and supply costs, then the shorter the life must be.[22]

It is apparent, then, that although Kennecott had felt that certain benefits might have gained through joint bargaining, experiences proved to be different from the expected results. The Company's position was that it had no interest in enlarging the scope of negotiations to include its refining, mining and fabricating operations in other geographic areas nor in other facets of the industry, beyond the primary metals production areas.

The Coalition Formation

As has been noted above, the International Union of Mine, Mill and Smelter Workers had long been the dominant union in the copper industry; its main rival, the United Steelworkers of America was, late in 1966, in the process of absorbing Mine-Mill, and a large segment of the industry was facing a common contract termination date of June 30, 1967. It soon became apparent that the Industrial Union Department, and the Steelworkers, anxious to prove its new strength, chose to engage the copper industry in its first major test of industry-wide coalition bargaining.

The IUD had been working for some time on the formation of at least five separate company committees in order to bring about coali-

---

[22]*Ibid.*, p. 178.

tions with those firms which were involved in the nonferrous industry to some degree.[23] It was in Chicago, however, between October 26 and 28, 1966 that the IUD held a major meeting of the "Copper and Brass Industry." At that time, some 320 people were in attendance, including 94 from Mine-Mill, 91 from the Steelworkers, 51 from the United Automobile Workers (UAW), 32 from the International Association of Machinists (IAM), 8 from the IUD, 3 individuals from the Federal Mediation and Conciliation Service who acted as observers, and a host of others. In all 13 international unions were represented, including at least one which has no members employed in the copper industry.[24]

At the Chicago meeting, the IUD presented the delegates with a three-part, 130-page document which was simply entitled "Copper and Brass Conference," but which provided a detailed analysis of the operations, financial analysis, plant locations and organizational status, contract analysis, and pension examinations for each of 10 companies which it included in its definition of the nonferrous industry.[25] In addition to the individual corporate breakdowns, the IUD also provided the delegates with detailed intercompany comparisons in regard to sales, profit, return on investment, all of which were designed to encourage the representatives to seek greater demands in 1967 bargaining. The Chicago meeting also served to sell the various local leaders on the virtues of coalition bargaining on an industry-wide basis under the leadership of the IUD and the Steelworkers.

"HEAVEN IN '67"

It is apparent that sufficient interest was elicited at the October meeting sponsored by the IUD so that the Steelworkers, and their new "affiliate," Mine-Mill, had decided to work with the IUD in preparing a total coalition effort against the copper industry in 1967. The result was a second conference involving USW and M-M in Salt Lake City from March 14 to 16, 1967 where the assembled representatives adopted the "1967 NON-FERROUS BARGAINING POLICY GOALS as formu-

[23]Apparently, the earlier plan was to engage each of these firms in separate coalition effort, prior to the decision to operate on the larger scale.

[24]See "Attendance List," IUD—Copper and Brass Meeting, Chicago, Illinois, October 26–28, 1966. Prepared by the Industrial Union Department, AFL-CIO.

[25]See "Copper and Brass Conference," *op. cit.* The 10 companies analyzed were: ASARCO, Anaconda, Calumet and Hecla, Cerro, Kennecott, Magma, National Distillers, Phelps Dodge, Revere, and Scovill.

lated and adopted by the NON-FERROUS INDUSTRY CONFERENCE."[26] The 38-page booklet in which the unions presented the bargaining demands quickly became known as "Heaven in '67" by the less respectful union leaders, while the industry representatives chose to refer to the document as the "Best Seller," or the "Arizona Joke Book."

Although the demands contained in the "Bargaining Policy Goals" booklet were specific in some areas, they were deliberately vague in others. In assessing the USW-Mine-Mill demands, it becomes apparent that in order to satisfy all parties, it was necessary to seek the highest common denominator—which meant that in some cases, companies were facing demands that were not even applicable to the situation at hand. One union goal was industry-wide uniformity on all issues, which it hoped to gain in the single set of negotiations in 1967.

The demands specified in "Heaven in '67" were practically all-inclusive. (Of course, too, there were thousands of local demands.) The demands themselves began with "Cost-of-Living Escalator Clause," on through wage and salary changes ("substantial"), equalization of rates, job and income security, group insurance benefits, vacations, holidays, etc., on to length of agreement and pension plans. In order to protect further its position created by having painted with such a broad brush, the unions also included a demand that stated: "All existing provisions which are superior to the proposals in this statement of Bargaining Policy Goals shall be preserved."[27]

The unions never publicly attached any dollar value to the proposals contained in the "Best Seller" for any company. It was estimated, however, by one company, that to apply all of the demands to its operation, including an estimate of the "substantial" wage increase, would have resulted in added labor costs of nearly $2.85 per hour. As a percentage increase, such an estimate would have been equal to about four times the increase gained by the UAW in settling with the Ford Motor Company, the most widely heralded union victory at that time.[28] Although industry and union negotiators often differ in their estimates of the costs of a particular proposal because of different as-

[26]"1967 Non-Ferrous Bargaining Policy Goals" as formulated and adopted by the Non-Ferrous Industry Conference, Salt Lake City, Utah, March 14–16, 1967. Prepared by USW and M-M.

[27]*Ibid.*, p. 18.

[28]See "Situation Facing Companies . . . ," *op. cit.*, p. 3.

sumptions, it is doubtful that the unions, using their own assumptions, could have priced the total package at less than $2.00 per hour.[29]

The single outstanding theme running through the "Best Seller" was that of uniformity. The unions stressed the need for uniform conditions, wages, benefits, insurance, vacations, and all other contractual items across the industry. It further sought to ensure this end through the negotiation of a master contract at each company. The goal with this end in mind was stated:

> *Master Agreements and Termination Dates*
>
> The major Companies in the non-ferrous industry still operate with separate collective bargaining agreements at each location. Many agreements even have different termination dates. This antiquated system has long since been abandoned by most major Companies and Unions. This should be done in non-ferrous also. Certain of the non-ferrous Companies have negotiated single economic settlements for most plants for several years. They should now convert these half-way arrangements to full Company-wide master agreements including coverage of all subsidiary units. This would facilitate both negotiations and contract administration. All agreements in each Company and in the industry should bear a common termination date and should provide for automatic inclusion of newly certified or recognized units.[30]

The unions adopted the bargaining goals as set forth in "Heaven in '67," and in fact made the booklet the official set of bargaining demands when a copy was sent to each of the targeted nonferrous companies with the required contract reopening letters, mailed early in April 1967. Additionally, as contracts in isolated parts of each company expired, the unions presented the booklet as their official demands. In most cases, there was no elaboration of demands other than that contained in the booklet; it was up to the companies to decide whether or not priorities were assigned, and what the impact upon bargaining would be.

THE COALITION IN ACTION

In light of the fact that many of the companies in the copper industry faced contract termination dates for a substantial number of

[29] *Ibid.*
[30] "1967 Non-Ferrous Bargaining Policy Goals," *op. cit.*, p. 13.

locations on June 30, 1967, they prepared for customary bargaining to begin several months in advance of that date. When negotiations did get under way, all copper producers faced similar situations. The Mine-Mill—Steelworker coalition had been joined by some 25 other unions who had representation rights in some area of operation maintained by one of the companies. (See Table 9–2 for the list of coalition unions.) In most cases the sessions were marked by a full group of coalition union representatives, where the unions again reiterated the fact that "Heaven in '67" was submitted as the official list of demands upon which they intended to bargain. It was further emphasized that the recognition of the coalition on a joint basis, for bargaining a single master agreement at each company, was a precondition to further negotiation.

The response by the individual companies in the industry was a rejection of the union plan for master agreements through company-wide coalition bargaining. Each company, except ASARCO, did agree to permit the coalition representatives to attend negotiating sessions, and all four companies attempted to engage in meaningful bargaining, without any success whatsoever. The result of the unions' intransigence was an effective cessation of all collective bargaining.

As the June 30 termination date approached, the company representatives continued to attempt to avoid a strike by seeking to negotiate with the unions either on an individual or collective basis, while continuing to maintain the integrity of the legally certified bargaining units. The result was further refusal on the part of the coalition to participate in any productive bargaining. The unions simply repeated demands as espoused in the "Best Seller," and reiterated the fact that company-wide bargaining would have to be agreed to in order to avoid a major work stoppage.

In a further effort to get bargaining off dead-center, each of the major producers made at least one economic bargaining proposal to the coalition participants. In most cases, the companies made the offer directly to the traditional negotiating units. For example, Kennecott's offer was made to the Western Mining group, while ASARCO made a series of proposals directly to each of the units of the ASARCO Council. Each of these proposals—meant to be a start for negotiations—were substantially in excess of the amounts that had been settled for during the previous contract negotiations in 1964, and generally amounted to about 50 cents an hour over three years. No counterproposal was elicited from the unions.

TABLE 9–2

UNIONS IN THE NONFERROUS COALITION

United Steelworkers of America (including former Mine, Mill and Smelter Workers)
United Automobile, Aircraft, and Agricultural Implement Workers of America
International Union of Electrical Workers
International Brotherhood of Electrical Workers*
International Association of Machinists
International Brotherhood of Teamsters, Warehousemen and Helpers
International Union of Operating Engineers
Laborers International Union of North America
Brotherhood of Railroad Trainmen
Order of Railway Conductors and Brakemen
Brotherhood of Locomotive Firemen and Enginemen
Brotherhood of Railway Carmen of America
International Brotherhood of Boilermakers, Iron Ship Builders, Blacksmiths, Forgers and Helpers
United Brotherhood of Carpenters and Joiners of America
Brotherhood of Painters, Decorators and Paperhangers of America
United Association of Journeymen and Apprentices of the Plumbing and Pipe Fitting Industry of the United States and Canada
Office and Professional Employees International Union
Pattern Makers League of North America
Sheet Metal Workers International Union
Switchmen's Union of North America
Bricklayers, Masons and Plasterers International Union of America
International Chemical Workers
International Association of Bridge and Structural Iron Workers
Brotherhood of Locomotive Engineers
International Molders and Allied Workers Union
Office Employees Independent Union

*The IBEW at Phelps Dodge in Arizona stayed out of the coalition at first, but later joined with the four wire and cable plants at Yonkers, New York when those contracts expired.

Source: Copper Strike Information Bureau.

Role of the IUD

Although the Steelworkers have taken the credit (or blame) for leading the 26-union coalition against the copper industry, the influence of the IUD was very evident in the early stages of bargaining. In addition to the local and staff representatives of the various international unions, a typical presidents' committee was established to aid in the guidance of the coalition efforts. It was reinforced through the participation of Richard T. Leonard, Director of the IUD Collective Bargaining Services Section. Evidence of IUD strategy also came to the fore in negotiating the sessions that did take place when it became apparent that the union representatives were interested primarily in discussing benefit items such as pensions and insurance which might have greater similarity in plans across the operation of a particular company. The local union officials also quickly found that they were no longer the spokesmen for their respective unions, but that representatives assigned by the coalition leaders were in charge of the negotiations.[31]

A second IUD strategy maneuver also became apparent as the contract termination date of June 30 drew nearer: failing to engage in meaningful bargaining until after a strike is in progress. From the coalition standpoint such a strategy serves at least two purposes. The first is to solidify the rank and file, both as to the degree of militancy required to maintain a strong front, and as to attempting to force the company to deal with all striking unions on a single basis. A second reason for the refusal to bargain prior to the contract expiration is simply to provide a delay to permit more contracts to expire at the same time, thereby bringing greater pressure to bear on the employer as well as solidifying and fortifying the ranks of the strikers. As the copper strike progressed, at least in the early stages, the coalitions were able to add new units to their ranks on a regular basis, thereby increasing the possibility of a larger bargaining group on the next round if the unions were successful in gaining common termination dates and master agreements.

The Strike

In most instances in the past, copper unions had struck employers on a selective basis. If the local union was unable to reach agreement

[31]Personal interview with officials of Anaconda, *op. cit.*

with its employer, and chose to strike, it would do so. In the situation with Kennecott at its western properties, the coalition already in existence had the same prerogative. The 1967 coalition situation, however, presented a different case. It is reported that initial coalition plans called for a strike against a single employer on July 1, but that USW Vice President Joseph P. Molony argued successfully for an industry-wide shutdown two weeks later. His views apparently prevailed, and although ASARCO's Omaha plant was struck on July 1, on July 15, 1967 a walkout began at 73 locations of eight copper-producing companies which was to eventually include some 60,000 workers in the copper industry for more than 260 days.[32] It was a long and extensive strike that was clearly a product of a coalition bargaining attempt on a massive scale. The coalition unions were often not as anxious to maintain strikes against the so-called independent producers as they were against the larger firms in the industry. For example, the Pima (Arizona) Mining Company was allowed to continue production past the August 31 expiration date of its contract with the Steelworkers, Teamsters, Operating Engineers, and the IBEW. Settlement was reached, without a strike, on October 13 for about 75 cents an hour over three years.

Similarly, three contracts with secondary metals operators in the Chicago area were concluded early in September by the Steelworkers for packages that ranged from 50 to 65 cents over three years, at a time when ASARCO had offered employees in its competing plant a similar deal. At Balmat, New York, the USW had been negotiating since July 1 with St. Joseph Lead Company while production continued. Settlement was reached in October for a 50.2 cent package (without impact) for a 42-month contract. Other lead producers remained on strike. Five contracts were settled between September and December by the IBEW and IAM at wire and cable plants for packages that ranged from 36 cents to 56 cents over five years. The major integrated producers had more substantial offers on the table during that period, but the coalition leaders would not negotiate on them because of the issue of company-wide bargaining. Meanwhile, they continued to settle with smaller producers at less than the Big Four were offering.

---

[32]Some 73 operations in 44 cities and 21 states were struck on July 15 immediately idling some 50,000 workers, according to the Copper Strike Information Bureau.

INTERVENTION AND OUTSIDE PRESSURES

Although the nonferrous strike largely shut off domestic production of copper, its related by-products and much of the lead, zinc, and silver production, caused thousands of workers to be laid off, (in addition to those striking), resulted in the crippling of the economies of several states and numerous dependent communities, it is apparent that the union leaders greatly miscalculated its ability to force the companies to their knees, or to bring about governmental intervention.

Indeed, some observers felt that during the early period of the strike a primary aim of the coalition was to bring about the invocation of Taft-Hartley emergency provisions for an 80-day cooling-off period.[33] The use of such a measure would benefit the unions in two ways. First, it would permit the unions to present an industry-wide approach to bargaining before a government-convened forum. This would tend to legitimatize the demand for joint bargaining to the detriment of the company's position on the issue. The issuance of an injunction would also serve to provide a respite to the workers who were forced to strike in the early period of the conflict, and would permit them to join with others at the end of the 80-day period without severe loss of earnings, in the interim, if necessary.

On the other hand, the coalition obviously was of the opinion that a Taft-Hartley injunction would not be in its best interest as the strike progressed. The most significant reason for the change in position lies in the fact that the USW would simply be overtaxed if it had to bargain with copper at the same time negotiations were being conducted with the can and aluminum industries, followed by the basic steel industry during the summer of 1968. Similarly, the USW strike fund would be extremely pressed to support two or more major industry strikes, if the copper workers chose to strike again.

The Government chose not to make use of Taft-Hartley measures. Spokesmen rationalized the decision by noting that while a problem of national importance had been caused with respect to the United States balance of payments, and that, although serious harm was being done to the national economy, that such problems had not been dealt with previously in Taft-Hartley proceedings, and that the courts might have

[33]W. M. Kirkpatrick, Vice-President of Anaconda, for example, made such a point in an address to the American Mining Congress in Denver, Colorado, September 13, 1967.

been unwilling to issue an injunction on such grounds. As we shall note in Chapter XI, however, court precedents appear to indicate that whenever the President has seen fit to request relief under the Taft-Hartley emergency procedures, such relief is not likely to be rejected by the courts.

A second reason for the reluctance to make use of the established machinery for halting the strike would seem to have been based on a fear by the government that settlement may not have been forthcoming within the 80-day cooling-off period and that the strike may have begun anew. This would have forced the President to turn to Congress for compulsory arbitration, as was the case in the railway cases. It is difficult to assume, however, that a second strike would have occurred given the length of the strike.[34] It is for this reason that some company spokesmen, while publicly opposing Taft-Hartley intervention, later began, privately, to express some interest in an 80-day injunction.

Governors

Other attempts to settle the strike, however, were made by third parties, beginning as early as August 2, 1967 when the governors of the five Western states met to discuss the strike, its effects, and means of inducing settlement. On August 24, the same group of governors called on President Johnson, urging him to appoint a fact-finding board to look into the possibility of invoking the emergency provisions of the Taft-Hartley Act, followed by a second appeal on August 29. The President chose not to act on the request.[35]

Cabinet Members

While bargaining continued on a sporadic basis at some locations, with no movement whatsoever on the part of the unions with respect to the demands for national bargaining, the Federal government was beginning to become involved on an informal basis. On September 6 and 7, the Secretaries of Labor, Commerce, and Defense summoned representatives of the four major producers, and of the coalition unions to Washington for separate exploratory meetings with the Secretaries in order to seek a common ground for settlement of the dispute. Labor

---

[34]For Taft-Hartley experiences, see Herbert R. Northrup and Gordon F. Bloom, *Government and Labor* (Homewood, Illinois: Richard D. Irwin, Inc., 1963), Chapter 13.

[35]Copper Strike Information Bureau, "Strike Chronology," August 24, 1968. The chronology is a daily summary of events which transpired during the entire course of the dispute. It is reproduced in Appendix B.

Secretary Wirtz announced that the negotiations in the strike were at a "complete and absolute stalemate."[36]

The first apparent movement by the Steelworker-IUD-led coalition came about on October 2, 1967 at the request of Utah Governor Rampton in what has been described as a "fishbowl" public bargaining session in a counterproposal to Kennecott. The unions had promised to respond to the outstanding Company offer by revising their demands to a package of less than a dollar. The union counteroffer presented was never fully costed by the unions, but was claimed to amount to 99 cents. After almost three weeks of continuous bargaining Kennecott reduced its original estimate of $1.75 per hour to $1.35 per hour. (See Table 9–3) At that time, too, one coalition leader reaffirmed the union stand that all Kennecott operations were to be included in bargaining, and stated that "Company-wide bargaining is a must issue."[37]

TABLE 9–3

UNION COUNTEROFFER

Here is the union counterproposal as costed by Kennecott:

Wages—13 cents per hour for each of the three years plus an additional 4 cents the first year.

Increments—17.25 cents per hour.

Impact—12.05 cents per hour.

Pensions—39.8 cents per hour. (Union costing: 29.8 cents)

Insurance—13.34 cents per hour. (Union costing: 9.16 cents)

Holiday—One additional per year 1.27 cents per hour. (Union agrees)

Job and Income Security—3.3 cents per hour. (Union costing: None)

Other Miscellaneous Benefits—5 cents per hour. (Union costing: None)

TOTAL $1.35 (Kennecott) $0.99 (Union)

Kennecott costs the union counteroffer at 11 percent annually, nearly twice the recent settlement accepted and widely hailed by the United Auto Workers in its strike against Ford Motor Company. Settlement at the latter high level has been generally regarded by the Administration and the nation's economists to be an inflationary increase for wage-benefits settlements. In key settlements for the first nine months of 1967 the median wage and benefit increase was 4.9 percent, according to the October 30, 1967, B.L.S. report.

Source: Copper Strike Information Bureau, November 1967.

[36] *Ibid.*, September 7, 1967.
[37] *Ibid.*, October 3, 1967.

In a similar manner, Anaconda met with the unions to receive a counterproposal at the request of Montana Governor Tim Babcock on October 17 and 18. The coalition submitted a revision in its demands for a contract to include all Anaconda locations and subsidiaries in the United States, which would have increased the Company's labor costs in Montana in excess of 50 percent. Anaconda rejected the coalition counteroffer.[38]

In December, Governor Babcock again attempted to intervene in Montana by announcing the appointment of a fact-finding commission to examine the issues in the strike—then 144 days old. Anaconda announced a willingness to participate and cooperate with such a plan for its Montana operations, but union officials refused.[39]

Senators

On November 15 when the copper strike entered its fifth month, a bill was introduced on the floor of the U.S. Senate by Republican Senator Fannin of Arizona, which would provide for new machinery to permit workers to end a protracted strike. Essentially, the bill provided that 20 percent of the workers involved in a strike "affecting commerce" could, after 30 days of striking, petition the NLRB for a referendum on the work stoppage. If a majority of those voting in the referendum favor a cessation of the strike, the union representing the workers must halt the work stoppage for at least a 90-day period. The coalition unions were unequivocally opposed to the Fannin bill, which was referred to committee.[40]

Two weeks later, Senators Mansfield and Metcalf, both Democrats, of Montana, announced that they had written to President Johnson proposing that he appoint a fact-finding board to seek settlement of the strike. The reaction was swift from both sides in the dispute. The Steelworkers' officials, then in Miami Beach attending the AFL-CIO convention, responded by stating that the unions "welcome the opportunity to state our position in this strike and shall stand ready to participate and cooperate fully in the proposed fact-finding."[41]

The very nature and composition of the proposed board was op-

[38]*Ibid.*, October 17–18, 1967.
[39]*Ibid.*, December 6, 1967.
[40]See *Congressional Record*—Senate, November 15, 1967, S-2667 at p. S-16539.
[41]*Wall Street Journal*, December 8, 1967.

posed by most firms in the copper industry. The panel suggested by the Senators would consist of two members chosen by the companies, two by the unions, and three more selected jointly by the parties or by Cabinet members to represent the public. The function of the panel was to be one of fact-finding, with powers of recommendation for settlement. The companies in the industry declined to endorse the panel proposal, and in so doing indicated a belief that such a simple forum would give an undeserved legitimization to the coalition demand for company-wide bargaining. Some of the industry spokesmen suggested instead a series of local fact-finding panels to look into the individual disputes outside of the national context, a proposal rejected by the unions.[42]

Taylor Panel

Bargaining between union and company representatives continued to take place, with varying degrees of success, while the strike continued on through January 1968, with other plants being struck as contracts expired. Again, Senator Mansfield urged the President to appoint a fact-finding board, this time consisting of three members. With the support of AFL-CIO President George Meany, and over the opposition of Senator Fannin, the President announced, on January 24, the appointment of a three-man fact finding panel under the chairmanship of Dr. George W. Taylor, prominent mediator and Professor at the University of Pennsylvania's Wharton School of Finance and Commerce, to seek a way to end the 195-day strike.[43] The panel was to be acting at the request of the Secretaries of Labor and Commerce, and would be reporting to them.

The panel members announced that public hearings would be held on four separate days in order to uncover the core of the dispute, and to make the public aware of the fact that the copper industry had been essentially shut down for six months.[44] It was also the intention of the panel to act as mediators, if possible, to attempt to establish grounds for settlement in private sessions, as well as public, without making "recommendations" as such.

---

[42]*Ibid.*, December 11, 1967.
[43]Philadelphia *Bulletin*, January 24, 1968.
[44]*Wall Street Journal*, January 29, 1968.

Much of the struck portion of the copper industry objected in principle to the appointment of the Taylor Panel for the same reasons noted above. Additionally, some industry representatives were of the opinion that the coalition unions were showing signs of weakness, and that the unions were about to lose the strike. ASARCO had actually reopened some locations. Some settlements had been reached with independent operators, decertification and back-to-work movements were afoot in several locations, and many workers were apparently beginning to question seriously the wisdom of the protracted work stoppage. The announcement of the Panel's appointment served to bolster the union hopes.

Although all of the copper producers agreed to participate in the panel proceedings, they did so with certain strong misgivings. One of the big four producers voiced extreme displeasure with the convocation of an extralegal proceeding,[45] while an industry spokesman offered the following statement:

> While willing to be helpful to the extra-legal Board appointed by the Secretaries of Labor and Commerce to ascertain solutions to the six-month old copper strike, the major producers are disappointed that the Administration has not adopted a more practical method of resolving the many disputes that exist. The companies believe that the jurisdiction of the Board should be limited to those operations concerned with the primary production of copper and the recognized bargaining units therein.
>
> Collective bargaining is finally showing the results in the dispute and the pressures necessary to bring about bargained settlements are mounting. According to the statement issued by the Department of Labor, "the national interest will not permit the continuation of this situation." If this has now become true, then the Administration had available the means designated by Congressional enactment to deal with the dispute, namely Taft-Hartley. Use of this Act would return the copper properties to production, cut the flow of dollars to foreign sources, and help revive hard-hit local economies, putting a prompt end to a situation which is adverse to the national interest.
>
> The appointment of a panel could delay a return to work while its members learn what the problems are and how, and in what way, the Board could be helpful in further bargaining and negotiations.

---

[45] *Ibid.*, January 30, 1968.

> As a result of collective bargaining the Copper Range Company reached a settlement this week with the Steelworkers Union at the White Pine mining property in northern Michigan. The Anaconda Company, Wednesday, made a new and substantially increased offer to the unions representing its Montana operations.
>
> We sincerely hope that the Government intervention will not carry this dispute further into the political arena and will not slow down collective bargaining while the parties to the dispute await the thoughts of the Board.[46]

Thus, the industry leaders expressed their objection to the panel and its proceedings. It was supported in its opposition by an editorial in the *New York Times* which stated in part:

> . . . The normal economic issues are secondary to the unions' determination to establish bargaining on a company-wide basis, in place of the localized bargaining system that now prevails in copper.
>
> In intervening, the President has chosen not to get an 80-day injunction under the national emergency provisions of the Taft-Hartley Act. That law would have restored domestic copper production but would not have provided an approach to settlement of the stubborn basic issue. The present recourse to White House improvisation has the disadvantage of throwing the whole dispute into an industry-wide framework of settlement, thus automatically putting them well on their way to winning the central strike goal even before any recommendations are made.
>
> The panel now has the difficult task of demonstrating that its appointment has not, in and of itself, stacked the deck against the companies on an issue of great importance to employers and unions in most major industries. . . .[47]

When the panel began its hearings it became quickly evident that the unions' failure to budge from its fixed position on the nonmandatory subject of bargaining—the company-wide issue—was the single major impediment to settlement. Although numerous economic and other issues were raised in the hearings, the panel found that three issues related to the coalition demands were the source of the problems. The panel reported to the Secretaries who in turn released the findings of the Taylor Panel which stated in part:

---

[46]Copper Strike Information Bureau News Release, January 25, 1968.
[47]*New York Times,* January 25, 1968.

> The unions insist that whatever else companywide bargaining may mean, there are three basic ingredients which represent absolute preconditions for negotiations:
>
> (a) Common expiration dates for all labor-management contracts within a company including its subsidiaries in the non-ferrous metals industry.
>
> (b) A companywide economic "package" to be applied equally to each unit within a company, making some minor allowances for local conditions.
>
> (c) An accepted rule within each corporation that settlement must be achieved at all operations before any operations are resumed.
>
> The companies, on the other hand, rejected these preconditions and said the present bargaining arrangements (perhaps with minor modifications) should be retained. They asserted that there must be separate economic treatment for the several "different businesses" within their corporate structures.[48]

The Panel viewed these as the "roadblock" issues, and in setting forth recommendations, indicating that the parties should "shelve" the existing positions that had been taken, and begin negotiating on the substantive issues within three groupings: (1) Copper mining, smelting and refining; (2) Units producing other nonferrous metals; and (3) Copper wire and cable and brass fabrication.[49]

Three days after the report of the Taylor Panel had been made public, the Associated Press reported that the coalition had failed to accept the findings of the extralegal board which it had sought. The report stated:

> Chances appeared bleaker today for any break in the nation wide copper strike after union leaders slapped down a government proposal to get talks moving again in the seven-month old walkout. "It looks pretty grim," said strike leader J. P. Molony after his committee . . . rejected a federal suggestion that unions drop their demands for company-wide bargaining.[50]

Thus, it would appear that the unions were seeking support from the Taylor Panel, and in the absence of a favorable result—a failure to gain through intervention what they had been unable to do through

[48]Joint News Release by the Departments of Commerce and Labor, February 17, 1968.
[49]*Ibid.*
[50]Associated Press Dispatch, February 20, 1968.

bargaining—elected to continue to hold out, and to continue the strike against the major producers.

The President

After rejecting the recommendations of the Panel whose establishment it had sought, the coalition unions under the leadership of the Steelworkers continued to exert pressure on the Administration in efforts to achieve its goal of company-wide bargaining. Steelworker Vice-President Molony even went so far as to threaten government officials with a withdrawal of labor support at election time when he told a group of strikers, "if our friends in Washington are 'neutral' in the strike, then I'll be 'neutral' next November. Remember, the hottest corner in hell is reserved for those who remain neutral in a crisis."[51]

Real collective bargaining, in any sense, began only after the strike had been in progress for more than seven and one-half months, and only after the President called both parties to Washington to begin intensive negotiations. Beginning on March 4, the parties began to use the recommendations of the Taylor Panel as a *beginning* for collective bargaining. Phelps Dodge, Kennecott, and ASARCO met separately with the unions. ASARCO and the USW agreed to begin talks on the basis of the Taylor Panel Report instead of the company-wide basis that the coalition had demanded.[52]

Apparently, however, other companies were not so fortunate in obtaining agreement to begin talks on a basis other than company-wide. In spite of the fact that both sides had "agreed" to a news blackout, it became evident that the parties were having difficulty in determining what basis was to be used in determining bargaining groupings.

Although Phelps Dodge reached a tentative agreement covering its Arizona mining operations, and its El Paso, Texas copper refinery, it quickly became apparent that the coalition was still attempting to force a common contract termination date, and to seek to have all other Phelps Dodge contracts consummated prior to having any strikers return to the job.[53] Bargaining did progress, however, and the first contract to be ratified was that of the Steelworker locals who were to be covered by a single contract for the Phelps Dodge Arizona mining

[51]*The* (Baltimore) *Sun,* February 29, 1968.
[52]"Strike Chronology," *op. cit.,* March 5, 1968.
[53]*Ibid.,* March 8–11, 1968.

operations and the El Paso refinery—for an estimated $1.13 an hour for 40 months. Thus, the first significant break came on March 16, eight months after the start of the strike.[54]

Gradually, real collective bargaining began to work, and settlements were reached by the copper producers and their unions. By the end of March, most of the major issues had been settled, but many operations were prevented from reopening because of outstanding *local* issues which had been previously submerged and subordinated to the demands of the coalition.

Throughout the period of Washington negotiations some company officials felt that Administration representatives who were acting as mediators were engaged in a constant effort to induce the industry to make substantially higher wage and benefit offers. This would assuage the unions who were obviously unable to obtain the primary goal of company-wide bargaining.

OTHER ISSUES

In examining the copper situation, at least three other issues are worthy of note, and have direct bearing on the length and depth of the coalition strike. The first is the role of the NLRB, the second is the role of copper imports and attempts to deplete the supply of processed product, and the third deals with the strength of the coalition and the manner in which the Steelworkers have brought about and encouraged a competitive imbalance through earlier settlements with smaller companies in certain segments of the industry.

The NLRB

On October 18, 1967 Kennecott filed charges of unfair labor practices against the Steelworkers and the other coalition unions with which it dealt.[55] The Company, it is noted, did not file the charges until the coalition leader *publicly* stated the union position that had been evident to industry negotiators for more than six months. The petition filed at the Denver Regional Office of the Board declared that since May 8, 1967 the coalition had engaged in bad faith bargaining by conditioning demands for new contracts upon the expansion of the bargaining to

[54] *Ibid.*, March 16, 1968.
[55] *Ibid.*, October 18, 1968.

include common expiration dates for all units, company-wide economic package, and a uniform back-to-work date for all employees. The Board's General Counsel failed to act on the petition, because the union, in a telegram disclaimed any intention of pursuing company-wide bargaining. It was not until February 28, 1968 that the regional Board office under great outside pressure issued a complaint against the Kennecott coalition unions, charging an unfair labor practice.[56] By that time, too, other companies had also filed charges, and had requested injunctive relief under Section 10(j) of the National Labor Relations Act in order to force the unions to withdraw demands for company-wide bargaining. Such a 10(j) injunction was never formally sought. After the intervention of the Taylor Panel, the White House bargaining and, eventually, the settlements the General Counsel finally activated the machinery to determine the merits of the basic unfair labor practice charges.

It has already been noted that it appeared that the coalition unions sought Taft-Hartley intervention in the early stages of the dispute, but later found it undesirable. It was the position of the industry, too, that such intervention was unwarranted, and unnecessary, although it expressed a definite preference for the use of the existing disputes law over the extralegal, or "arsenal of weapons" approach that was eventually utilized.[57] The government apparently felt that it would find it difficult to convince the courts that a Taft-Hartley emergency back-to-work was warranted under the existing definition of "national emergency."[58] The national emergency that was predicted by the coalition as a result of the strike simply failed to develop because of the existing copper inventory, and because of the high level of imports that resulted from the work stoppage. The Administration apparently felt that the domestic situation was not severe enough to be classified as an emergency—although officials in many Western states might disagree strongly—and that the balance of payments problem which was aggravated by the strike was not a viable issue to place before the court. The role of politics as regards the means of government participation in the collective bargaining process is difficult, at best, to assess. However, it is

---

[56]*Ibid.*, February 28, 1968.

[57]Such an observation was made in personal interviews with several officials of the embroiled copper firms.

[58]Such an opinion was expressed by Panel Chairman George W. Taylor in a speech at the University of Pennsylvania on April 16, 1968.

sufficient to state that the coalition leaders were attempting to exert all possible pressures to support the demands for industry-wide settlements in the copper confrontation.[59]

Imports and the ILA

It has already been noted that one of the aims of the strike leaders was to bring pressure to settle by eliminating all supplies of copper through a strike affecting more than 90 percent of the industry. The single largest supply of copper during the strike came from imports. Thus, on February 22, 1968 the president of the International Longshoremen's Association (ILA) announced that his union would boycott the handling of copper at Eastern and Gulf ports. He stated:

> The International Longshoremen have decided in the interest of helping their fellow trade unionists on strike against the copper companies to refuse to handle all imports and exports in the U. S. and Canada.[60]

Faced with a suit for creating a secondary boycott, the ILA quickly announced a change of position, attributing the earlier announcement to a "clerk's error."[61] The fact remained, however, that the union continued to refuse to handle copper consigned to some firms, while granting permission for delivery to others.[62] Despite these measures, the supply of copper never really dried up; and although some users were forced to curtail operations or to seek substitutes, and pay vastly higher prices for imported copper, the strike never brought about a "copper crisis."

Solidarity of the Coalition

A constant demand of the coalition unions in dealing with the four major copper producers, and the four others which were on strike for extended periods, was that of sustaining the strike until all workers were satisfied. The coalition spokesman framed the issue thus:

> I doubt very much that you, or we of the unions, or anyone else, can persuade the members of these unions involved in the strike to

[59]See footnote 51 above.
[60]"Strike Chronology," *op. cit.*, February 22, 1968.
[61]*Ibid.*, February 23, 1968.
[62]*Wall Street Journal*, March 15, 1968.

> settle at one property of one of these companies and leave fellow trade unionists, their brothers, at another property out on strike and walking picket lines. They just can't propose to abandon their fellow members.[63]

It is interesting to note, in the light of such proclaimed solidarity, that the coalition unions had been in the process of systematically reaching agreements with competitors of the major producers during the entire course of the strike. In some cases, the settlements reached were for packages substantially less than the initial offers extended by the four major producers at that time. For example, a tube mill was sold by a Phelps Dodge subsidiary to an independent operator after the strike there had begun. Two days later, the Steelworkers settled for 43 cents an hour, a figure less than that offered by Phelps Dodge in its initial package.[64]

A similar situation will tend to put Anaconda's wire and cable operations at a competitive disadvantage. Coalition unions settled with six independent wire and cable producers for packages that ranged from 30 to 38 cents per hour, for contracts that ran from 30 to 60 months. Likewise, unions settled disputes with other producers in the secondary metals market, in lead and zinc, mining, and even in copper mining. In most cases, the settlements were for substantially less than the expected settlements among the major producers.[65]

Within the coalitions union at the major producers, there are only slight public indications of unrest or loss of control by the leadership. It has been reported that in at least one case a Steelworker local in a strike-bound Washington plant voted to disaffiliate from USW and join instead with the independent Northwest Metal Workers Union while other decertification and back-to-work movements were developing.[66] A second factor which apparently began to shake the strength of the coalition was the reopening by ASARCO of some of its struck plants. In all, however, the coalition seems to have done a good job at maintaining discipline, at least until the period of the White House negotiations.

---

[63]Transcript of *Proceedings . . . , op. cit.*, pp. 87–88.
[64]"Strike Chronology," *op. cit.*, August 28, 1967.
[65]Press Release by the Copper Strike Information Bureau, February 16, 1968.
[66]*Wall Street Journal*, December 26, 1967.

ANALYSIS

The copper strike which ran nearly nine months for most workers —and still longer for others—cannot be viewed as a union victory, nor as a major economic triumph for the copper companies. The basic agreements reached under the prodding of government officials provided a wage and benefit package that amounted to $.70 to $1.04 an hour, although some packages were reported at slightly higher figures.[67] The unions did not succeed in gaining any of the "must" demands of the coalition. No single contract was signed to cover all operations within a company; and in fact, some companies are bargaining on smaller units than they had in the past. There are at least three contract termination dates applicable to the operations of each of the major producers, separated by as much as six months. No common economic package was extended across the operations of a company; and the amounts of the settlements vary considerably from company to company. Some workers went back to work before their striking brothers, while others continued on strike for nearly a year. Some marginal operations have been phased out because the added labor cost has made them unprofitable to operate.

The settlement amounted to an increase of from five to eight percent per year for three years but actually covered periods of up to four and five years in some cases. The settlement brought about a price increase in copper, which was promptly and soundly denounced by the chairman of the President's Council of Economic Advisers. The strike resulted in a worsening of the balance of payments by about $500–700 million, resulted in a loss of about $215 million in wages, about $300 million in profits, about $120 million in federal taxes, and resulted in inestimable costs to state and local economies.[68]

The coalition leaders also found that they were not able to "have their cake and eat it too." A poignant example came about as a result of bargaining at ASARCO. Although the unions had sought intervention from a fact-finding panel, and later rejected its findings, they were forced to bargain with ASARCO according to the Panel guidelines. The result was the breaking up of the ASARCO Council which they had hoped to expand, but which ASARCO obviously preferred restructured.

[67]Most companies did not release exact figures, although the approximate ranges were widely reported in the various news media.

[68]See various editorials—especially in western newspapers—between May 1 and May 6, 1968.

The Steelworkers paid out more than $6.2 million in strike benefits, the average worker lost about $4200 in wages, and none of the "must" issues were gained. It must be said that the total effort was a failure to inflict coalition bargaining or coalition aims on the industry. But the IUD, the Steelworkers, and the other coalition unions are in the strategic position to repeat the confrontation in 1971, and have already threatened to do so.[69] Although they do not have the single contract expiration date that was sought, they now have three basic sets of contracts which *may* again be drawn into a second coalition effort—if the workers should choose to support it, if the memory of the 1967–1968 strike has not brought about a fundamental change of attitude. In order to attempt such a further effort, it would be necessary to regroup the unions and then begin to prolong bargaining or engage in a strike that would extend for almost six months in order to shut down the three segments of the industry. Such a prospect is not likely.

[69]Steelworker Press Release, May 19, 1968.

CHAPTER X

OTHER COALITION ATTEMPTS: A BRIEF EXAMINATION

The several detailed case examinations of union bargaining coalitions already presented have served to illustrate the basic techniques utilized by the AFL-CIO's Industrial Union Department (IUD), and have provided a basis for evaluation of the coalition effort. The purpose of this chapter is to examine further IUD efforts to achieve coalition bargaining. Because many attempts have been made to engage chemical manufacturing and chemical-related firms in coalition programs, special emphasis is placed on that industry, followed by other illustrations of IUD-led coalitions in bargaining with employees.

The Chemical Industry

The chemical-related industry firms have been a favorite target of the IUD unions for several reasons. By the very nature of chemical manufacturing, many companies operate numerous, small, capital-intensive plants and therefore negotiate with a large number of separated, small bargaining units. Furthermore, these employees are often represented by relatively weak international unions which have found it necessary to obtain outside assistance in order to gain strength, both internally and in dealing with employers. The Oil, Chemical and Atomic Workers International Union (OCAW), the International Chemical Workers Union (ICWU), and the United Glass and Ceramic Workers of North America (UGCW), all have numerous locals in the chemical industry, and each finds itself in a relatively weak position when contrasted to such industrial unions giants as the United Automobile, Aerospace and Agricultural Implement Workers (UAW) or the United Steelworkers of America (USW).[1]

A further factor which has eased the organizational task of the IUD in forming coalition bargaining committees has been the historical existence of company "councils" of OCAW local unions. The councils were formed under the direction of the international and served as an informal source of information exchange regarding contracts, rates, benefits, and other items of mutual interest. Thus, when the IUD and the OCAW international officers began to develop an interest in coalition bargaining, the OCAW councils provided a ready nucleus to which other local unions of a particular company could be added to form a coalition for bargaining.

Koppers Company

The IUD efforts at such companies as Allied Chemical and Koppers have met with little, if any, success to date. Koppers Company, for example, has about 90 plants. The exact number is changing constantly because of new plant start-ups, plant phase-outs, and because of the seasonal nature of some operations. Furthermore, the organized plants are represented by more than 40 different international unions. Contracts have always been negotiated on a strictly local basis for the bargaining units that range in size from ten employees to locals that represent several hundred. The contract termination dates vary considerably in the scope of company operations across the nation, as is the

[1]Further evidence of a desire to increase union strength by the predominant chemical unions has been the recent interest in union mergers involving such internationals as OCAW, ICWU, UGCW, Glass Bottle Blowers, United Rubber Workers, and others.

case with pensions, benefits, and wages. All are negotiated locally, and all vary greatly when compared. For these reasons, it is to be expected that the IUD would find it difficult and expensive to bring about a strong coalition effort against the Koppers Company despite the fact that it maintains a committee of more than a dozen locals which have sought to band together for extra bargaining strength.[2]

Allied Chemical

A situation exists with some of the unions representing workers at Allied Chemical Corporation that is similar in many respects to that of Koppers. Allied has more than 125 separate plant locations, about half of which are organized. Of these plants, OCAW represents about 16, ICWU about 14, and District 50 formerly of the United Mine Workers represents about 24, including all Allied locations where large numbers of people are employed.[3]

In July 1967, a "committee representing the international unions" met for the purpose of furthering coalition bargaining at Allied. Among the actions taken by the group was a resolution that "the Industrial Union Department attempt to interest District 50 UMW in a practical working arrangement with the IUD-Allied Committee. Such an agreement [was] to include a bilateral no-raiding agreement."[4] Thus, the IUD was attempting to join forces with the District 50 locals, the largest union group at Allied, in order to bolster its own economic strength in bargaining with the Company. To date, there is reported to be some evidence of interest by the District 50 locals to bargain on a multiunit basis, but little reported indication of IUD activity or results in dealing with Allied on a coalition basis.

Paint Industry

There had historically been an informal group of union representatives which met for the purpose of exchanging information of use to the representatives in the paint industry. Again, the group of unions in-

[2]See, for example, various memoranda to "All IUD-Koppers Committee Local Unions," from E. D. Kuhns, Coordinator, Industrial Union Department, AFL-CIO, Washington, D.C., March 1966 to January 1967.

[3]See "Allied Chemical Corp.," a report prepared by the IUD for distribution at a meeting of Allied Chemical union representatives, November 21–22, 1966, Washington, D.C., pp. 9–16. District 50 was expelled from the United Mine Workers in 1968.

[4]*Report of Meeting,* Committee of Representatives—IUD Allied Chemical Committee, July 6, 1967. Prepared by the IUD.

cluded OCAW, ICWU, and UGCW, as well as the Brotherhood of Painters, Decorators and Paperhangers of America (BPDP). Late in 1966, the IUD convened a Paint Conference at which time an attempt was made to establish the groundwork for bargaining which would include the "big four" of the industry: Glidden, Sherwin-Williams, Pittsburgh Plate Glass, and National Lead, along with several smaller producers.[5] Apparently failing in so large an undertaking, the IUD concentrated on portions of Glidden and Sherwin-Williams.

Sherwin-Williams

In the summer of 1966, four Sherwin-Williams plants represented by OCAW had contract expirations. Included in this group, with the earliest termination date, was the large Chicago, Illinois local which had been the traditional pattern-setter.[6] Despite past practice, negotiations at all plants were reported to have been greatly slowed, and the locals did not seem anxious to reach agreement, until three of the four contracts had expired, and were being continued on a temporary basis. It is reported that an off-the-record meeting was held whereby a settlement was reached that was satisfactory to all of the locals with regard to pensions and insurance, although three-year contract expiration dates were maintained at the same intervals.[7]

Glidden

A parallel situation developed which involved three locals of the Glidden Company in September 1967.[8] One OCAW-represented plant at New Orleans, and BPDP locals at Reading, Pennsylvania, and St. Louis, Missouri had agreements terminating within a two-week period.[9] The IUD committee had drafted common proposals with regard to pensions, insurance, severance pay, hospitalization, vacations, cost of living, and a provision to bring all company contracts to termination at the same time in order to increase the coalition strength on successive rounds of bargaining. When the Company announced, just before negotiations began, that the New Orleans plant was to be closed, the IUD

---

[5]See "Paint Conference," a report prepared by the IUD for distribution at a meeting of union representatives of different paint manufacturing firms, November 1966.

[6]*Ibid.*, pp. 21–27.

[7]Personal interview with Sherwin-Williams Company official, November 1967, Cleveland, Ohio.

[8]"Paint Conference," *op. cit.*, pp. 5–13.

[9]Personal interview with Glidden Company official, November 1967, Cleveland, Ohio.

demands were expanded to provide that a satisfactory shutdown agreement be reached as part of the total settlement.

Apparently, Glidden agreed to "explore" the possibility of dealing with the coalition on many of the common issues, and did finally reach settlement for the three plants through the IUD coordinator. Three-year contracts were negotiated to cover the three plants which carried the same termination dates as had their predecessors. Since that time, however, the New Orleans plant has continued its closing plans, and the Glidden Company has been merged into the SCM Corporation. The impact of this three-plant coalition and its future remain to be evaluated in light of these more recent developments.

Rohm and Haas

The Rohm and Haas Company first faced a demand for joint bargaining in the early fifties when two UGCW local unions at Bristol, Pennsylvania and Knoxville, Tennessee presented such a request. At that time, the Company refused the demand, but did permit observers from Knoxville to attend Bristol negotiations.[10] After only a few days, the observers left town, thus ending that attempt to break down the Company practice of local bargaining. The locals, however, occasionally continued to have observers attend negotiating sessions within the international, and maintained communications with the OCAW local representing Rohm and Haas employees in Houston, Texas.

In 1965, the IUD formed a Rohm and Haas committee of three locals,[11] and subsequently added locals of three other international unions as well, although there is little evidence to indicate that any of the latter three participated to a great degree, or became directly involved in any coalition effort. After an extensive "educational" program was conducted by each union for its members, a collective bargaining program was established, and the three largest bargaining units were asked to sign pledges supporting the IUD effort. (See Table 10–1.) Thus, the two UGCW locals, and the one represented by the OCAW, whose combined membership is responsible for about two-thirds of the Company's output, decided to attempt to bargain pensions, insurance, savings plans, and other "policy" items on a joint basis.

[10]Personal interviews with Rohm and Haas Company officials, summer 1967, Philadelphia, Pa.

[11]See "Attendance List." IUD-Rohm and Haas Meeting, January 14–15, 1965, Washington, D.C.

TABLE 10–1

COORDINATED BARGAINING RESOLUTION

TO: Don Doherty, Coordinator
IUD-Rohm & Haas Committee
815-16th St. N.W.
Washington, D.C. 20006

This is to certify that Local ......, International Union ...., has adopted the Collective Bargaining Program of the IUD-Rohm & Haas Committee.

This adoption of the Program was made with the complete understanding that we will work with the other unions in the Committee to the end that we will obtain the highest possible level of improvements in our collective bargaining with the Company. It is further understood and agreed to that our union will take whatever action is necessary in order that we may obtain such a settlement.

____
President

____
Secretary

Date ______________________

(LOCAL SEAL)

1 copy to be sent to the IUD-Rohm & Haas Coordinator
1 copy to be sent to your International Union
1 copy to be kept by the local union.

Source: Industrial Union Department, AFL-CIO, Collective Bargaining Services Section.

When the Company refused to submit to formal proposals from international officers of the unions involved, the IUD began to direct a bargaining campaign which was designed to obtain the same end result, *viz:* national bargaining on "policy" issues. When negotiations opened for the Houston OCAW local, outsiders were present, and bargaining on pension issues was conducted by the IUD coordinator on behalf of the union. After some five months of periodic meetings between the Company and union, which eventually saw the withdrawal of both outsiders and IUD coordinator, settlement was reached which closely paralleled other area settlements, as had traditionally been the case.[12]

Two major gains were won by the IUD, however. Although both of these were small in terms of economic costs, both could prove valuable to the long term IUD effort. While bargaining was in progress at Houston, negotiations were also in progress at Bristol where a settlement was reached prior to the contract termination. The IUD gain, however, was an agreement reached with Rohm and Haas which would permit the UGCW local to reap the benefits obtained at the Houston plant when the newly negotiated contract expired. This meant little in the way of tangible benefits, for the local still had to bargain for the benefits; but it did establish an important "tag-along" precedent that has had at least publicity value to the IUD.[13]

A second major gain of the 1966 coalition effort was in the substantial shortening of contract termination date spread between the three major agreements—a spread that was reduced to about three and a half months in recent negotiations. Thus, the IUD-led coalition has now gained the advantage of being able to prolong early negotiations until it is in a position to threaten the Company with a three-plant strike early in 1969.

In some sense, the Rohm and Haas situation is a model for the IUD program. There are only three plants involved, of the seven operated by the Company. These three, however, are the major production

[12]See *Memorandum* to "IUD-Rohm & Haas Committee," from Don Doherty, Coordinator, Collective Bargaining Section, IUD, March 9, 1967.

[13]The main value to the IUD was one of publicity, for Company policy had always made benefits generally available to all employees. For example, a letter to Mr. Don Doherty, Representative [of the OCAW Committee at Houston] from Mr. Robert C. Landon, Manager of Industrial Relations of Rohm and Haas, August 18, 1966, stated:

> . . . With very few exceptions, our Company has always been willing to offer at all locations what it has offered at one location so long as a given proposal was applicable to the area in which our plant is located and to chemical manufacturing generally. We are quite willing to assure you that we are considering no change in this policy.
>
> * * *
>
> We have already said that Company-wide benefits we offer to the OCAW Local in our Houston Plant we will offer to Bristol and to Knoxville, in turn, and to any other unions with which our Chemicals Division Plants have a collective bargaining relationship. Likewise, these benefits will be offered to our nonunion employees and, in most instances, to our salaried employees. Thus you can see our purpose is to avoid any discrimination between employee groups rather than to create or maintain unjustifiable distinctions in wages, benefits or working conditions.

units, and the plants with the strongest unions.[14] It is also interesting to note that the IUD committee includes all of the other unions having representational rights, and has made arrangements to permit certain international unions to attempt to organize the remaining nonunion plant units. It would seem that the unions view their program as having produced some benefit to this point, and are reinforcing the effort through the mechanism of the "president's committee," and through increased communication, from the IUD, and to the union membership.[15]

Olin Mathieson

The efforts of the Industrial Union Department to bring about a coalition to bargain with the Olin Mathieson Chemical Corporation apparently have met with very little success to this point. The IUD has had an Olin Committee in existence since 1964,[16] and has attempted to use it to bring about extra concessions for the few Olin unions involved in the effort. When, for example, Olin's local management representatives began negotiating with the OCAW officials at Beaumont, Texas for that location in the fall of 1965, the Company was informed of the IUD desire to standardize fringe benefits throughout the Company. The international representative even went so far as to withdraw the local's demands for pension changes and substituted the IUD-drafted demands, coupled with a demand for a contract termination date to coincide with two other large OCAW locals in the Northeast.[17] Neither demand was won.

When preparations were being made for bargaining a new contract for the 2,500 employee local at New Haven, Connecticut, in the spring of 1966, Olin was first directly confronted by the IUD coalition. Olin and Local 609 of the International Association of Machinists (IAM) had agreed to hold preliminary meetings on two separate days in May: one for general Union proposals, and one for pension demands. The IAM then informed the Company that it would have "observers" from other Olin locations present for pension meetings, and that Steve Harris of the IUD would be present to assist in pension bargaining. When

[14]The combined size of the remaining coalition locals is less than 300, and these are small craft units within a larger plant.

[15]See *Memorandum, op. cit.*, February 9, 1968.

[16]See "Attendance List," Olin Mathieson Chemical Corporation, a report presented at a meeting in Washington, D.C., September 14–15, 1964.

[17]Personal interview with Olin Mathieson Chemical Corporation officials, August 1967, New York.

meetings opened, the first day was devoted to general demands, to which was added the Union demand that the existing pension plan be scrapped and replaced with a new one. The Union further reinforced its position that it would be assisted in bargaining by "observers" from other locals, and by the IUD.

On May 26, when pension meetings were scheduled, Harris did show up and introduced the outsiders as "assistant committee members." The Company promptly filed an unfair labor practice with the NLRB, but offered to meet with the local committee and Harris, but not with the outsiders. The IAM also filed a refusal-to-bargain charge because the Company had refused to meet with the outsiders present. Union communications to the Olin employees stated that the Company was refusing to meet with the outsiders because it wanted to prevent the Union from negotiating a nationwide pension plan. Negotiations were finally resumed only after Harris and the outsiders agreed to sign a letter specifically denying any intention of expanding the scope of the bargaining unit.[18] Bargaining then proceeded until agreement was reached on all contract issues, and for a separate pension plan to cover only the New Haven plant employees.[19] The pension agreement reached during those negotiations had no tie with possible changes under other Company plans—rather than driving an opening wedge toward a new Company-wide plan, the IUD only achieved a local pension plan for one local.

Further IUD attempts were made to engage Olin Mathieson in coalition bargaining in the Southwest in 1966, and in Wisconsin in 1968. In each instance negotiations were held off Company property. Olin polled the delegates to determine whom outsiders were representing in order to ascertain that all those who were now called "committee members" disavowed any intention to expand the bargaining unit.

Another confrontation faced by Olin from the IUD came about at the Baraboo, Wisconsin, munitions plant operated by Olin for the United States Government. Negotiations were nearly completed for a new contract to replace one that expired on Tuesday, February 7, 1968.[20] On the Friday before termination, a group of outsiders ap-

[18]*Ibid.*

[19]See *The New Haven Retirement Plan,* sent by the IUD to member locals, dated July 12, 1966.

[20]See "Olin-Mathieson Chemical Corporation," a report prepared by the IUD for presentation at a meeting held April 20–21, 1967 at Washington, D.C., p. B2.

peared at the bargaining table, at which time the Company requested a caucus. When meetings were resumed, only the local committee was present, and agreement was reached without further reference to the IUD or to the outside "committee members" who had been present.

OTHER COALITION SITUATIONS

In addition to the specific cases discussed up to this point, including the number of specific coalition efforts under way in the chemical industry, many of the other ninety-odd committees have prepared for or made attempts to pool union strength in dealing with employers. Although it is impractical, if not impossible, to examine the progress and/or results of each of these separate unions efforts, a few brief examples will be cited to present a better picture of coalition bargaining in other companies to date.

Eaton Yale & Towne

A situation developed at Eaton Yale & Towne in the fall of 1967 that presented evidence of an IUD coalition in which the dominant group was the United Automobile, Aerospace and Agricultural Implement Workers of America (UAW). Eaton maintained a "master agreement" that was applied to eight divisions and seven plants represented by the UAW, although some of the plants were forced to shut down because of adverse economic conditions.[21]

The union coalition attempted to force the Company to enlarge the scope of the master agreement to include at least two other locals of the Auto Workers. Eaton firmly resisted, with the result being a lockout which was eventually turned into an official strike action at one location, and a settlement at the second location. When negotiations opened for the master agreement, the UAW committee also included representatives of the IAM, Allied Industrial Workers of America (AIW), as well as other coalition unions—a total of 33 in all. The UAW, however, took a firm lead in handling bargaining, and the negotiations centered only on issues concerning those unions which were a party to the master agreement.[22]

[21]See "Eaton Yale & Towne, Inc.," a report prepared by the IUD for presentation at a meeting held July 27–28, 1967, Cleveland, Ohio, pp. 1–11.

[22]Personal interview with officials of Eaton Yale & Towne, Inc., November 1967, Cleveland, Ohio.

In retrospect, it would appear that the IUD coalition effort at Eaton Yale & Towne produced only a work stoppage, and that the member unions were either abandoned by the UAW or chose to settle without any significant amount of support from the coalition group. It is also likely that the UAW has sufficient bargaining strength to attain its goals, and that the others merely hoped to benefit from the UAW position. Apparently, this did not materialize.

International Telephone and Telegraph

ITT, a company with 11,000 of its 44,000 employees in the United States represented by a wide range of international unions, has always maintained a strict policy of local bargaining with its certified local unions. This policy has resulted in widely divergent pension plans, benefit patterns, and wages, based on local conditions and employee needs.

The IUD-sponsored committee which is attempting to coordinate bargaining at ITT has apparently decided, after two weak attempts to bring the Company under the coalition umbrella, that the task was either too great, or that the local unions were unwilling to participate. Despite claims to the contrary, there has been no IUD-coalition bargaining at ITT.[23]

H. K. Porter

A similar situation exists with respect to the H. K. Porter Company with a single significant difference. Whereas ITT does provide staff services and general direction regarding labor relations matters to its operating units, Porter places a greater degree of autonomy on its divisional and plant personnel. The individual responsible for overall labor relations is the Company president.[24]

The very nature of the decentralized business that H. K. Porter maintains in some 50 different product lines, and dealings with about 40 different unions, all on a local basis, has resulted in great diversity of pension, insurance, and benefit programs which have been bargained for, and tailored to the needs of the employees in a given area.

---

[23]Personal interviews with officials of International Telephone and Telegraph, August 1967, New York.

[24]Personal interview with officials of the H. K. Porter Company, Inc., November 1967, Pittsburgh, Pennsylvania.

The Industrial Union Department does maintain an H. K. Porter committee, and has named the Company as one of the giant conglomerates with which it hopes to advance the cause of coalition bargaining. Thus far, however, it is difficult to find any significant gains that have been made by the IUD through coalition.

Campbell Soup

The Campbell Soup Company, like many other firms, has long upheld a policy of local bargaining.[25] When the IUD announced that a five-union president's committee had endorsed coalition bargaining for its 14 locals in July 1967, the Company resolved that it would not deal with the coalition nor would it succumb to joint bargaining as proposed by the IUD.[26]

The thrust of the IUD attack was first felt when bargaining began to renew a United Packinghouse, Food and Allied Workers of North America (UPFAW or Packinghouse Workers) contract at the Company's plant in Paris, Texas. At that time, Company representatives were faced by both an IUD coordinator and a "traveling squad" of representatives from four other plant locations. Although the parties appeared close to agreement, the Packinghouse Workers international representative refused to endorse the Campbell offer. When the offer was presented to the local membership, in the presence of the traveling squad, a voice vote rejection was obtained.[27] Campbell Soup, however, unilaterally put the wage increase into effect and stopped union dues checkoff. The local refused to call a strike and worked without a contract while awaiting contract terminations at other coalition locations.

Similar events transpired when bargaining took place with Packinghouse Workers, Amalgamated Meat Cutters and Butcher Workmen of North America (Meat Cutters), the IAM, and the International Brotherhood of Teamsters at five other Campbell plants between De-

---

[25]A single exception to the local bargaining came about as the result of acquisition of the Swanson frozen food division whose contracts for five small midwestern plants were negotiated together.

[26]See "News Release for A.M. Papers, Monday, July 31, 1967." The release from the IUD was carried by the *Daily Labor Report* three days earlier, July 28, 1967.

IUD Executive Director Jack Conway also sent a letter to the president of each international involved which provided a sample letter to be sent to Campbell Soup President, W. B. Murphy requesting joint bargaining.

[27]Personal interviews with Campbell Soup Company officials, August 1967, Camden, New Jersey.

cember 1967 and May 12, 1968. In each case, the local, under direction of the internationals and the IUD, failed to accept the final offer of the Company, but refused to strike upon termination of the contracts. In each case, too, Campbell unilaterally installed the wage portion of the offer and stopped collecting union dues.

Throughout the five-month period over which the IUD dragged the bargaining, the Company was subjected to a series of requests from various union officials to engage in joint bargaining, and to grant common termination dates to the coalition unions. Also, during this time, the unions had been discussing a nationwide "Don't Buy" campaign to be used if necessary, but apparently decided against going ahead with it for the time being. It is also reported that the unions involved prepared a war chest to support a massive strike by collecting per capita assessments from other union members in the canning industry.[28]

In 1968, during the period when the coalition unions were working without contracts at Campbell, the two primary coaliton unions announced a merger. Thus, the Packinghouse Workers and the Meatcutters further solidified their alliance within the coalition and became more resolute in joining the other unions in all out effort directed toward the achievement of coalition bargaining at Campbell Soup Company.

The five participating coalition locals, after failing to reach agreement or new contracts, permitted their members to work without contracts, in some cases for more than five months. Then late in July 1968, at the height of the tomato harvesting season, a multiplant strike began which crippled the Company's heat-process operations at the single most important time of the year. Strikes began at Camden, New Jersey; Sacramento, California; Paris, Texas; Napoleon, Ohio; and following vacation shut-down on August 12, 1968, the plants at Chestertown, Maryland and Moorestown, New Jersey, also struck the Campbell Soup Company.

Although there were two major issues brought to the fore in the Campbell strike—wages and coalition bargaining—it soon became apparent that the latter was the primary union goal. Because the employees were receiving wages which were increased to reflect the Company's first year offer, the strikers found that they later returned to

[28]See *Business Week,* February 17, 1968, pp. 125–126.

work at essentially the same rates as existed at the outset of the work stoppage.

The coalition issue, however, was clearly the prime concern of the unions. The Company had long been aware of the various IUD efforts to engage Campbell in coalition bargaining, and again noted this fact when it was informed that the local bargaining committees had been dissolved and had assigned bargaining responsibility to a corporate-wide union bargaining committee which was composed of one or two representatives from each participating local, several international representatives of the unions, and a chairman from the IUD.

The single committee notified the Company that it had set a specific date when it would come to Camden to negotiate all contracts. Campbell did meet with this committee in the offices of the Federal Mediation and Conciliation Service, but insisted that discussions be confined only to matters concerning the Camden contract. It refused to agree to the union committee precondition for bargaining of common expiration dates and joint, company wide bargaining. The union broke off the meeting.

The strike at Campbell had a major impact upon the economics of southern New Jersey and other agricultural areas in which it operated. The Company usually purchases about 300 million pounds of tomatoes and other vegetables a year, much of which would have been processed in late July and August, and much of which are bought from "contract" farmers whose entire crop is destined for Campbell Soup Company. Although the Company agreed to pay these farmers their costs for producing plus a "reasonable profit," the forced plowing under of thousands of pounds of vegetables also caused losses for migrant workers and others vitally interested in the vegetable crops.

Campbell, shortly after the start of the strike, filed unfair labor practice charges with the NLRB, alleging that the unions' insistance on common termination dates and multiplant bargaining constituted a violation of Section 8(a)(5) of The Taft-Hartley Act. It also requested injunctive relief under the terms of Section 10(j) of the Act. The NLRB began to "study" and to "investigate" for several weeks. The strike had been settled before a decision was made on the 10(j) issue.

The AFL-CIO, in its first major coalition confrontation since the nonferrous dispute quickly backed the striking Campbell workers when its president said that the Company's bargaining attitude was "a threat to the whole American labor movement."

After some five weeks of striking, marked by state court injunctions, mass picketing, arrests, and unexplained general-alarm fires, bargaining was resumed at the local levels, and individual settlements were reached which bore different termination dates and which reflected the needs of the workers in different parts of the nation. It was obvious that the coalition unions failed completely either to establish coalition bargaining or to set up common termination dates that would facilitate such bargaining in the future. Moreover, the final wage and benefit package was either the same, or very close, to the Campbell pre-strike offers at each plant.

Summary

In examining the above ten additional situations wherein the IUD has made some claim for the success of coalition bargaining, it becomes evident that in most such cases such IUD claims of victory are at best premature. It is felt that the sample presented herein is reasonably representative, that there may be cases where IUD gains have been significant, but probably a greater number of cases where progress of a coalition has been insignificant, and even cases where IUD committees have been abandoned because of lack of interest on the part of local unions or inability to increase bargaining strength enough to justify continuation in an IUD program.

Part Three

PUBLIC POLICY AND CONCLUSIONS

CHAPTER XI

COALITION BARGAINING AND PUBLIC POLICY

The history of coalition attempts in various industries, as set forth in previous chapters, has involved cases before the National Labor Relations Board, appeals courts, and in some instances intervention by members of the President's Cabinet, or even by the President himself. This chapter analyzes the overall public policy which is emerging as a result of union attempts to promote coalition bargaining. The two principal areas of concern are interpretations of the National Labor Relations (Taft-Hartley) Act and the statutory and extralegal activities of government intervenors attempting to settle labor disputes arising out of coalition bargaining.

COALITION BARGAINING AND THE NLRB

Coalition bargaining, by its very nature, becomes immediately involved in potentially conflicting interpretations of the Taft-Hartley Act. Section 7 of the Act states that "Employees shall have the right to self-organization, to form, join, or assist labor organizations, *to bargain collectively through representatives of their choosing* . . . and shall have the right to refrain from any or all of such activities . . . ." Section 8(a)(5) provides that it is an unfair labor practice for an employer to refuse to bargain collectively with the representatives of his employees, subject to the provisions of Section 9(a), and Section 8(b)(3) provides that it is an unfair labor practice for a union "to refuse to bargain collectively with an employer, provided it is the representative of his employees subject to the provisions of Section 9(a)." In turn, Section 9(a) states in part:

> Representatives designated or selected for the purpose of collective bargaining by the majority of the employees in a unit appropriate for such purposes, shall be the exclusive representatives of all the employees in such unit for the purposes of collective bargaining. . . .

The Taft-Hartley Act then charges the National Labor Relations Board (NLRB) with the duty of determining the appropriate bargaining unit and of ascertaining whether a bargaining representative has been chosen by the majority of that unit to represent the employees therein for the purpose of collective bargaining.

Two questions immediately present themselves when coalition bargaining is attempted: Can an employer refuse to bargain with a committee which includes members who are actually, whether or not admittedly, representatives of another bargaining group than that bargaining unit for which negotiations are being held? On the other hand, can a union force the employer to bargain for employees who are not part of the bargaining unit certified by the National Labor Relations Board, but who may be part of another unit separately certified? The record shows that the NLRB has answered the first question in the affirmative, by overlooking the stated purpose of coalition bargaining as defined by its union adherents; and that as to the second question, it has avoided coming to grips with the thrust of its own case law in coalition bargaining cases, at least until the nonferrous metal dispute reached a climactic stage.

There are other issues concerning the NLRB which will be discussed below. They involve the attempts of the NLRB to obtain injunctive support for coalition bargaining; the use of the lookout by management to thwart coalition strategy; and the possible impact of the NLRB's decision to expand the bargaining unit to support a union demand even though no question of representation is before the Board.

The Bargaining Committee Question—the Strategy

There are several subsidiary and one principal reason why the IUD coalition program puts so much emphasis on placing "outsiders"—that is, IUD representatives and those of unions other than the one directly involved in the negotiations—on the negotiating committees of local unions which are attempting to obtain coalition agreements. These reasons obtain whether the outsiders are acting, or classified, as "observers," "assistant committee members," or actual members of the bargaining committee. The basic purpose, and one only thinly disguised, is to make a show of force and solidarity which will convince the employer to engage in company or industry-wide bargaining, first on a few key issues, such as pensions and insurance, and then as propitious on more and more. In the meantime, if this strategy does not succeed, the coalition organization, nevertheless, may net several auxiliary benefits.

If, for example, the IUD is able to report in its various communications and publications that a "coordinated" effort is under way and is able to cite the exchange of committees as evidence, real gains in the form of attracting new locals to the effort may be realized. Second, in light of the pledge or understanding which is apparently required of each participating local in the coalition, and in light of repeated pronouncements that no local would settle on terms that were unacceptable to the president's committee, steering committee, or coalition members, it is helpful to the bargaining to have representatives of other locals at hand to participate in the decision-making process, and to insure that the local in question remains solidly committed to the program of the IUD.

A third benefit to the IUD-coalition unions gained through the presence of outsiders is improved communication. With representatives of various locals on each bargaining committee, a greater opportunity is afforded each local to exchange information and therefore, to obtain identical contracts, and especially move toward identical contract expiration dates, a key step toward obtaining the goal of company-wide or industry-wide bargaining.

To achieve these goals and advantages, the coalition unions must maintain the facade that the outsiders are merely representing or observing for the bargaining unit for which the negotiations are concerned. Despite the fact that the goals and strategies of coalition bargaining are a matter of public record and that this record has repeatedly been brought to the NLRB's attention, the NLRB has thus far accepted this explanation, basing its actions on a number of prior cases which deal with employees' right to representatives of their own choosing.

The Bargaining Committee Question—The Legal Background

The case involving *Kentucky Utilities,*[1] decided by the NLRB on March 22, 1948, was one of the first instances in which the Board gave its weight to the concept that the unions are free to choose for its bargaining agent whomever they desire. The NLRB brought a charge pursuant to Section 8(a)(5) against the employer because the company refused to deal with a union representative who had been discharged as an employee, but now worked for the union. The individual had been widely quoted as stating that he would do all in his power to hurt the company financially, and thereby force it "to sell out" to the government-operated Tennessee Valley Authority. The NLRB admitted the troublesome nature of the employee, but ordered the company to deal with him nonetheless because "the employer has no right to veto . . . [the employees' choice] by refusing to deal with a bargaining representative."

The Court of Appeals for the Sixth Circuit overturned this decision because it felt that collective bargaining could not lead to peaceful settlement in an atmosphere such as this union representative would induce.[2] In a companion case, however, where the company refused to deal with another local because its bargaining committee contained persons other than its own employees, the Court concurred with the NLRB, that such refusal violated the Taft-Hartley Act. The general rule seems to be that, unless there are special circumstances in a particular situation which may absolve a party from the obligation to deal

[1]*Kentucky Utilities Co.,* 76 NLRB No. 121, (March 22, 1948) 21 LRRM 1258.
[2]*NLRB* v. *Kentucky Utilities Company,* 186 F. 2d 810 (CA6, 1950) 26 LRRM 2287.

with a specific representative, an employer (or a union) has practically an almost uninhibited right to select whomsoever it desires to be its representatives. For the employer (or the union) to refuse to deal with that representative is a violation of the Act.[3]

It was on the basis of this theory that trial examiners in cases involving both General Electric Company[4] and the 3M Company[5] recommended that both companies be found guilty of violating Section 8(a)(5). In both instances, as was detailed in Chapters VI and VIII, the union committee included outsiders, whose disguise as representatives of the bargaining unit directly involved, was thin and transparent. In the *General Electric* case, the company was not even obligated to bargain at that time. Rather, it had arranged a prenegotiation meeting where the outsiders showed up. In both cases, however, the trial examiner accepted the union assertion at its face value, and despite considerable evidence to the contrary, ruled that the outsiders were, in effect, solely and legally there to represent the existing contractual bargaining unit employees, and that therefore, the companies had violated the Taft-Hartley Act by refusing to bargain with the committees of whom the outsiders were a part.

Despite the obvious aims of the coalition unions in the *General Electric* case, including the numerous public pronouncements of the Unity leaders, the NLRB, in October 1968, upheld the union's right of having "outsiders" participate in collective bargaining negotiations, thereby giving further sanction to the concept of coalition bargaining. The Company has appealed the Board decision.

In the *American-Standard* case, the NLRB took the same position, again ignoring the fact that the outsiders signed a roster as representing units other than that involved in the negotiations at hand.[6] The Court of Appeals for the Sixth Circuit found the Board's evidence wanting, and declined to enforce its order.[7] American-Standard, as the reader

---

[3]The doctrine that there are special circumstances which limit the right of a party to select representatives has been upheld in *NLRB* v. *Garment Workers Union* (Slate Belt Apparel Contractors Association) 274 F. 2d 376 (CA3, 1960), 45 LRRM 2626; *Bausch & Lomb Optical Company,* 108 NLRB No. 1555, 34 LRRM 1222; and *General Electric* v. *NLRB* (CA6, 1968), 21 LRRM 2690.

[4]"Trial Examiner's Decision," *General Electric Company* and *International Union of Electrical, Radio and Machine Workers, AFL-CIO,* 2-CA-10991, June 8, 1967.

[5]"Trial Examiner's Decision," *Minnesota Mining and Manufacturing Company* and *Oil, Chemical Atomic Workers International Union, AFL-CIO,* 18-CA-2443, November 22, 1967.

[6]*American Radiator, and Standard Sanitary Corporation* v. *NLRB,* 381 F. 2d 632, (CA6, 1967) 65 LRRM 3073; also *American Radiator,* 155 NLRB 736, (September 15, 1967) 65 LRRM 1385.

[7]*Ibid.*

will recall, did bargain with committees on which outsiders sat "under protest," after first declining to do so. The Court did not pass on the question of the propriety of the outsiders being present; in effect, it found merely that the NLRB had not presented sufficient evidence that a violation of the Act had occurred.

In the *Union Carbide* situation, the company did not refuse to bargain with a committee on which outsiders sat. Instead, Union Carbide required that the outsiders emphasize that they represented the bargaining unit in question and were present for the sole purpose of negotiating a contract for that unit only. The Company thereby avoided litigation on this particular issue although its tactics, including the lockout, have been extensively litigated, as will be again noted later in this chapter.

Several companies examined in this study have tended, like Union Carbide, not to challenge the right of outsiders to be present, but rather to force them to stress that they are present solely as representatives of the bargaining unit in question and to negotiate a contract only for that unit. The advantage of this approach from the company viewpoint is that it is likely to avoid losing litigation over the issue of outsiders on the bargaining committee. On the other hand, it does permit, as the trial examiner in the *3M* case noted, "the union camel . . . sticking its nose under the tent." If the coalition-minded unions can force a company, directly or through NLRB action, to admit outsiders to a bargaining table under the facade that they are representing just one bargaining unit, then the first step toward coalition bargaining has been accomplished—unless, of course, a company can and will maintain its position as did Union Carbide.

It would seem, nonetheless, that the litigation thus far, although certainly not definitive, is tending toward acceptance of the theory as enunciated by the trial examiner in the *3M* case: the company must accept the outsiders on the committee unless there is an overt attempt on their part to embrace more than a single unit of bargaining. The fact that such an expansion of the unit is the avowed purpose of coalition bargaining has thus far been no company defense. Apparently, companies are required to sit back and wait until unions feel strong enough to push openly for their goal: company-wide bargaining and an expanded bargaining unit.

Unilateral Change of Bargaining Unit—The Issue

Put in terms consistent with the legal framework of the Taft-Hartley Act, the aim of coalition bargaining is to alter the bargaining unit now extant, which is usually one plant, and to enlarge its scope to a multiplant or company-wide basis. The law would seem quite clear, and the cases so indicate, that the parties may mutually agree to expand the bargaining unit, but that either a company or a union, may refuse to bargain over expansion of the appropriate unit, and that for either to insist on doing so is a violation of Section 8(a)(5) or (b)(3).[8]

It should be emphasized that bargaining units are single plants in most cases because both the company and union desired it thus. A single plant is easier for a union to organize at one time, and this is what unions usually request. Indeed, since 1961, the NLRB has often tended to move toward smaller units at union behest, and quite obviously in order to assist union organization. This was the policy of the original Board under the Wagner Act which Congress sought to restrain by inserting Section 9(c)(5) in the Taft-Hartley amendments which states: "In determining whether a unit is appropriate . . . the extent to which the employees have organized shall not be controlling."

That the existing NLRB is following the "extent of organization" criterion in bargaining unit determination has been often noted.[9] Once the union is certified, however, and a coalition movement begun, the unions which asked originally for single plant bargaining units may join in a push for a broader unit. Here again, the NLRB has come to their aid, first, as already noted, by ignoring the basic motives and objectives of having "outsiders" on bargaining committees, and requiring employers to deal with such committees; second, by requiring employers to bargain on issues which in effect make coalition bargaining almost a *fait accompli;* third, by use of its power to seek injunctions in a one-side

---

[8]See for example: *NLRB* v. *International Brotherhood of Electrical Workers,* 266 F. 2d 349 (CA5, 1959) enforcing 119 NLRB No. 1792, 41 LRRM 1392 (1958); *United Mine Workers* (Central Soya Company), 142 NLRB 930, 53 LRRM 1178 (1963); *Evening News Association,* 154 NLRB No. 121, 60 LRRM 1149 (1965); *Detroit Newspaper Publishers Association* v. *NLRB,* 372 F. 2d 569 (CA6, 1967); 64 LRRM 1149, *Hearst Consolidated Publications, Inc.,* 156 NLRB No. 16, 61 LRRM 1011 (1965).

[9]See for example: Note, "The Board and Section 9(c)(5): Multi-Location and Single-Location Bargaining Units in the Insurance and Retail Industries," *Harvard Law Review,* Volume LXXIX (February 1966), pp. 811–840; Also, John E. Abodeely, "Collective Bargaining Unit," *Boston University Law Review,* Volume XLVII (Winter 1967), pp. 139–149, and Herbert R. Northrup, *Restrictive Labor Practices in the Supermarket Industry* (Industrial Research Unit Study No. 44, Philadelphia: University of Pennsylvania Press, 1967), pp. 149–156.

manner; fourth, by dismissing or ignoring employer unfair charges, until it was almost literally impossible to do so; and fifth, by its attempt to expand the bargaining unit when no question of representation existed.

Required Bargaining on Contract Termination Dates

That contract termination dates are a legitimate area of mandatory bargaining was established in one key case before coalition bargaining became an issue, but nonetheless in a coalition case. Two locals of the United Steelworkers and one of the International Molders and Foundry Workers in plants of the U.S. Pipe and Foundry Company in Alabama and New Jersey joined in a demand upon the company for common contract termination dates. The company charged the unions with violation of Section 8(b)(3)—bad faith bargaining—contending that they were attempting to alter the bargaining unit by forcing the company to bargain on a multiplant basis. Both the NLRB[10] and the Court of Appeals, Fifth Circuit dismissed the company charge and the United States Supreme Court denied certiorari.[11]

The issues were well put in Court of Appeals, which found for the NLRB in a split decision. According to the company, the issue was:

> Whether a union, the certified representative of a plant bargaining unit may require of an employer as a condition to its agreement that its contract and all contracts under negotiation between the employer and other certified representatives of different bargaining units plants shall expire upon a common date.

The NLRB, on the other hand, argued that:

> . . . where, as here two or more unions are simultaneously negotiating separate contracts with the same employer, such unions have just as much right to insist that the contracts shall on the same date as the employer has to insist that they shall expire on different dates.[12]

The Court did agree with the company that more was involved than the simple matter of contract duration being a bargainable issue, but after examining the evidence and record of negotiations decided that the question of expansion was merely an *apparent* one. The Court

[10] *Steelworkers Union* (U.S. Pipe & Foundry Company) 129 NLRB No. 42, 46 LRRM 1542 (1960).

[11] *U.S. Pipe & Foundry Company* v. *NLRB*, 298 F 2d 873 (CA5, 1962) 370 U.S. 919 (1962); 50 LRRM 2412.

[12] *U.S. Pipe & Foundry Company* v. *NLRB*, 298 F. 2d 873 (CA5, 1962) 49 LRRM 2540.

held that it was the right and duty of the Board to define the scope of the bargaining unit, and that the question of expansion of the unit by the parties was *not* a subject of mandatory bargaining. But, it went further, and ruled that the frustration experienced by the unions when striking because of the employer's shifting of production to other plants, had made the question of bargaining for *common* contract dates a valid one because the question had become a part of "wages, hours and other terms and conditions of employment" of the employees at each plant. "Without a common expiration date, any union striking for a new contract on a different date might have to 'bail with a sieve' while the employer shifted its production activities to the other plant or plants."

Thus the Court took it upon itself to shift the balance of economic power between the employer and the employee, while at the same time maintaining that the alteration of the bargaining unit was only a matter of *apparent* expansion. The Court conceded that "there is no legal obstacle to the right of the petitioner-employer to insist adamantly that the three contracts continue to expire on different dates . . . [and that] each union can insist just as adamantly that all three contracts expire on some common date." This, the Court felt was an adequate remedy against such a coalition which seemed to alter the scope of the bargaining unit.

The dissenting opinion in *U.S. Pipe,* written by Judge Carswell, is significant in several respects. He stated: "Because I cannot agree that the action of the Union here was only *apparently* beyond the scope of bargaining units . . . respectfully, I must dissent." Judge Carswell believed that for separate bargaining units to insist upon a common expiration date as a condition for agreement is in violation of the Act. He had no doubt about the legality of a bargaining agent insisting upon a specific expiration date for *its own contract,* whether or not it be the same as for other bargaining units; but to couple such demands, he felt, was not proper.

Judge Carswell maintained that it was not a specific date, as such, that was the key to the controversy, but the demand of the *separate* bargaining units *having no authority to bargain for each other,* as condition precedent to an agreement for all:

> The Court here finds that the common expiration date "vitally affects the ability of each union separately to bargain," stating that the sepa-

rate unions face a "very real, hard problem" in this regard. *Its preoccupation and concern with respective difficulties of the parties that have fashioned, it seems to me, a new microscope of legal detection to see that which is and that which is not apparently visible in the Congressional language.* . . . As I see it, this so extends and confuses the separability of unit duties and responsibilities as to enshroud the process with additional problems, which new problems themselves might just as logically be made the justification for even more expansion. *Does not this mean, for example, that like demand can be made for industry-wide wages and hours by units of heretofore limited scope or that employer demand as condition to agreement (to the) same wages as paid to other units?*

* * *

Industry-wide or plant-wide bargaining may well be desirable for one or the other party, or for both, but this determination can be made by the Board. . . . The problems of negotiation asserted by the bargaining unit here are made by the Court the justification for an expansion of unit authority. These contentions are more properly for the consideration of the Board. . . . *Under the holding here the Court, in effect, is approving joint negotiation without consent of the parties and without plenary proceedings before the Board for determination of the need or desirability of such joint negotiation.* (Emphasis added).[13]

It would appear that when the Supreme Court denied certiorari in this case, considerable legitimization had been given to coalitions of separately certified bargaining units. Although the question of whether each unit must bargain for itself was not answered either by Board or Court, it would seem that both decisions tended in that direction.

Withholding Agreement Until All Units Have Settled

The case that involved the Standard Oil Company (Ohio) and the Oil, Chemical, and Atomic Workers International Union (OCAW)[14] is one that represented both a victory and small setback for the proponents of coalition bargaining. It was a victory in that the unions were reaffirmed in their right to select representatives "of their own choosing;" and a setback in that the Board, with support of the Court, ruled

[13]*Ibid.*

[14]*Standard Oil Company* v. *NLRB*, 322 F. 2d 40 (CA6, 1963), 54 LRRM 2076, enforcing 137 NLRB 690, 50 LRRM 1238.

that it was improper for a union to withhold signing of an agreed upon contract pending completion of negotiations with other units.

The company had separate agreements with locals at each of its four refineries, all of which expired at the same time. After negotiations had begun at each location, the OCAW Sohio Council decided to appoint "temporary international representatives" to sit in on each negotiating session, allegedly to improve communications between the four committees. The plant managers at each refinery refused to meet with the committees so long as they contained members of another certified bargaining unit—the temporary representatives. The company continued to refuse to bargain until the union finally agreed to resume meetings with its regular negotiating committees.

When bargaining recommenced, the company and the locals came to agreement on terms for three of the refineries. The union, however, refused to sign the contracts, ostensibly because international approval was needed; but actually because the Sohio Council had bound its members to accept no settlement until agreement was reached at the fourth location. When the last of these negotiations came to a successful conclusion, all contracts were signed in a period of a week.

It was the contention of Standard that the union was trying to force it into a position where it would be effectively involved in company-wide bargaining. The NLRB ruled that although such an intention may have been a real possibility, the company, by refusing to meet with the union committees, had not given the OCAW an opportunity either to support or to disprove the existence of a coalition. The NLRB also ruled, however, that OCAW was in violation of the Act by refusing to execute an agreement already reached until agreement was achieved at other locations.

The Sixth Circuit affirmed both aspects of the NLRB's finding of facts in the company-wide bargaining aspect. Said the Court:

> We are of the opinion that the inference and conclusion drawn by the examiner with respect to company-wide bargaining was correct and supported by the evidence. *Where undisputed facts are open to more than inference, this Court is bound to accept the inference drawn by the Board. We may not draw another inference, even though we think it is more logical.* (Emphasis added).[15]

[15]*Ibid.*

Thus the Court stated that it was obligated to accept the decision of the lower body, although it may have had some doubt or reservations. It then built upon the decision of the Board and, in the absence of proved bad faith or ulterior motive of the union, found Sohio guilty of the refusal to bargain charge. Both the NLRB and the Courts overlooked the potential impact of approving this step in the development of coalition bargaining.

The impact of *Standard Oil* falls, then, into two specific areas bearing on coalition bargaining. The first is that a union may not refuse to execute a labor agreement by refusing to sign when agreement has been reached on all issues until satisfactory settlement has been reached at other coalition locations. The simple expedient available to the unions, however, is to reach an artificial impasse by failing to agree on one or more issues until such time as other locations are also in a position to settle.

Second, the *Standard Oil* decision, however, also served to reinforce the right of the unions to be permitted to assign representatives of other bargaining units to a particular negotiating committee as long as no overt attempt is made to enlarge the scope of the established bargaining unit.

The Nonferrous Cases

Although the copper cases are the first coalition ones given serious attention by the NLRB since *Standard Oil,* in which companies complained that the unions were demanding that the bargaining unit be expanded and no settlement could be made with one unit until all units came to agreement, they are not the first brought to the Board's attention. Both General Electric and Union Carbide made charges to the Board that they were victims of the same conduct; General Electric even noted in its charge that the coalition unions "pledged that no one of them would consummate a contract covering any bargaining unit . . . until all should do so." Nevertheless, the General Counsel of the NLRB summarily dismissed both cases without a hearing.

The General Counsel handled the Kennecott charge, the first of the nonferrous cases, most gingerly. It was filed in October 1967; the complaint was issued in February 1968. The bases of the Kennecott complaint (and later, those of Phelps-Dodge and Anaconda) were demands, widely publicized for several months by the United Steelworkers of America and its coalition partners in the nonferrous industry, that there were three absolute preconditions for agreement:

1. Common expiration dates for all labor-management contracts within a company, including its subsidiaries in the non-ferrous metals industry.
2. A company-wide economic "package" to be applied equally to each unit within a company, making some minor allowance for local conditions.
3. An accepted rule within each corporation that settlement must be achieved at all operations before any operations are resumed.

When the Steelworkers representatives publicly stated these demands in October at a hearing called by the Governor of Utah in Salt Lake City, Kennecott filed its charge, but the General Counsel did not process the charge because the union sent a telegram "withdrawing" the demands, although in fact they continued to be pressed and publicized, as described in Chapter IX. Only after union officials had publicly repeated these demands before a factfinding board in Washington, D.C., did the General Counsel issue a complaint.

Since then, Phelps Dodge and Anaconda have also filed charges against the Steelworkers and other coalition unions. All three cases will probably involve long hearings and decisions may not be expected until late in 1968. Thereafter the NLRB rulings may be appealed to the courts. The possibility exists, however, for a realistic review of the tactics of coalition unions, and the support given to them by the NLRB to engage in activities which are designed, under one guise or another, to expand the bargaining unit unilaterally.

The copper cases will also afford an opportunity to see if the NLRB will apply the same reasoning to unions that it has to companies in another area. For example, in a case growing out of the 1960 General Electric-IUE negotiations, but decided four years later,[16] the NLRB ruled that General Electric had not bargained in good faith because its communications to employees "froze" its stance at the bargaining table. Then in the *H. K. Porter* case,[17] the Board ruled that the

[16]*General Electric Company,* 150 NLRB 192 (1964) 57 LRRM 1491.
[17]*H. K. Porter,* 153 NLRB 1370 (1965); enforced 363 F. 2d 272 (D.C. Circuit, 1966).

company's refusal to grant the checkoff of dues was an unfair labor practice.

Will, one wonders, the NLRB find that the Steelworkers public stance on its three demands and its communications relating thereto "froze" its stance or that the union's refusal to grant companies the security of lower wages in fabricating than mining an unfair labor practice?

NLRB Tactics and Section 10(j)

Section 10(j) of the Taft-Hartley Act provides that:

> The Board shall have power upon issuance of a complaint as provided in subsection (b) charging that any person who has engaged in or is engaging in an unfair labor practice, to petition any district court of the United States . . . within any district wherein the unfair labor practice in question is alleged to have occurred or wherein such person resides or transacts business, for appropriate temporary relief or restraining order. Upon the filing of such petition, the court shall cause notice thereof to be served upon such person, and thereupon shall have jurisdiction to grant to the Board such temporary relief or restraining power as it deems just and proper.

The limits of NLRB power to seek injunctions pursuant to Section 10(j) have not been set by the United States Supreme Court, partially at least, no doubt, because prior to recent years, the NLRB has been reluctant to seek this avenue of redress. That Congress expected this to be an extraordinary and not widely used remedy seems also to be well understood. Nevertheless, the present Board members have on several occasions, as recounted in previous chapters, attempted to use the injunctive weapon to aid the union coalition movement.

General Electric's situation is a case in point. The International Union of Electrical, Radio and Machine Workers (IUE) has filed an unfair labor practice charge against the company in every bargaining year since the early 1950's except for one.[18] Prior to 1960, all were dismissed by the NLRB. The 1960 case, as already noted, was decided in 1964, four years after General Electric and 100 unions had signed a three year agreement and eighteen months after a successor three year agreement had been reached. In 1963, despite a peaceful negotiation,

[18]See, Herbert R. Northrup, "Boulwarism v. Coalitionism—The 1966 GE Negotiations," *Management of Personnel Quarterly*, Volume V (Summer 1966), pp. 2–12.

the IUE filed another charge. The General Counsel of the Board had neither issued a complaint nor dismissed the charge by mid-1968! Moreover, the appeal of the Company from the 1960 case decision before the Second Circuit Court of Appeals has not been heard because the NLRB has delayed repeatedly to avoid proceeding with the case.

With this background, it is all the more remarkable how rapidly the NLRB moved with the 1966 complaint of IUE and the coalition unions against General Electric. Within a few days after the charge had been filed, a complaint was issued, and then an injunction was sought pursuant to Section 10(j). The District Court granted the injunction,[19] but the Court of Appeals sharply rebuked both the District Court and the NLRB, with these words:

> . . . It is difficult to imagine a case that presented more vividly the need for prompt action by the Labor Board. For reasons that escape us, the Board decided not to utilize with dispatch its adjudicatory machinery but to proceed instead at cross purpose with that envisaged by Congress in the National Labor Relations Act.[20]

As noted in Chapter VI, the Supreme Court stayed the vacation of the injunction by the appeals court, but the case later became moot. The Board promptly set the matter for hearing before a trial examiner, who rendered his report in June 1967.[21] A decision on the case by the NLRB had not been issued by mid-1968.

In the *3M* case, the NLRB was in even more haste to come to the aid of coalition bargaining. Two days after issuing a complaint, which itself was speedily handled, the General Counsel sought an injunction, which was granted by the District Court.[22] Again, however, the injunction was struck down on appeal,[23] and this time the NLRB sought no Supreme Court action. The Board, again, speedily set the case for hearing and the trial examiner's decision was handed down in November 1967.[24] A Board decision may come in conjunction with that issued in the *General Electric* case.

---

[19] *McLeod* v. *General Electric Company,* (D.C., So. D. of N.Y., August 1966) 62 LRRM 2809.

[20] *Ibid.*

[21] "Trial Examiner's Decision," *General Electric Company* and *International Union of Electrical, Radio and Machine Workers, AFL-CIO,* 2-CA-2443, (June 8, 1967).

[22] *Meter* v. *Minnesota Mining and Manufacturing Company,* (D.C. Minn., 1967) 66 LRRM 2203, reversed (CA8, 1967), 66 LRRM 2444.

[23] *Minnesota Mining and Manufacturing Company* v. *Meter,* (CA8, 1967) 66 LRRM 2444.

[24] "Trial Examiner's Decision," Minnesota Mining . . . *loc. cit.*

In the *Union Carbide* case,[25] the NLRB not only acted with questionable speed, but also with questionable tactics. Although Section 10(j) clearly makes no provision for *ex parte* injunctions, the legal representative of the General Counsel sought such an injunction at the Bluefield, West Virginia, District Court, without any notice to the company, rather than at Charleston, which was closer to the plant in question and which was where the parties were negotiating. The Court refused to agree to this procedure, and when the hearing was held in the Charleston District Court, the injunction was refused.[26] The case then went through the regular trial examiner stage to the Board, as discussed below.

In sharp contrast to the hasty actions in these three cases was the due deliberation in the Kennecott matter. Here the company requested that the General Counsel seek an injunction in October 1967; he finally issued a complaint in February 1968, announced that an injunction action would be sought, and then rescinded the injunction request when President Johnson called the parties to Washington to negotiate under the aegis of the Secretaries of Labor and Commerce. In defending his actions (or lack thereof) in the Kennecott case, the General Counsel has noted that the issuance of complaints and the prompt use of injunctive procedures is not necessarily the best means of reaching settlement. He stated in part: ". . . that when parties are engaged in critical negotiations . . . throwing a lawsuit into the hopper isn't a help."[27]

One might fully agree with the General Counsel's position; then logically ask why the unnatural speed on his part and that of the NLRB in seeking injunctions to force General Electric, Union Carbide, and 3M back to the bargaining table to deal with union coalitions who apparently sought the same objectives as did the copper coalition unions. Such an issue is even more apparent when it is considered in light of the fact that the General Counsel deliberated more than four months in the copper situation before issuing a complaint, but took only two days to seek an injunction against 3M, and not much more time to move against General Electric and Union Carbide.

---

[25]*Union Carbide Corporation, Mining and Metals Division and Oil, Chemical and Atomic Workers International Union,* 165 NLRB No. 26 (June 15, 1967) 65 LRRM 1282.

[26]*Farkes* v. *Union Carbide Corporation* (D.C., So. Dist. W. Va., August 12, 1966).

[27]See statement of NLRB General Counsel Arnold Ordman before the U.S. Senate Judiciary Subcommittee on Separation of Powers, May 13, 1968, as reported in the *Daily Labor Report,* No. 94 (May 13, 1968), pp. A-3–A-5.

The Chairman of the NLRB has stated that the injunctive power of the Board should be used only in cases of extraordinary circumstances. He has maintained that the Board has exercised its power "not as a broad sword, but as a scalpel, ever mindful of the dangers inherent in conducting labor-management relations by way of injunction."[28] Again one finds little disagreement with these thoughts. What is missing is a concept of equity. It is noteworthy that as the Chairman of the NLRB spoke these words, and lamented in the same speech that the Supreme Court's ruling in the *General Electric* case "robbed the Board of guidance in Section 10(j) matters," the Kennecott charge was waiting on the General Counsel's desk where it lay for four months.[29]

The Defensive Lockout—Union Carbide Case

In one area, the United States Supreme Court has regularly overruled attempts by the NLRB to enhance union power by curtailing management's right to counter union tactics.[30] This is in the use of the lockout, a fact which may account for the only major NLRB decision which was found in a company favor in a coalition case.

In this case, as noted above, the NLRB, after dismissing company charges against the union, first attempted to obtain an injunction ordering Union Carbide to cease locking out its employees at Alloy, West Virginia. The District Court Judge not only declined the NLRB request, but stated that in his opinion, the lockout was entirely legal.[31] A Board trial examiner then found against the company, although the record before the District Court was stipulated to the Board record. It should be noted that the company had made repeated offers to settle the dispute, and that the lockout occurred only after an impasse resulted from the failure of the unions to demonstrate any interest in settlement. The NLRB then reversed the trial examiner, and dismissed the complaint.[32] The union has appealed to the Court of Appeals for the District of Columbia, but the nature of the record and the strong support of lock-

[28]See Frank W. McCulloch, "Past, Present and Future Remedies Under Section 8(a)(5) of the NLRA," *Labor Law Journal*, Volume XIX, (March 1968), pp. 131–142.

[29]*Ibid.* See also remarks by Frank W. McCulloch entitled "New Remedies Under the National Labor Relations Act," Twenty-first Annual Conference on Labor in New York City sponsored by the New York University Institute of Labor Relations, May 14, 1968, as reported in the *Daily Labor Report,* No. 95 (May 14, 1968), pp. F-1–F-6.

[30]See for example: *American Ship Building Company* v. *NLRB,* 380 U.S. 300 (1965) and *NLRB* v. *Brown Food Stores,* 380 U.S. 278 (1965).

[31]*Farkes* v. *Union Carbide Corporation, loc. cit.*

[32]*Union Carbide Corporation,* note 23 above.

outs by the Supreme Court do not indicate that the decision will be lightly overturned.

Because Union Carbide was careful to make repeated efforts for settlement, and because it did not refuse to bargain when outsiders were present, although rigorously confining matters to the certified bargaining unit involved, it was in a good position to take the offensive and to win the lockout. Even under these favorable circumstances and with obviously careful planning, the litigation involved was extensive and is still not completed.

Libby-Owens-Ford and Bargaining Unit Expansion

A recent Board decision rendered in a situation involving the Libby-Owens-Ford Glass Company[33] and the union representing most of its plants, the United Glass and Ceramic Workers of North America (UGCW or Glass Workers) is one which had no direct connection with a coalition bargaining case *per se,* but one which if upheld, could have tremendous impact upon the formation of coalitions in the future.

The ten production units of L-O-F have been represented by different locals of the Glass Workers union. Eight of these plants were placed into a single unit for bargaining purposes by voluntary agreement by the company and union in 1939. Since that time, two nonintegrated plants were opened at Brackenridge, Pennsylvania, and Lathrop, California, where employees also elected the Glass Workers as bargaining representative. These two locals, however, were separately certified, maintained separate contracts and were never included in the master agreement.

The first demand for inclusion of a local in the "big unit" came during bargaining in 1961, with a repeat in 1963. In those instances, the company refused to accede to the union's demands, and the demands were withdrawn. In 1965 a demand was made to include both locals, and in 1966, was the primary bargaining goal of the Lathrop, California local (the nucleus of which was composed of laid-off workers from other L-O-F plants who moved there during startup). Because of

[33] *Libby-Owens-Ford Glass Company and United Glass and Ceramic Workers of North America, AFL-CIO-CLC,* 169 NLRB No. 2 (January 12, 1968) 67 LRRM 1096. In the summer of 1968, the Chemical Workers began an attempt to expand the L-O-F doctrine by seeking a bargaining unit "clarification" at American Cyanamid Company. Further similar efforts have also been recently directed toward PPG Industries and American St. Gobain Glass Company to engage in joint bargaining by adding separately certified units to a master agreement.

L-O-F's inability to take a strike at that time (which would have also shut down some General Motors operations as well) the union was given a clause which would permit the membership the right to strike on the issue after one year.

Apparently, one of the reasons for the demand for the expansion of the bargaining unit was based upon a fear of raiding the Teamsters. The local officers felt that the union was not receiving adequate attention from the international. When the Teamsters attempted to gain bargaining rights at Lathrop, the international awakened and sought ways to protect itself, one of the results being the demand for expansion of the unit to include the two locals.

Having failed in collective bargaining attempts to expand the master contract group, the UGCW turned to the Board for assistance by requesting an election to determine whether the *membership* of the two locals desired to be included in the larger unit.

Although no representation was at issue, the NLRB, by a three to two vote, ordered an election at the Brackenridge and Lathrop plants to "clarify" the situation—that is to see if the employees involved desired to be included in the broader unit. The Board majority stated in part:

> We conclude from the above review of outstanding principles and the arguments herein that the Petitioner [UGCW] has adopted a procedure which would appear to encompass its desired relief. We are unable to perceive any reason why a further delay should be required where, as here, no question of the presumptive propriety of the employer-wide unit exists and only the technical problems of bargaining history and employer opposition have prevented its establishment.
>
> * * *
>
> As is clear from the above discussion, we are persuaded that the Board's authority and practice in determining units and conducting elections, including the weight given to employee wishes as one fact and the holding of self-determination elections as an investigatory, fact-finding tool, are firmly based on the Act. And we are satisfied that our present decision is within our statutory competency. There will be time enough to treat with the other questions which our dissenting members foresee if they in fact arise. We deal only with the immediate question presented to us, and we do so by using a new combination of long-established procedures, in order to put at rest a controversy that has

admittedly been disturbing the relations of the parties for a number of years.[34]

In a vigorous dissent, Board Members Fanning and Jenkins took significant exception to the view of the majority. They stated in part:

> Although our colleagues readily recognize that no established principles cover this situation, they ignore the fact that the void they undertake to fill—"to mark out the appropriate unit for future bargaining" without affecting existing contracts and, obviously, with reference to a representation issue—is a statutory void. Authorization for this type of election is completely lacking under the Act. Representation is not in issue in this case. Unit scope is.
>
> One cannot quarrel with the majority statement that "it is not a difficult matter" for the Board to make available a secret ballot election tailored to this situation. Mechanically this is quite true. What is difficult is to find in the Act the statutory authority for so doing in these circumstances, and hence for the expenditure of funds for this purpose. There simply is no present statutory authority for permitting employees to decide, in a representational vacuum, which *contract* unit they wish. True, in "Globe," or so-called self-determination elections, the Board has long given weight to employee expression of unit preference *in connection with selection of a bargaining representative*. This is because a question concerning representation exists and Section 9(c)(1) of the Act specifically authorizes an election in those circumstances. The election is held to select a bargaining representative, and only by reason of the selection of a particular representative rather than another representative does the employee register a preference as to unit.
>
> * * *
>
> The existence of this void in the statutory scheme is not denied by our colleagues. Instead they speak of the "technical problems of bargaining history and employer opposition" having prevented establishment of a presumptively appropriate employer-wide unit, and perceive no reason for further delay in supplying a solution to the problem, or for leaving the parties with no early source of relief. At best it seems cavalier to treat employer opposition to a request for bargaining on a country-wide, multiplant basis as a mere technical problem. It is a factor to be seriously considered. The mere fact that the Employer and the Union here take opposite positions on the question of enlarging the

---

[34]*Ibid.*

unit for future bargaining does not, to our way of thinking, justify rationalizing the existence of the requisite authority for solution by the employees.[35]

Immediately after the announcement of the NLRB's decision, Libbey-Owens-Ford obtained a temporary injunction from the District Court, District of Columbia,[36] which was granted on the grounds that the NLRB had exceeded its authority. The NLRB, however, turned to the Court of Appeals, District of Columbia Circuit, which set aside the injunction and permitted the vote to be held.[37] The Appeals Court did, however, order the Board to refrain from certifying the results of the vote (which was overwhelmingly in favor of both units joining the company-wide unit) until its decision, which was reached on June 7, 1968.

The Court of Appeals for the District of Columbia ruled in favor of the Board by a two to one majority. The order stated in part:

> The Board's action in this case, if at all inconsistent with the Act, was certainly not so "plainly beyond" its bounds or so "clearly in defiance" of it. We therefore remand the case to the District Court with directions to dismiss the complaint.[38]

A dissent, however by Judge Tamm, is significant. He stated:

> It is my view of this case that the Board has arbitrarily exercised a power that has neither been conferred upon by Congress nor is implied by any phraseology contained in the Act.
>
> The case illustrates the consistent tendency of administrative agencies to assume and exercise by accretion powers not granted to them specifically or by necessary implication. Undoubtedly in most instances this grasping for non-authorized powers is motivated by sincere desire to perform more effective and efficient functions. I believe that the courts must insist, however, that the administrative agencies confine their operations specifically to those fields of activity which are bounded by the statutes which create their authority and authorize

---

[35]*Ibid.*

[36]*Libby-Owens-Ford* v. *McCulloch,* (District Court, District of Columbia, 1968), 67 LRRM 2712.

[37]The United States Supreme Court has ruled that an injunction against an action of the NLRB will be granted if, and probably only if, it can be shown that the Board has clearly overstepped its authority as set forth in the Act. See *Leedom* v. *Kyne* 358 U.S. 184 (1958).

[38]*McCulloch* v. *Libby-Owens-Ford Glass Company* as reported in *Daily Labor Report* (June 12, 1968), pp. A-1, A-4.

> their operations. If additional power or functions are essential to a proper discharge of an agency's responsibilities, those powers or functions should not be self-created but should be sought from the Congress.[39]

Libby-Owens-Ford has appealed this order to the Supreme Court. It may also gain an additional review by refusing to recognize the Board's ruling, and then, after an unfair labor practice charge, reappeal the whole matter.

It is then apparent that if the Board position in this case is upheld by the Supreme Court, coalition unions may have a new tool designed to accomplish goals previously unattainable through collective bargaining. Extension of the Libby-Owens-Ford doctrine would permit unions simply to petition for an election to "clarify" the scope of the bargaining unit to include from time to time any local or group of locals as the opportunities arise. If the NLRB can join several units into one where one union is involved without regard to history or employer concern, there is no logical reason why it cannot do the same thing where several unions are concerned. This would open a clear path to coalition bargaining without the necessity of using the various subterfuges which have been a hallmark of the movement to date.

UNION LEGAL STRATEGY—AN EXAMPLE

In the light of the aforementioned NLRB and court decisions, an examination of some of the legal developments that have affected the coalition programs, it is helpful to examine the legal strategy developed by the International Chemical Workers Union (ICWU) as it "directs increasing attention toward the achievement of coordinated bargaining [where] the field staff should have a clear grasp of the basic legal problems involved."[40]

The ICWU document notes that the Board has held that the duty to bargain in good faith requires that company and the union meet on a basis as certified by the NLRB. It is therefore a violation of the act to attempt to force an employer to engage in multi-plant bargaining, although such a combination is acceptable and within the law if both

[39] *Ibid.*

[40] From a document entitled *Legal Problems in Coordinated Bargaining,* prepared by the International Chemical Workers Union, a copy of which is in this writer's possession. Undated, probably 1966.

parties voluntarily mutually agree to enlarge the scope of the bargaining unit.

The union, as a second step, recommends that the locals within a company attempt to gain joint bargaining by an alternative method, if a situation exists where there is a uniformity of pension or other programs. The alternative calls for the adoption of a

> . . . resolution which (1) authorizes the joint committee council to bargain with the company on behalf of the local on pensions and/or insurance, and (2) specifies that any agreement reached in such bargaining will preclude local bargaining for the term of that agreement. With such a setting, there is a good chance that the Board will hold that the company must bargain on a national basis with the joint committee or council which has been designated as the representative of the locals concerning the uniform pension or insurance plan.[41]

The ICWU then notes that such a strategy is not applicable in the absence of some uniform plan which may be used as a wedge. In that case, the union turns to "coordinated" bargaining combined with a plan for individual contract clause which would permit individual locals "to support united action." Under the specified plan, the local unions continue to bargain unit-by-unit, but a single joint steering committee participates in negotiations at each location.

The union is careful to state that the bargaining committee members must be fully appraised of the fact that negotiations can be conducted only for the terms of the contract at that particular unit. It further states that an unfair labor practice charge could result from an agreement reached by the locals that no agreement would be *signed* in the absence of agreement at another location. A way is left open by the ICWU, however:

> *It is therefore a mistake to have any agreement that no union will sign until a satisfactory offer is made at another location. But the desired objective can be reached through other completely lawful means* . . . . (Emphasis in original).[42]

The basic principle then enunciated is one which concerns itself with bargaining only for the unit in question, but with emphasis placed on common contractual demands. This means that a local would simply

---

[41] *Ibid.*
[42] *Ibid.*

demand, and hold out for, provisions that would eventually result in identical contractual terms across the scope of the coalition group. It is further suggested that most important coalition demand is one for common contract termination dates, which if achieved, would permit simultaneous bargaining, and would give all locals the power to withhold agreement until all were satisfied with the terms of the company offer. Thus joint or national bargaining would have been achieved nonetheless.

In the event of the inability to attain such goals as noted above, the ICWU suggests further alternatives which would serve to advance the cause of a coalition. A potent coalition weapon can be forged through the inclusion of an exception to a no-strike clause which would permit a local to engage in a work stoppage in support of a lawful strike at another company location. A further modification is suggested to permit employees to refuse to perform work which may have been diverted to a plant due to a strike at another plant. And, a further alternative is suggested in the form of a clause which would simply give employees the right to refuse to cross a picket line established by another local within the same company.

Although not specifically cited, the ICWU document also alludes to the use of other common coalition bargaining practices such as slowing down of bargaining, continuing to work beyond contract expirations in order to seek coterminous contract terminations, and others which all point toward an eventual forcing of management to engage in joint negotiations on company-wide or national basis.

A Proposal For NLRB Reform

This examination of NLRB rulings and activities in situations involving coalition bargaining emphasizes two facets of public policy: 1) the difficulty of defining realistically what is meant by "bargaining in good faith," and 2) the tendency of the NLRB to support the union view whenever the rationalization of that position seemed at all possible.

The difficulties of defining good faith bargaining are not indigenous to coalition bargaining situations. It has been most complicated to do so under many circumstances throughout the history of the Wagner and Taft-Hartley Acts. The pursuit of definitions of good faith at the bargaining table has led the NLRB to go "beyond the scope of attempting to maintain an atmosphere in which private agreement-making could function and into regulation of bargaining tactics, bargaining content, and contract administration."[43] The coalition bargaining case carries government intrusion further into the tactics of the parties, and in addition produces decisions that are more fantasy than real. Rendering rulings, for example, as to when an "outsider" is not an outsider, but instead represents a local union other than the one which elected him or pays his salary, or when management can or cannot refuse to deal with a committee on which an outsider is present, not only takes the NLRB deep into the bargaining process, but also yields decisions which solemnly state that the union spokesmen do not mean what their leaders have publicly sworn to accomplish.

The tendency of the NLRB (at least as presently constituted) to support the enhancement of union powers is, of course, clearly revealed by its hasty pursuit of injunctions to force companies to bargain with coalition-constituted union committees. The fact that the courts found this activity contrary to the Taft-Hartley Act, and the slowness which the NLRB moved in the Kennecott situation, add to the evidence of NLRB partisanship.[44]

Both the tendency of the NLRB to move more deeply into the collective bargaining process and its apparent partisanship increase the potential for the Board to become entangled in the tactics of the parties. The close association of union charge, General Counsel complaint, and Board seeking of an injunction, and the speed of the processes, the prompt dismissal of charges of General Electric and Union Carbide, and the leisurely Board pace in the Kennecott dispute, raise questions not only of Board partisanship, but of a careful union-NLRB coordinated tactical effort to ensure union coalition victories. The more such things appear to occur, the more unions will attempt to bring the NLRB into a case for support; and the corollary is often a management tactic to use the Board's processes as a defensive maneuver.

Many proposals have been made to alter the combination of NLRB self-aggrandizement and partisanship. Some would more rigidly

[43] Paul A. Abodeely, *Compulsory Arbitration and the NLRB,* Industrial Research Unit, University of Pennsylvania, Labor Relations and Public Policy Series, Report No. 1, (Philadelphia: University of Pennsylvania Press, 1968), p. 85.

[44] See the discussion earlier in this chapter.

define NLRB powers, others would abolish the Board's jurisdiction in unfair labor practice cases and transfer them to a labor court, and still others would extend the terms of NLRB membership in order to reduce political influence on them.

These suggestions do not appear to go to the heart of the matter. As Paul A. Abodeely has pointed out:

> If we see as the basis of the problem, and a cause thereof, the attempt at prescribing regulations on collective bargaining beyond merely requiring the meeting and conferring on subjects both can agree upon, the obvious answer is to repeal such regulation. Any other answer requires a different basic assumption as to the cause of the problem. Repealing NLRB powers and placing a court, either an existing one or a newly established labor court, in charge of its duties will only serve to replace Board regulation with judicial regulation. Extending the terms of Board members to avoid the political control of labor relations and the reversal of Board policy incident to it will not reduce government control in any way. Further, the "good" or "bad" choice of members will be accentuated and the aim of Congress to make government policy reflect current public interests will be frustrated.[45]

Essentially, what is recommended is the repeal of Sections 8(a)(5) and (b)(3). This is not a new suggestion—it has been recommended by a host of authorities with varying philosophies. For example, the Independent Study Group, composed of several eminent scholars, stated:

> Basically, it is unrealistic to expect that, by legislation, "good faith" can be brought to the bargaining table. Indeed, the provisions designed to bring "good faith" have become a tactical weapon used in many situations as a means of harassment.[46]

Dr. George W. Taylor, a member of that Study Group has long believed that Sections 8(a)(5) and (b)(3) should have been deleted from the Taft-Hartley Act. He has remarked:

> . . . I think it was a mistake, under the Taft-Hartley Act, for a government agency to be charged with responsibility for defining the

[45]Abodeely, *op. cit.*, p. 86.

[46]Independent Study Group, *The Public Interest in Collective Bargaining* (New York: Committee for Economic Development, 1961), p. 82.

subject matter of compulsory collective bargaining as a matter of national labor policy.

> When the Wagner Act was passed, it seemed to me to be unwise to include Section 8(5) . . . [A] legally required obligation to "bargain" in the Act would make it necessary to define what was meant by collective bargaining and the subjects that would have to be mutually determined.[47]

Dr. William Gomberg, a veteran of the labor movement agrees:

> It is my conviction that the so-called good faith bargaining clause has made the NLRB an extension of the tactics of the parties. It provides a whipping boy for the frustration of a party to the bargain who refuses to face the consequences of overplaying his hand and then goes running to papa government.[48]

Dr. Herbert R. Northrup also concurs. He has recommended the abolition of Section 8(a)(5) and (b)(3), rather than other proposed remedies, because "the need is to remove the *raison d'etre*—not to alter the method."[49]

If Sections 8(a)(5) and (b)(3) were deleted from the Act, the controversy over union committee membership and recent size would be largely irrelevant to the law. If unions desired to pack committees with representatives of other local or national unions, they would have a perfect right to do so—but management would have an equal right to decline to bargain with them. Essentially economic power would arbitrate the result.

One might point out that some inequities might result from such an arrangement, and to be sure, that is correct. Certainly, however, the inequities would be no greater, and probably, far less than under a situation where the NLRB intervenes to support one side and renders decisions which appear neither realistic nor objective. If collective bargaining is to be supported, then it must be understood that the parties must both be permitted maximum flexibility in their private decision making and also be forced to live with the results of their decisions.

47George W. Taylor, "Collective Bargaining in Transition," in Arnold Weber, (ed.), *The Structure of Collective Bargaining* (Chicago: Free Press of Glencoe, Inc., 1961), p. 347.

48William Gomberg, "Government Participation in Union Negotiation and Collective Bargaining," *Labor Law Journal,* Volume XIII (November 1962), pp. 941, 944.

49Herbert R. Northrup, *Compulsory Arbitration and Government Intervention in Labor Disputes* (Washington: Labor Policy Association, Inc., 1966), p. 104.

Lacking the NLRB to "mother hen" then, as Dr. Taylor has noted,[50] is likely to be the most effective restraining force against rash confrontations yet devised. Certainly, the device of *less* rather than more legislation is worthy of trial in view of its broad and wide-spread support.

COALITION BARGAINING AND INTERVENTION IN LABOR DISPUTES

Besides intervention by the NLRB, coalition bargaining cases have involved government action on a variety of other fronts. The Federal Mediation and Conciliation Service, as part of its regular mediation function, has been active in nearly all coalition cases. The President has invoked the emergency procedures of the Taft-Hartley Act twice; and the Secretaries of Labor, Commerce, and Defense and the President himself have intervened directly in a number of ways.

In some ways, these actions of government officials in coalition cases have indicated the same harmony of action with IUD strategy and aims as has been demonstrated by the NLRB's cooperation with union tactics and goals. For example, there have been several obvious instances of attempted pressure by government officials in support of both bargaining structure and economic settlements for which IUD backed coalitions were striving. This support of unions has, in turn, encouraged management to seek support of its political friends. The results have varied.

In the Union Carbide case, for example, the Secretary of Labor put heavy pressure on the Company to send its top executives to Washington in order to bargain with top union officials representing all the unions in Carbide coalition group. If Union Carbide had agreed, coalition bargaining would have been a *fait accompli*. Since, however, the rationale for the Secretary's interest was Carbide's Kokomo, Indiana plant, which manufactured a critical item for the Viet Nam War, Carbide sent only local officials from Kokomo to Washington. The union officials left disappointed and the strike at Kokomo ended after the Taft-Hartley Act was invoked.

General Electric's situation was similar. In fact, General Electric and its largest union, the International Union of Electrical, Radio and Machine Workers, had all but reached agreement when the parties were "invited" to the White House and told to negotiate under the aegis of the Secretaries of Labor, Commerce, and Defense. Indeed, there is a

[50]Taylor, *op. cit.*, p. 348.

persistent rumor that the IUE representatives had voted to accept General Electric's offer when they were dissuaded by a call from union officials in Washington, telling of a meeting between George Meany and the President which preceded the summons to the White House.

General Electric went to Washington, but declined to make any radical change in its offer, and the IUD eventually settled for a slight rearrangement of the cost of living formula. The Auto Workers struck the Evendale, Ohio, jet engine plant, and other locations, but a Taft-Hartley injunction stopped the former strike, and the others ended without tangible union gains. On the other hand, the call to Washington was a propaganda triumph of sorts for the IUD and the coalition concept, for it marked the first time the General Electric-IUD negotiations have been subjected to such pressures. This has enabled the IUD and IUE spokesmen to call their General Electric drive "a victory."

Taft-Hartley Intervention

As already noted, the Taft-Hartley Act has been invoked twice by President Lyndon B. Johnson in coalition bargaining cases—for the Kokomo, Indiana, plant of Union Carbide, and the Evendale, Ohio, jet engine facility of General Electric. Both plants manufacture products regarded as essential for the Viet Nam War, and this was the rationale for use of the Act. Because the Act was invoked in these cases, and not in the nonferrous industry dispute, it is pertinent to review the provisions of Title II of the Taft-Hartley Act.

The Act provides that *"whenever in the opinion of the President of the United States"*[51] an emergency situation exists, he may invoke a procedure which begins with the appointment of a Board of Inquiry to investigate and to report, without recommendations, on the issues of a dispute which "threatens" the national health or safety. The President can then direct the Attorney General to petition a federal district court for an injunction to prevent or to terminate the strike or lockout. If the injunction is granted, the conditions of work and pay are frozen for the time being, and the parties are obliged to make every effort to settle their differences with the assistance of the Conciliation Service. If these efforts are unsuccessful after 60 days the Board of Inquiry is required to make a public report on the status of the dispute, again without recommendations. The National Labor Relations Board then within 15 days

[51]Emphasis added.

must poll employees as to whether they will accept the last offer of the employer and to certify the result to the Attorney General within five days. The injunction then must be dissolved, and a strike is legal. By this time, 80 days have elapsed since the first application for an injunction. If the majority of workers refuse the employer's last offer, then the President can submit the complete report to Congress, with or without recommendations for action.

In both the Union Carbide and General Electric cases, the strikes were ended by injunctions, and settlement was reached by the parties before it was necessary to poll the employees concerning the employers' last offers. It is likely, however, that the last offer vote requirement was a factor in the result. There was apparently, at both plants, considerable doubt about whether the employees would support a new strike after the 80-day injunction period and this allegedly induced the unions to settle. Although all fifteen polls taken on last offer votes under the Taft-Hartley Act have resulted in rejection of the employers' last offers (but usually not in a strike except in the longshore industry), the last offer provision in at least two other cases has apparently induced settlements for the same reason, once on the part of employers, and the other, of a union.[52]

In both the General Electric and Union Carbide cases, the coalition unions were unhappy about Taft-Hartley use. If the Act was invoked, they had hoped that it would cover the entire unionized section of each company and thus result in a coalition confrontation before a government board.[53] This, they hoped would be the least result from the Washington negotiations induced by the President in the General Electric case and unsuccessfully requested by the Secretary of Labor in Union Carbide. The former's successful bargaining and the latter's refusal to yield to the Secretary's pressure resulted in little choice for the President but to invoke the Act for the key defense facilities only.

The Nonferrous Intervention

The nonferrous intervention was of a different character, being basically extralegal. Initially, as was noted in Chapter X, the unions

[52]Reference is to the 1959 steel strike and to the 1962 strike at Lockheed Aircraft Company. See George W. Taylor, "The Adequacy of Taft-Hartley in Public Emergency Disputes," *The Annals,* Volume CCCXXXIII (January 1961), p. 79; and Herbert R. Northrup and Gordon F. Bloom, *Government and Labor* (Homewood, Illinois: Richard D. Irwin, Inc., 1963), p. 365.

[53]This view is based on interview with union and company officials.

seemed to favor a Taft-Hartley intervention. As the strike continued, however, and copper needs continued to be met, then tactics shifted. In their own publications, and through their friends in public life, particularly Senator Mansfield, Democrat of Montana,[54] they called for Washington negotiations under Johnson Administration aegis. Undoubtedly, the desire to avoid an 80-day injunction that expired when metal can or basic steel negotiations were under way was a factor.

Meanwhile, governors tried to intervene and senators proposed solutions, all without success. When it seemed that proposals for extralegal intervention were gathering force, the industry and its friends countered with proposals to invoke the Taft-Hartley Act. The Secretary of Labor, however, let it be known that he did not believe that the courts would sustain the request for an injunction because of an insufficient showing of emergency; and that the employees might go back on strike after the 80-day period of the injunction were granted.[55]

Whatever the merits of the use of Taft-Hartley procedures in the nonferrous strike, the fact does remain that the law gives the President wide discretion by providing that *his "opinion"* shall determine whether an emergency exists, and the courts have demonstrated great reluctance to substitute their views for his as to whether the Act should be invoked.[56] In addition, of course, one can only speculate as to what nonferrous employees might have done if an injunction had terminated their strike. After eight months on strike, however, it would seem that few employees would lightly undertake another.

In any case, the President twice gave the nonferrous unions what they wanted: first, an extralegal factfinding board, and second, bargaining at the White House level. Their failure to secure their basic coalition demands in the light of these favorable developments is ample evidence of the weakness of their case.

Government Intervention—Final Comment

Coalition bargaining is likely to involve government intervention not only because the increased scope of bargaining affects a greater number of the public, but also because the tactics of the parties include

[54]See Chapter 10.

[55]In private meetings with the parties, the Secretary repeatedly gave these opinions. Our source is interviews with several nonferrous employer representatives.

[56]*United Steelworkers* v. *United States,* 361 U.S. 39 (1959).

attempts to bring the government into the dispute. Union tactics particularly have sought this intervention. The results have, in balance, aided the coalition, but not to the extend to which the coalition unions hoped. Their failure in this regard is partially the result of employer counter tactics, and partially the result of the inherent weakness of the coalition philosophy. The following and final chapter will examine this latter aspect, together with other factors affecting the future of coalition bargaining.

CHAPTER XII

CONCLUDING OBSERVATIONS

The preceding chapters which describe some of the methods and efforts of the Industrial Union Department of the AFL-CIO (IUD) have raised some questions concerning the future of collective bargaining and its impact. In addition, such recent events as the rift between Walter Reuther and the AFL-CIO, and the rapprochement of the UAW and the Teamsters also affect the coalition movement. It is therefore appropriate to examine these factors as they may bear on coalition bargaining. First, however, it is pertinent again to examine briefly other union cooperative efforts or joint bargaining situations which may be contrasted to the efforts of the IUD.

The Unique Character of the Coalition Movement

As noted in Chapter II, cooperation among various unions in preparing for and engaging in collective bargaining is not all new to the American labor movement. The various forms have ranged from the loose amalgamations of locals of an international within a geographic area into the familiar district councils or joint boards; to the cooperation among locals of different craft unions into building trades councils, metal trades councils, and to cooperation among different national unions concerned with a specific employer or industry.[1]

When the alliance has involved various locals of the same international, the relationships have often been effective and lasting. The common interest in bargaining and contract administration on a regional market-wide basis has apparently been sufficient to bind the groups with some semblance of permanency. A grouping of various locals of different international unions has usually been subject to more strain, competitive pressures, and to a lesser degree of cooperation and permanence. A significant exception, however, has been the durable alliance of railroad shopcraft unions. Cooperation among international unions is the most recent form of alliance, and is the least durable.[2]

In most of these instances, the cooperating local unions have a common interest based on craft relationships, dealing within a certain geographical region or specific market. In a situation such as involves a building trades council, the usual aim is to band together for strength in dealing with an employers' association, and effectively to control the labor supply in the market place. Metal trades bargaining through a council provides negotiating power by presenting a united front, but also provides the locals with added insulation from the threat of raiding by other unions, which was an especially important consideration during the period of time following the formation of the CIO and the rise of industrial unions.[3]

Company-wide bargaining with one industrial union also leads to a form of joint bargaining. Each automobile producer has engaged in bargaining with the United Automobile, Aerospace, and Agricultural Implement Workers International Union (UAW) for all employees represented by the union for what becomes the master contract for that firm. In practice, the first settlement reached in the industry becomes the pattern which other automobile makers usually follow. This is an example of a coalition of local unions affiliated with the UAW bargain-

---

[1]See, for example, Herbert J. Lahne, "Coalition Bargaining and the Future of Union Structure," *Labor Law Journal,* Volume XVII: VI (June 1967), p. 353 ff.
[2]*Ibid.*
[3]*Ibid.*

ing with a single employer for a single contract. A situation has evolved in the basic steel industry where the major producers have joined together to bargain with the United Steelworkers of America (USW) on a national basis to reach an agreement which covers all of the employees of the several companies represented by that union. Thus, there is a coalition of locals of the same international dealing jointly with several employers.

The Coalition Distinctiveness

The current thrust of the drive for coalition bargaining as espoused by the Industrial Union Department differs from most cooperative efforts of the past in several significant aspects.

Nearly all previous cooperative efforts that have existed in the past involved locals of a single international union, with the significant exception being the councils of craft unions. In Chapter II, it was noted that occasionally two meatpacking unions which have now merged have bargained with major meatpackers on a coalition basis. In addition, the two pulp and paper unions, sometimes with some maintenance craft unions, often bargained on a coalition basis for employees of pulp and paper mills in a particular region. The pulp and paper coalition evolved from a craft situation and is not much different than the multicraft bargaining by metal trades councils.

Interestingly enough, in the automobile industry where the UAW is led by Walter Reuther, the leading exponent and probable intellectual father of coalition bargaining, the UAW bargains alone. The International Union of Electrical, Radio, and Machine Workers (IUE), for example, which represents the workers in the Frigidaire and Delco-Remy Divisions of General Motors, bargains separately with the Corporation. On the other hand, the UAW and the International Association of Machinists and Aerospace Workers (IAM) have engaged in a form of coalition bargaining in the aerospace industry, as was noted in Chapter II.

In actual fact, it was the aerospace experience, not the automobile experience with Reuther and the IUD have attempted to emulate. In the automobile industry, the UAW has the option of applying pressure to any employer and can, in effect, divide and rule. Coalition bargaining would seem to offer no advantage to the UAW in the automobile industry. In aerospace, the unions are relatively weaker. The coalition approach is obviously directed toward a twin objective: to prevent employers from forcing a bargain on a weaker local bargaining agent, and to make use of the critical character of the work by encouraging friendly government intervention and support both for companywide and industrywide coalition bargaining and for union wage and other objectives.

WAGE COMPETITION AND UNION STRUCTURE

Unions have long sought to "take wages out of competition" and to provide levels of remuneration that are equal throughout an industry, community or company. When a company or industry operates in more than one area, the task of equalization becomes more difficult. Likewise, when a company operates in more than one industry—and in reality, no single industry—as is the case with many conglomerates, the task of the unions is further magnified. To introduce a third factor of different international unions again makes the goal of nonwage competition even more difficult to attain. Thus, the rule in most multiplant corporations which have continued to bargain on a local basis has been one of differential wages, usually arrived at as a result of a combination of union bargaining strength, prevailing area rates, and economics of the plant, product market, and/or corporate situation.[4]

Most companies have attempted to maintain different wage structures, and for good reason. In the case where a firm operates in different industries, it is necessary to provide a rate structure for different operations which will allow it to compete with other producers who operate only in that particular industry. Most firms attempt to treat all employees equally, but recognize other competitive factors such as community or area rates, differential labor input and productivity ratios, as well as varying profit margins from plant to plant. Major firms attempt to weigh each of these factors—while seeking equal treatment of all employees—through several devices. General Electric, for example, maintains separate community base rates, but grants equal incremental increases to all employees; Union Carbide maintains wage and benefit levels comparable to the area in which the plant is located. In each

[4]See, for example, Neil W. Chamberlain, "Determinants of Collective Bargaining Structure," in Arnold R. Weber (ed.), *The Structure of Collective Bargaining* (New York: Free Press of Glencoe, 1961).

case, the primary desire is to remain competitive, and to operate the facility at a profit. If uniform wage rates are imposed, these objectives can become difficult or even impossible to achieve.

The nature of coalition bargaining contains two elements to eliminate differences in labor costs among producers in a given industry and thus to enhance union power: the desire for uniformity and the threat of a multiplant strike. If an employer normally has sufficient strength to withstand a strike by the members of a single bargaining unit acting alone, the union would be unable to attain all of its demands. If that same employer is faced with a coalition strike at all, or most of his production facilities, his ability to resist the demands is obviously diminished. On the other hand, striking large groups can be a difficult and expensive union undertaking.

By its very nature, a union coalition is designed to enhance the power of the participating unions in bargaining by presenting a unified front, and by posing the threat of a multiunit work stoppage, thereby forcing a more costly wage and benefit settlement upon the employer. If a union coalition is extended to all, or even a substantial number of producers in a given industry, the unions are then in a strategic position to broaden and to intensify the effect of a joint strike against firms in the industry. When the target of a coalition is a diversified or conglomerate corporation, a similar long reaching effect is attained which then increases the probability of government intervention, and if the Administration is friendly toward the unions, increases the opportunity for union achievement of its aims. Certainly, experience has shown that such intervention can result in gains for the unions that appeared to be unattainable through the normal exercise of collective bargaining.[5] Moreover, when a coalition effort further leads unions to pursue a bargaining posture of failing to engage in meaningful bargaining until after a strike has begun,[6] it then becomes evident that the unilateral action of that coalition can have a very definite impact on the effective bargaining unit, and presents the threat of expanding the strike potential in any bargaining situation.

---

[5]For discussion of experience under Taft-Hartley Emergency Strike Provisions, see Herbert R. Northrup and Gordon F. Bloom, *Government and Labor* (Homewood, Illinois: Richard D. Irwin, 1963), Chapter 13.

[6]J. Ward Keener, "Why We're Having Strikes," *Dun's Review*, December 1967. Mr. Keener is chairman of B. F. Goodrich Company.

UNION WEAKNESSES—AND STRENGTHS—IN COALITION BARGAINING

Professor George H. Hildebrand has hypothesized that the demand for coalition bargaining has come about as a result of basic weaknesses on the part of some industrial unions *vis-a-vis* the employer.[7] Considerable evidence presented in earlier chapters tends to support Professor Hildebrand's hypothesis. Especially in an industry such as chemicals, unionism has exhibited bargaining weaknesses. In the chemical industry, for example, neither the International Chemical Workers Union (ICWU) nor the Oil, Chemical and Atomic Workers Union (OCAW) has been able to exert sufficient strength to alter substantially the bargaining patterns of the major producers.

Such bargaining deficiencies have also caused other relatively small and impotent international unions, such as the United Glass and Ceramic Workers of North America (UGCW) (in the chemical industry) and the American Federation of Grain Millers (AFGM), as well as other unions having relatively small industrial bargaining leverage, to seek participation in coalition efforts. It is this group of unions that has usually supported IUD-led attempts to form union coalitions.[8]

On the other hand, powerful international unions such as the UAW, Steelworkers, and the IAM have also participated in major coalition efforts. It appears, however, that such participation comes about only under one of two separate conditions: when the locals of the strong international are in a relatively weak bargaining position *vis a vis* the target company such as the UAW in General Electric; or when the international is in a position to dominate and to provide leadership for the entire coalition effort, as was the case in the nonferrous situation.[9] Furthermore, unions which have demonstrated great strength within a single industry, such as rubber, steel or automobiles, have not as yet demonstrated any interest in joining other unions in order to advance the cause of a coalition there.

---

[7]From an address presented by George H. Hildebrand, Cornell University, entitled "Coordinated Bargaining: An Economist's Point of View," presented as part of a panel at the Industrial Relations Research Association Spring Meeting, Columbus, Ohio, May 3, 1968.

[8]An examination of the various IUD meeting attendance lists indicates that small, relatively weak unions are most often those supporting the joint bargaining programs.

[9]It is reported, however, that often when one of the stronger unions deems it advantageous to settle outside of the coalition bounds, it will often do so, leaving the remainder of the group to fend for itself.

Mergers

The IUD's former Executive Director has stated that the ideal situation from the standpoint of the industrial unions would be one in which there were only a relatively small number of strong internationals which would represent all employees.[10] This means that the number of internationals would have to be severely reduced through merger of unions that now often compete for membership and in bargaining. Although there have been reported discussions from time to time regarding such combinations, the only significant recent mergers in the industrial union field are those which involved the Steelworker takeover of the International Union of Mine Mill and Smelter Workers that preceded the copper coalition and the recent marriage of the meatpacking unions. Apparently problems such as union finances, internal politics, established tradition and pride, and the lack either of economic advantages or the needs of competitive realities, such as face corporations, have prevented other logical permanent mergers. In a sense, coalition bargaining has permitted a limited temporary merger among divergent interest unions for special purposes: attempts to bargain with new strength where weaknesses had prevailed without the sacrifice of leadership, patronage or potential for withdrawal.

The IUD Leadership

It is the Industrial Union Department which has acted as the catalyst in seeking to bring the diverse weak bargaining units under a single umbrella, usually within the context of bargaining with a single multiplant, multiunion firm. And, by so doing, the IUD has attempted to bring about a fundamental change in the bargaining structure, as well as a change in the structure of the unions themselves.

Traditionally, most bargaining has been conducted at the local level—negotiations have been conducted by a committee elected by the local membership who then deals with the local management representatives. Each side is often assisted and guided by experts from the next step in the respective hierarchies: the union by the international representative, and local management by corporate staff members. The cen-

---

[10]Statement of Jack T. Conway, former Executive Director, IUD, reported in the *Daily Labor Report,* March 16, 1966, p. A-14. Herbert R. Northrup, Professor and Chairman, Department of Industry, University of Pennsylvania, made the same point in a speech to the American Mining Congress, Denver, Colorado, September 10, 1967.

ter of interest in negotiations has remained, however, at the local level and deals specifically with the needs and desires of the rank and file *vis-a-vis* the economics of the plant operation.[11] Naturally, the economic power of the union in bargaining depends upon the potential impact of a strike against the company; and in the case of a conglomerate, the loss of production at a single unit may not be especially significant with respect to the overall corporate profit structure. A conglomerate may be able to shift production to parallel plants in other locations or merely absorb a loss by considering a work stoppage as a long-term investment.

The use of a coalition for bargaining, however, can bring about a fundamental change in the operating power structure of the union. By necessity, where a coalition is to be effective, it becomes essential to shift the locus of power and the decision-making responsibility not only from the local leadership to the international, but actually from the international to the federation—usually the IUD. This is not to imply that ultimate decision-making power rests with the IUD coordinator, but rather with the IUD-guided president's committee composed of designated staff members of the international unions, or in some cases, the presidents of the participating unions.[12] Such a move naturally tends to remove the political and bargaining power from the local level and move it to a point which is, in reality, beyond the grasp of the rank and file to change except when the coalition fails to produce results, and the rank and file are spurred to revolt.

Organizing

A necessary concomitant of coalitionism lies in the concept of total union organization of the firm or industry in question. It is axiomatic that extensive joint bargaining is impossible in a situation where a substantial portion of a corporation operates in a nonunion status. A major effort of the IUD, therefore, has been extensive use of "coordinated organizing" to supplant activities on the coalition front.[13] Coordinated organizing means that the remaining nonunion plants are assigned to the participating unions; then an intensive organizational drive

[11]See E. Robert Livernash, "Special and Local Negotiations," in John T. Dunlop and Neil W. Chamberlain (eds.), *Frontiers of Collective Bargaining* (New York: Harper and Row, 1967), pp. 27–49.

[12]"AFL-CIO Executive Council Report" to the AFL-CIO Convention, Bal Harbour, Florida, December 6, 1967, as reported in the *Daily Labor Report,* December 6, 1967, p. D-1.

[13]"AFL-CIO Executive Council Report," *op. cit.,* p. D-2.

is undertaken by teams of organizers from the different IUD affiliates. Thus, a Steelworker, Autoworker, or other organizer may be working for the OCAW in attempting to gain representation in a nonunion plant. The emphasis is solely on getting *a* union in the plant, knowing that all bargaining activity ultimately will be channeled through the IUD in an advanced coalition movement. The success of this aspect of the IUD program is difficult to assess at this time but evidence would tend to indicate that coordinated organizing has not had a significant effect on the strength of any coalition bargaining program.

Demands

The concept of coalition bargaining, too, dictates that bargaining issues be couched in terms of demands that will be applicable to all participating employee groups. Such a set of demands is an absolute necessity, for support could be expected to dwindle rapidly unless there is "something for everybody." As a concomitant, it becomes necessary to formulate demands in order that the highest common denominator is met, with the result being highly inflated demands upon which realistic bargaining often cannot be leased. To date, most coalitions have centered upon issues which are usually already somewhat similar throughout a company, and which may have wide applicability: pensions, insurance, and some other benefits. Coalition leaders have generally been hesitant to attempt to bargain all issues on a joint basis for two reasons: insufficient coalition strength, and a desire to permit local leaders to negotiate some items in order to gain political support for successive rounds of coalition bargaining. The nonferrous coalition, at its outset, provided a significant exception, and union leaders have readily pointed out that the eventual aim of any joint effort is to encompass all issues and to "go just as far and just as fast as we are able."[14]

A long-term goal of the IUD is to bring the negotiation of all economic issues under the umbrella of coalition bargaining. The attainment of such a step in bargaining with a particular company or industry would seem to result in one of two possible situations, both of which would pose structural problems for collective bargaining. The first of these would be the attainment of a single master contract affecting all

[14]Statement made by an IUE official in response to a question by this writer, Columbus, Ohio, May 3, 1968.

workers represented by the coalition unions (or individual identical contracts at each location) which would contain all items usually specified in the labor agreement. The second possibility would be that of a master contract covering "economic" issues with a separate local supplement applicable to each separate bargaining unit.

Consequences

The consequence of the first alternative is evident. Negotiations between the company and the coalition would quickly become overburdened with discussions of so-called "local issues" such as seniority practices, work rules, plant conditions, and a multitude of other specific individualistic items. Bargaining would become impossibly ponderous. If the unions chose, however, to ignore the local demands, a rank and file revolt would be the most likely result. Such a result occurred in the West Coast pulp and paper industry.

The second alternative is perhaps the more workable one from the coalition standpoint—that of a master agreement with local supplements to encompass the needs of employees at a particular plant location. Although such arrangements are nonexistent in some major industries today on a single company basis, one need only note the situation that has developed in the automobile industry to see the potential for problems. Although the major producers were usually able to settle the master agreements without regular strikes, it has become almost customary for a series of local strikes to cripple production for several months afterward. As of June 1, 1968 at least one local of General Motors had not yet reached agreement on local issues, six months after the basic package had been negotiated. It is difficult to assume that other practitioners of labor relations would seek to become engaged in similar situations, especially where the involvement of several international unions instead of just one would certainly tend to complicate the problems. Yet such is an aim of the IUD in its coalition program.[15]

Strikes

A further consequence of coalition bargaining lies in potential for more frequent, larger, and longer work stoppages. The experiences of

[15]A summary of one employer's view was presented by Earl L. Engle in a speech entitled "Coordinated Bargaining: A Snare—and a Delusion," presented at the Industrial Relations Research Association Spring Meeting, Columbus, Ohio, May 3, 1968.

Union Carbide, 3M, and especially copper have all indicated that the primary cause for strikes was the demand for joint bargaining, and the concomitant actions inherent in the coalition approach for what the employers judged to be unreasonable demands. Such actions are necessarily repeated in each instance where interlocked unions attempt to force the coalition approach upon unwilling company targets. In order to justify their policies, the promise of great rewards for the rank and file almost becomes a union tactical requirement.

Nor is there reason to suppose that established coalitions would record a better strike record than has been the case with fledglings. For the reasons noted above, demands of the expanded group are likely to be inflated and would tend to produce companywide strikes. And most likely such an approach would also result in a protracted series of local strikes made necessary by the inability of workers to satisfy their most immediate demands when confronting an employer who has "already given away all there is to give" at the master negotiating sessions.[16]

A recent address by the Director of the Federal Mediation and Conciliation Service (FMCS) would tend to support the above hypothesis. In discussing an FMCS study designed to determine causes for the rejections by union members of contracts negotiated by their officials, he noted, among other things, that when combined, three reasons were given as responsible for 54 percent of such rejections: dissatisfaction of skilled workers, leaders had not understood real feelings of the membership, and dissatisfaction of other groups. He stated:

> The basic reason for joint consideration [of the above] is that all three causes illustrate a central feature of collective bargaining.
>
> Except for the sophisticated, there is inadequate recognition of the fact that most unions, industrial unions in particular, do not represent a homogeneous group on many subjects.
>
> * * *
>
> The "something for everybody" answer to this problem may be expensive to the union. Perhaps more important, if the degree of response to any one interest is too great, others may be alienated and not appeased by what they consider to be only token recognition of their problems.[17]

---

[16]*Ibid.*

[17]Address by William E. Simkin, Director, Federal Mediation and Conciliation Service in an address to the Graduate School of Business, University of Chicago, November 17, 1967.

One might logically ask, then, what the effect of a further amalgamation of workers with extremely diverse interests through coalitionism might be expected to produce on contract rejection experience, and resultant strike records. It would not appear to justify optimism.

A problem closely related to that of settlement ratification by the rank and file is that of communication breakdowns between union officials and union membership. The problem faced by leaders in attempting to ascertain worker needs for bargaining; and of typing to sell an optimal "package" to the workers is becoming increasingly difficult. Local leaders have had experience in gaining acceptance of locally negotiated settlements. Further evidence indicates that these difficulties become increasingly greater as the decision-making and bargaining power is removed farther from the worker. The coalition concept requires that bargaining be centered at a step beyond the highest now commonly seen: that is, to move bargaining decisions from the local to the international and to the federation, with the inevitable result being less efficient communications and more frequent rank and file rejections of tentative settlements.

Intervention

The incidence of more frequent, longer strikes involving larger numbers of workers and more significant amounts of production losses is also bound to produce a further result: that of more frequent intervention by government and other third parties. Citing again copper, General Electric and Union Carbide experiences, as well as those in basic steel, airlines, railroads, and others, it becomes evident that when work stoppages are threatened, or when strikes occur that have a substantial impact on the national well-being or economy, the public will force the government to make use of either the legal machinery available, or to engage in a form of extralegal intervention. Furthermore, the case for intervention, on terms favorable to them, is often pressed by politically-powerful union leaders who are only too well aware of the historic fact that intervention often serves to deliver extra bargaining gains for the union cause. And, as the size of the bargaining unit increases—either by legal definition or by operating reality—the potential for a "public interest strike" becomes far greater.[18]

---

[18]Union leaders in the copper strike threatened publicly to withhold support from "friends in Washington" at election time if they remained "neutral." *The* (Baltimore) *Sun,* February 29, 1968.

The Future of Coalition Bargaining: Observation and Speculation

The role of coalition bargaining in labor relations in the future cannot be predicted with any degree of certainty, although an examination shows that some of the factors which will serve to shape that role are already observable. One of the most important factors facing the future of coalitionism lies in the current suspension of the UAW by the AFL-CIO.

UAW Suspension

Although the Industrial Union Department was a product of the merger of the American Federation of Labor and the Congress of Industrial Organizations in 1955, it would now appear that the marriage was one of convenience rather than love. Since that time, Walter Reuther had maintained the presidency of the IUD and had utilized it for a platform and a program. The current dispute between Reuther and AFL-CIO president George Meany has resulted in the suspension of the UAW, the largest financial supporter of the IUD, from the Federation and the removal of Reuther from office.[19] When Reuther's UAW elected to withhold per capita dues in an effort to force the calling of a special AFL-CIO convention, IUD lost its leader and most staunch supporter. One may only speculate as to the results, but it is now evident that the IUD budget has been severely reduced, that many of its activities have been curtailed, and that several key personnel have taken other jobs—including Executive Director Jack Conway, whose resignation was effective in June, 1968. It is therefore possible that Meany, who embraced and supported the coalition against General Electric, will continue to nurture and lead the IUD in its coalition bargaining; or will create a new organizational structure for that purpose. A recent meeting of the IUD Executive Board saw the election of the Steelworkers' I. W. Abel as the new president of the Industrial Union Department. At that time, he stated that the future of the Department would be studied, but that no changes were to be made in the immediate future.

---

[19] The UAW was suspended, but not expelled by the AFL-CIO on May 15, 1968 for nonpayment of per capita dues. As of this writing the suspension is still in effect, and no further action has been taken by either side.

New AFL-CIO Department

As further evidence of Meany's commitment to support of activities such as those pursued by the IUD, the AFL-CIO recently announced the formation of a Conference of Transportation Trades with more than 50 internationals representing three million members. The primary purpose of the Conference at this time was:

> . . . that the Conference of Transportation Trades serve as a clearing house on ideas, and as a forum for exchange of views, and that it develop programs dealing with the issues and problems which affect any and all segments of this industry.
>
> . . . that the ultimate objective of bringing together all of these unions concerned with transportation should be the creation of a constitutional Department of Transportation Trades within the National AFL-CIO.[20]

Although the participation of a Transportation Trades Department in an extensive coalition effort could bring about substantial bargaining strength, such a department would be immeasurably benefited by the return of the Teamsters to the AFL-CIO, and its support of the envisioned department.

New Labor Movement

On the other side of the coin, it now seems that Walter Reuther will elect to use his 1.5 million-member United Auto Workers Union as a base for a new labor organization which would be in direct competition with the AFL-CIO. There are some indications that other international unions such as the United Rubber Workers, the OCAW, the ICWU, and some others would support Reuther in a break with the Federation to begin a separate labor movement. And, evidence indicates that the UAW and the Teamsters engaged in discussions which permitted the Teamsters to join with Reuther in a mutual alliance known as the Alliance for Labor Action (ALA). Such an amalgamation could provide a powerful base upon which to build the new movement. The chances of other so-called "outlaw" unions, such as District 50, joining with Reuther seem remote, however, due to the fact that an independent union gains much of its strength because of the fact that it is able

[20]*Daily Labor Report,* May 21, 1968, p. A-8.

to serve as an alternative to federated unions. To affiliate would remove this benefit, and would largely weaken the overall position of District 50.

Popular Support

The future of coalition bargaining also depends heavily on the amount of support that will be given it through rank and file and local union leadership. Up to this point the IUD—as opposed to industry in general—has maintained a most effective communication campaign to "enlighten" union members as to the virtues and success of such programs. The rosy picture, however, might not appear quite so bright to the workers when they finally begin to realize the prices that have been paid for coalition efforts: Union Carbide, 3M, and copper are examples. And, as evidence presented in earlier chapters indicates, the claimed victories have often been quite exaggerated. Whether employees will continue to support these programs in the long run is problematic. A lot depends upon industry's willingness and capacity to communicate the other side of the picture which heretofore has not been presented.

Management Policy

The experience of the companies that have undergone coalition bargaining attempts by the IUD-led unions has demonstrated that a firm which is willing to bear the costs can effectively prevent the coalitions from altering the scope of the bargaining unit, and can prevent the unions from reaching their goal of companywide bargaining. It is essential, however, to take a determined stand, and then to do all that is necessary to maintain a solid position against the coalition front. Moreover, the immediate costs in terms of production losses may be large.

One of the most important aspects of management policy would seem to be one of communicating with the employees on a regular basis. The IUD, and the unions have been extremely effective in their communication, whereas most companies have not. Although General Electric, 3M, and Union Carbide did engage in considerable communicating to their employees, it was not until the copper strike was well under way that the nonferrous firms began to wage a major communication campaign which was aimed at both the copper employees and the general public. It was only then that some understanding of the concept of coalition bargaining was readily disseminated.

Management, too, must begin to reassess its position with regard to bargaining on pension and insurance matters. It cannot "have its cake and eat it too." If companies are to continue to insist upon bargaining according to the unit certifications as defined by the Board, as would seem just and proper, they must not continue to insist upon bargaining on pension and insurance matters on a national basis. In fact, the situation is even more complex than that in many situations: where management simply offers benefit improvements to union bargaining representatives after such improvements have been granted to nonunion and other groups, the union contention of inadequate bargaining would tend to be supported. What is needed is a policy of actual local bargaining on all matters, including pensions, insurance, and other items which are now uniform throughout many companies. Experience of some has shown that such a policy is neither extremely difficult nor expensive to implement. By basing bargaining strategy on costs rather than benefits, and by the use of modern electronic computing equipment, it is possible to bargain for, and to administer a large number of pension and insurance programs with little, or no added costs, thereby permitting the local union leadership to bargain for all matters on a local basis. Such an approach appears absolutely essential if local union leaders are to feel that they are accomplishing something. Otherwise, local union leadership will not support local bargaining. Moreover, by varying benefits according to local employee needs and desires, disenchantment by the membership over settlements, and their consequent rejection, can be avoided. In short, if management desires local bargaining, it must bargain on a local basis.

Labor Law Reform

Although the Supreme Court has not ruled upon the legality of coalition bargaining, other factors outside the usual realm of industrial relations will also serve to place legal parameters around coalition programs. Certain committees of Congress and industry groups are studying the need for labor law reform. Among issues being studied is the need for some sort of restriction to be placed upon unions which would engage in coalition programs. As noted in Chapter XI, the repeal of Sections 8(a)(5) and (b)(3) of the National Labor Relations Act which would eliminate NLRB enforcement actions against companies which declined to bargain with coalition committees and would also allow unions to refuse to settle in one plant until other plants had reached agreement. In short, this would return bargaining to the parties for economic arbitrament, a much more satisfying solution.

The success of any such legislation is, of course, dependent entirely upon future Congresses and Administrations. Should the voters continue to elect a Democratic Executive and Congress, backed heavily by labor, little change could be expected. If, however, the Republicans are successful in gaining the Presidency, and sufficient additional Senate seats and control of the House of Representatives, chances of meaningful labor law change would appear much more likely.

Presidential elections could also produce a significant effect upon the future of coalitionism. Because the National Labor Relations Board is an administrative agency whose members are appointed by the President and confirmed by the Senate, a change of party in the White House could serve to change the composition of the present NLRB which has favored the union coalition movement in several key decisions.

The state of the economy in the immediate future will also bear on the future of coalition bargaining. During the current period of prosperity and high employment, unions are operating in a tight labor market, and are therefore able to exercise greater leverage at the bargaining table, thereby extracting higher settlements, and in the case of coalitions, attributing much credit for high settlements to the existence of coalition bargaining. An economic downturn would alter this situation considerably.

Economic Implications

The economic implications of coalitionism, both in its success and failure are significant (as is evidenced in Chapters III through X) from the standpoint of the cost of bargaining and the cost of the bargain. As has already been discussed, coalition efforts have proved to be extremely costly as regards strikes—Union Carbide, 3M, and copper serving as examples—and strike potentials. Unfortunately, the future development of coalition bargaining would seem to portend more labor unrest and strike losses such as have occurred in the past.

Coalition bargaining experience also tends to support the hypothesis that IUD-led bargaining produces inflated settlements. The very nature of the bond cementing a group of unions for bargaining is one of uniformity of demands that will bring the lowest to a par with the highest, and at the same time provide enough in a settlement to satisfy the wishes of the workers in the unit which had previously been the leader in bargaining. When the demand for uniformity is continued as a primary negotiating goal, settlement becomes difficult and expensive for both company and coalition.

Although it is impossible to separate gains by coalitions from gains attributable to other causes, such as general economic conditions and comparable industry settlements, evidence supports the contention that determined coalitions have been successful in winning somewhat more costly packages than would have been otherwise possible. Several explanations can be offered to support such an argument: (1) a company may find it more advantageous to "buy off" the local bargaining units in order to prevent the formation of a solid multiunion coalition effort; (2) it is necessary to accede to the demands of a coalition in order to prevent a work stoppage; (3) inflated demands are met to bring to an end a coalition strike because worker aspiration level has been raised by the strike leaders; and (4) coalition settlements may be inflated through government or other outside intervening pressures which seek to assuage coalition unions that are unable to attain joint goals, and thereby encourage higher monetary settlements than would have resulted from the exercise of free collective bargaining.

THE QUESTIONS: RESTATED

The introductory chapter of this study posed a series of questions for which answers were to be sought. It is now appropriate again to examine briefly these questions.

1. *What is coalition bargaining?* Coalition bargaining is a new form of joint bargaining, generally under the sponsorship and leadership of the Industrial Union Department of the AFL-CIO, which seeks to bring together local unions of various internationals for the purpose of engaging a multiplant, multiunion employer in collective bargaining negotiations for all of the represented employees, and for terms applicable to all. It is a concept that has not been generally accepted by industry, and is a concept that has, in fact, been vigorously opposed by employers who seek to continue to bargain for its employees on a local basis to preserve the historic wage patterns and working conditions.

2. *How is coalition bargaining different from other forms of joint*

bargaining? Coalition bargaining is different from other types of joint bargaining in several respects. One is that the coalitions tie together locals of different internationals, and the bargaining programs are therefore guided by the IUD, a part of the AFL-CIO; whereas other types of industrial efforts at joint bargaining have been conducted by representatives of a single international. Also, coalition bargaining is the first joint sustained effort which has been designed to deal primarily with an employer on an industrial basis; others have operated with various craft unions, but have not generally sought to engage large industrial corporations in attempts to amalgamate the bargaining units for purposes of joint negotiations. And, the most important differentiating feature of coalition bargaining as contrasted to other forms of joint bargaining is that the other efforts have come about as a result of voluntary agreement between the employer and the union. Coalition bargaining programs are designed to force an employer to bargain with a representative of the various participating locals on a joint basis.

3. *Why does coalition bargaining occur?* Coalition bargaining has usually come about as a response by the unions to a bargaining weakness in dealing with large and diversified corporations. As firms have tended to expand, both as to numbers of plants and into diversified markets, the weaker among the unions have been unable to exercise sufficient bargaining leverage as contrasted to some other industrial unions. As corporations have become more able to withstand the threat, or the occurrence of a single plant strike, the various unions have sought ways to increase their economic power. Coalition bargaining is one such attempt better to deal with a diversified industrial corporation. A further reason for the formation of coalitions lies in the continuing drive for power on the part of some large international unions and their leaders. One such example would seem to be in the nonferrous situation.

4. *What is the impact of coalition bargaining?* The coalition efforts that have been described in this study point to the fact that such programs may have a very definite impact in several areas. One impact of coalition bargaining has been felt by the memberships of the unions which have participated in such programs. The locus of power and the power to make decisions has been removed one step further from the rank and file: from the local to the international, to the Federation and the IUD President's committee. The effect has been to make communi-

cation more difficult, and to increase the potential for membership dissatisfaction. Such a development means that day to day relationships which have been established by plant management personnel and local union leaders have been subject to disturbing elements. Furthermore, the evolution of coalition bargaining has had certain impacts upon the public, upon public policy and its administration. Analysis of the various coalition situations described in this study would lead to the conclusion that coalitions tend to increase the likelihood of more frequent, larger, and longer strikes, and therefore have an impact upon the public which is difficult for government to overlook. Coalition bargaining also encourages interventionist-minded politicians to intervene, and the parties to seek such intervention. The various major coalition attempts all point to the need for a thorough analysis of our labor legislation and its administration.

SUMMARY

On the whole, most coalition bargaining efforts have produced only minimal fringe-benefit gains, some increases in wage settlements, and, in some cases, a union membership which may be unwilling to participate in future coalition programs. A few other major, concerted efforts have indeed brought about significantly higher settlements, but only at the cost of extensive and protracted strikes which resulted in governmental intervention.

The long term future of coalition bargaining is open to question and supposition. One might logically ask whether, in light of the evidence now available, this form of bargaining will prove to be a viable factor in industrial relations. The unions have attempted to claim victories for some coalition efforts through their various communication channels; but have suffered definite setbacks of which the rank and file has not been fully apprised.

The future, too, must be evaluated in terms of the future of the IUD, of the National elections, of Court rulings, of the membership of the NLRB, and the state of the business cycle. The next important testing stage of the coalition concept will come about in the 1969–1971 period when unions who have engaged employers in the first test of bargaining will reopen contracts, and perhaps attempt a second coalition effort.

APPENDIX

IUD COLLECTIVE BARGAINING COMMITTEE LIST

Committee	*Committee*
Aeolian	Anaconda Company
Allied Chemical	Armour and Company
Allis Chalmers	Ball Brothers
American Brake Shoe	Bendix Aviation Corporation
American Home Products	Bestwall
American Machine & Foundry	Borg-Warner
American Metal Climax	Calumet & Hecla
American Optical Company	Campbell Soup
American Smelting & Refining	Celotex Corporation
American Standard	Cerro Corporation

IUD COLLECTIVE BARGAINING COMMITTEE LIST (Continued)

Committee	*Committee*
Certain-Teed Corporation	National Gypsum
Chicago Musical Instruments	National Lead
Copper & Brass	Olin-Mathieson
Dresser	Outboard Marine
Drug & Cosmetics Industry	Optical Industry
Eaton	Paint Industry
Flintkote	Paint—Pittsburgh Plate Glass
FMC	Paint—Glidden Company
Foote Minerals	Paint—Sherwin-Williams
Gar Wood	Pennsalt Chemicals
General Foods	Phelps Dodge
Globe Union	Porter, H. K.
Gulf & Western	Pullman
Harris Intertype	Purex
Honeywell	Quaker Oats
Hooker Chemical	Refractories
Ingersoll-Rand	Revere
International Minerals & Chemicals	Rexall
ITT	Robertshaw Controls
Johns-Manville	Rohm and Haas
Kennecott Copper Corp.	Scovill Manufacturing Co.
Koehring	Stauffer Chemical Co.
Koppers	Stewart-Warner
Ling-Temco-Vought	Sylvania Corporation
Litton Industries	Textron
McCord Corporation	Trailers Conference
Merck & Company	Union Carbide
Minnesota Mining & Manufacturing	Whirlpool
Modine Manufacturing Co.	

Source: Industrial Union Department, AFL-CIO, Washington, D.C., June 1967.

BIBLIOGRAPHY

Books

Abodeely, Paul A. *Compulsory Arbitration and the NLRB.* Industrial Research Unit, Labor Relations and Public Policy Series, Report No. 1. Philadelphia: University of Pennsylvania Press, 1968.

Anker, Jerry D. "Pattern Bargaining, Antitrust Laws and the National Labor Relations Act," in *Proceedings of the New York University Nineteenth Annual Conference on Labor.* New York: April 1966.

Chamberlain, Neil W. "Determinants of Collective Bargaining Structure," *in* Arnold W. Weber, ed., *The Structure of Collective Bargaining.* New York: Free Press of Glencoe, 1961.

Conway, Jack T. and Ginsburg, Woodrow L. "The Extension of Collective Bargaining to New Fields," in *Proceedings of the Nineteenth Annual Meeting.* Industrial Relations Research Association. San Francisco: December 1966.

Independent Study Group. *The Public Interest in Collective Bargaining.* New York: Committee for Economic Development, 1961.

Industrial Union Department, AFL-CIO. *Proceedings of the Sixth Constitutional Convention.* Washington: November 1965.

Jensen, Vernon H. *Collective Bargaining in the Nonferrous Industry*. Institute of Industrial Relations. Berkeley: University of California, 1965.

———. *Nonferrous Metals Industry Unionism 1932-1954.* New York State School of Industrial and Labor Relations. Ithaca: Cornell University, 1954.

Levinson, Harold. *Determining Forces in Collective Wage Bargaining.* New York: John Wiley and Sons, Inc., 1966.

Livernash, E. Robert. "Special and Local Negotiations," in John T. Dunlop and Neil W. Chamberlain, eds., *Frontiers of Collective Bargaining.* New York: Harper and Row, 1967, pp. 27–49.

Northrup, Herbert R. *Boulwarism.* Bureau of Industrial Relations. Ann Arbor: University of Michigan, 1964.

———. *Compulsory Arbitration and Government Intervention.* Washington: Labor Policy Association, 1966.

———. *Restrictive Labor Practices in the Supermarket Industry.* Industrial Research Unit Study No. 44. Philadelphia: University of Pennsylvania Press, 1967.

Northrup, Herbert R. and Bloom, Gordon F. *Government and Labor.* Homewood, Illinois: Richard D. Irwin, 1963.

Reuther, Walter P. *Agenda for Tomorrow.* Report to the Industrial Union Department, AFL-CIO, Sixth Annual Convention. Washington: November 1965.

Schultz, George P. and Weber, Arnold R. *Strategies for the Displaced Worker.* New York: Harper and Row, 1966.

Taylor, George W. "Collective Bargaining in Transition," in Arnold R. Weber, ed., *The Structure of Collective Bargaining.* New York: The Free Press of Glencoe, 1961.

Articles

Abodeely, John E. "Collective Bargaining Unit," *Boston University Law Review,* XLVII (Winter 1967), 139-49.

Conway, Jack T. "Coordinated Bargaining . . . 'Historical Necessity,' " *Agenda* (January-February, 1968), 22-25.

Gomberg, William. "Government Participation in Union Negotiation and Collective Bargaining," *Labor Law Journal,* XIII (November 1962), 941-44.

Keener, J. Ward. "Why We're Having Strikes," *Dun's Review* (December 1967), reprint.

Lahne, Herbert J. "Coalition Bargaining and the Future of Union Structure," *Labor Law Journal,* XVII: (June 1967), 353, ff.

McCulloch, Frank W. "Past, Present, and Future Remedies Under Section 8(a)(5) of the NLRA," *Labor Law Journal,* XIX: (March 1968), 131-42.

Northrup, Herbert R. "Boulwarism v. Coalitionism—the GE 1966 Negotiations," *Management of Personnel Quarterly, V:* (Summer 1966), 2.

Taylor, George W. "The Adequacy of Taft-Hartley in Public Emergency Disputes," *The Annals,* CCCXXXIII: (January 1961), 79–87.

Speeches and Addresses

Engle, Earl L. "Coordinated Bargaining: A Snare—and a Delusion," Industrial Relations Research Association, Columbus, Ohio, May 3, 1968.

Hildebrand, George H. "Coordinated Bargaining: An Economist's Point of View," Industrial Relations Research Association, Columbus, Ohio, May 3, 1968.

McCulloch, Frank W. "New Remedies Under the National Labor Relations Act," Twenty-first Annual Conference on Labor in New York City sponsored by the New York University Institute of Labor Relations, May 14, 1968.

Northrup, Herbert R. "Coalition Bargaining," American Mining Congress, Denver, September 10, 1967.

Simkin, William E. "Causes of Contract Rejections," Graduate School of Business, University of Chicago, November 17, 1967.

Interviews

Personal interviews were conducted with representatives of the following companies and unions. Most of those interviewed wished to remain anonymous, therefore, only the affiliations are here listed.

Companies

Allied Chemical Corporation
American Home Products Corporation
American Radiator and Standard Sanitary Corporation
American Smelting and Refining Company
The Anaconda Company
Armstrong Cork Company
Atlas Chemical Company
Bangor Punta Corporation
Boeing Company

Campbell Soup Company
Celanese Corporation
Continental Can Company
E. I. DuPont de Nemours and Company
Eaton Yale & Towne
General Electric Company
Glidden Company
Harris Intertype
Honeywell
Ingersoll-Rand Company
International Telephone and Telegraph Corporation
Johns-Manville Corporation
Kennecott Copper Corporation
Koppers Company
Libby-Owens-Ford Glass Company
Lukens Steel Company
Minnesota Mining and Manufacturing Company
Olin Mathieson Chemical Corporation
Phelps Dodge Corporation
Pennsalt Chemical Corporation
H. K. Porter Company
PPG Industries
Rohm and Haas Company
St. Regis Paper Company
Sherwin-Williams Company
Stauffer Chemical Company
Sterling Drug Company
Union Carbide Corporation
Westinghouse Electric Corporation
Whirlpool Corporation

Unions

Communication Workers of America
Industrial Union Department, AFL-CIO
International Association of Bridge and Structural Iron Workers
International Association of Machinists & Aerospace Workers
International Chemical Workers Union
International Union of Electrical Workers
International Union of United Automobile, Aerospace, Agricultural Implement Workers of America

Oil, Chemical & Atomic Workers International Union
United Association of Journeymen and Apprentices of the Plumbing and Pipe Fitting Industry of the United States and Canada
United Glass & Ceramic Workers of North America
United Rubber, Cork, Linoleum & Plastic Workers of America
United Steelworkers of America

Other

Copper Strike Information Bureau. "Situation Facing Companies in Present Copper Strike," New York: November 1967.

———. "Strike Chronology," New York: August 1968.

International Chemical Workers Union. *Legal Problems in Coordinated Bargaining*. Undated, probably 1966.

Proceedings of the Special Panel Appointed to Assist in Settlement of the Copper Dispute (Taylor Panel), January 30-February 2, 1968, Washington, D.C.

U.S. Department of Labor. Office of Labor-Management and Welfare Pension Reports. *Interim Report of Election of National President of International Union of Electrical, Radio and Machine Workers (IUE)*. Washington: April 5, 1965.

INDEX